MISSION TO THE MOON: A Critical Examination of NASA and the Space Program

MISSION TO THE MOON

*A Critical Examination
of NASA and the
Space Program*

*by Erlend A. Kennan
and Edmund H. Harvey, Jr.*

NEW YORK 1969

WILLIAM MORROW & CO., INC.

Library of Congress Catalog Card Number 69-14627

• •

Contents

List of Illustrations

Credit NASA Figures 1-5, 7

Introduction

by Ralph E. Lapp

Man's flight to the Moon must rank as the technological extravaganza of this century. Yet, ironically, the spectacle and the cost of the United States' Apollo program to land men on the Moon hinge upon the fragility of man. Exporting man from his ancestral Earth environment forces rocket experts to design a massive and complex manned space capsule. To sustain life in the void of space the designers have to imitate as best they can the various conditions to which man is habituated on the Earth's surface. One of the most obvious and important of these is provision for the capsule passengers to breathe.

Oxygen, present in our atmosphere as one part for every four of inert nitrogen, sustains life. But an atmosphere of pure oxygen can be a lethal weapon. Scientists and technicians long ago learned to treat oxygen with great respect.

Many scientists were shocked when three brave American astronauts perished in an Apollo experiment at Cape Kennedy—not because of the tragedy alone, but because of the atmosphere of pure oxygen used in the spacecraft. Those who were shocked at the time of the accident will be jolted when they read in this book about the lack of adequate safety precautions taken to prevent fire in the spacecraft.

The authors' account of this accident should not be viewed merely as a postmortem of this single grisly episode. Rather it has a much broader context—that of twentieth-century man caught in the clutches of remorseless technology. Who is master —man or the machine? This question is not new, having been raised when machines were crude and the problem was more identifiable. Today the question transforms to man versus systems. Thus, there is much to be learned from the authors' inquiry. One lesson is that human judgment should not be made inferior to the impersonal, but fallible, authority of engineering systems. In reading this authoritative and highly disciplined account of the Apollo accident, it is well to remember that Havelock Ellis wrote:

> The greatest task before civilization at present is to make machines what they ought to be, the slaves, instead of the masters of men.

Just before the Apollo 204 accident, the Subcommittee on NASA Oversight of the House Committee on Science and Astronautics made an exhaustive study of the lunar program. This study runs to 1219 pages of fine print, plus 288 pages of staff reports. Yet nowhere in this Congressional investigation of the Apollo program does one find real concern for astronaut safety. All attention focuses on the central question: "Will the hardware—the various space systems—be ready on time?"

All new ventures involve risks. In this respect the manned space program was extraordinary—it entailed near perfection in design and execution of plans to sustain life in a confined, hermetically sealed cabin destined to operate far from Earth. That degree of perfection was not achieved by the National Aeronautics and Space Administration despite the magnitude and cost of the Apollo program. Haste in space *can* spell disaster—and *it did*. America's pell-mell crash effort to beat the Russians to the Moon must be indicted as the villain in the Apollo accident. Compressed time schedules foreclosed more orderly development of life support systems and produced a space cabin which became an oxygen bomb.

Thus, the deaths at Cape Kennedy must in the final analysis be attributed to haste. In its mad rush to beat the Soviets to the Moon, the United States laid down an arbitrary and all-demanding timetable. The desire to reach the Moon "before the decade is out" demanded that all the elaborate pieces of the space program must fall in place by then.

I think that readers will be shocked to their eye teeth when they discover how the capsule fire hazard was assessed by those charged with responsibility for Apollo. Here the authors do an excellent job of reporting just what happened at Cape Kennedy on January 27, 1967. Although I had read the official reports of the Apollo 204 investigation, I confess that the turgid "official" prose obscured the true narrative of what happened when three

American astronauts were sealed up in an atmosphere of pure oxygen at sixteen pounds per square inch of pressure. Most U.S. scientists could not believe their ears when they learned that fact. Oxygen at such pressure comes in the category of an "oxygen bomb."

Little-known government reports which the authors have used make it clear *post facto* that oxygen fires had occurred in the U.S. space program long before the accident on January 27, 1967; but these had not been given realistic risk evaluation. U.S. space engineers failed to build adequate safety mechanisms into the Apollo capsule or to provide for rescue of the astronauts in case of a launch fire. Looking back on the modifications made in the capsule *after* the tragic accident, we see the measure of NASA's failure to deal with the fire hazard.

The haste in space is illustrated by decisions that NASA made regarding rescue missions should astronauts be trapped in a lunar orbit or stranded on the lunar surface. Rescue-relief missions were abandoned because they would involve additional programs that would slow down the pace of the Apollo program. There is no net for the astronauts' high-wire act in space.

Most certainly, NASA engineers learned a lesson from the Apollo accident. They took elaborate precautions in redesigning the space capsule and they were rewarded by the flights of Apollo 7 and Apollo 8. But in the magnitude of the capsule modification —quick-opening hatches, fireproofing, fire-resistant suits, and most of all in the two-component cabin atmosphere during launch—we find the measure of the deficiencies of the ill-fated capsule that burned.

Why were these clear deficiencies disregarded? This book attempts to answer this question. No simple answer is possible because of the sheer size of the organizational task force dedicated to fabricating the Apollo space capsule and the distributed responsibility thus engendered. Nonetheless, this book pieces together a chilling picture of bureaucratic ineptitude, industrial incompetence and shoddiness, an overly tight time schedule, and an engineering overconfidence in systems. Everyone is responsible and no one is found culpable. But three men died, imprisoned in a fiery container, helpless to save themselves. And what is more, though men were close at hand outside the inferno, they could not and did not cope with the emergency. High technology was put on trial January 27, 1967, and it was found wanting. You can't paste a guilty label on inanimate technology. Man becomes as anonymous as technology when he implicates himself in complex spaceware systems.

The reader may well ask: "If there was negligence, why did not the official inquiry define culpability?" But how does one judge one's self? The official investigation, largely an in-house NASA tour de force, was subject to Congressional review. Both the Senate and House committees that handle space activities held extensive hearings on the Apollo accident. But here the results are ambiguous. Both Congressional committees are so closely tied to NASA that they would be implicating themselves if they turned in an indictment of NASA. The NASA-Congressional umbilical cord binds the two parties together. As a result, the Congress is hard put when it finds itself a critic of the space agency.

This symbiotic relationship is especially significant today as we look beyond Apollo and seek to frame the future of the U.S. space program. Where do we aim in space after Apollo men reach the Moon and return to Earth? This question cannot be asked in a budgetary vacuum. Given unlimited funds, surplus scientific and technical manpower and a solid base of public confidence, it would appear an easy question to answer. Establish a lunar base and then set out for Mars, the planet most likely to sprout some forms of life, however rudimentary. But these are not normal times. The sheer expense of space travel forms an obstacle to post-Apollo programs.

In the past eight years the United States has spent almost $34 billion on civilian space activities. Almost all of this money has been focused on the manned space program, primarily because the life support systems for astronauts demand a heavy capsule and this in turn requires enormous booster rockets. Each Apollo rocket costs $250 million; this figure does not include the lunar excursion module and the launch costs. In view of the high costs of space travel and the need to attend to urgent domestic needs, the nation should take stock of the space program before authorizing more funds for new ventures to the Moon and beyond.

To put the question bluntly, we need to ask, "What good is man in space?" This query has been deferred much too long. Men have vaulted into space at an accelerated rate ever since Gagarin led the way in the spring of 1961. What have they accomplished? Actually, they have proved that man can survive in space. His value has been that of a pioneer in a prestige contest. So far as scientific results are concerned, the great bulk of experiments in space have been accomplished with unmanned devices. The latter can be made light in weight so that they can be shot into space aboard rockets much smaller than those needed for manned missions.

Space enthusiasts maintain that the practical benefits of the NASA program are of tremendous dollar value to the nation's economy. Indeed, they claim that the cash benefits greatly exceed the annual NASA expenditures. The argument goes that there is an unintended "technological spin-off" that brings new products and techniques to the American economic scene. I believe that it would be impossible for a federal agency to spend $5 billion per year without something of value falling back to earth, but in my view this is a slow "drip-out"—a scanty flow of benefits compared to the vast funds spent in space research. Most of the money spent in the U.S. space program is directed toward huge rockets that represent a kind of "freak-out" engineering having little relationship to the marketplace.

To make these candid assertions about the space program is not to label it a worthless national investment, but rather to bring it into rational perspective. There are sound values to the space program, especially in the scientific sector, which at present accounts for a very small percentage of the total space effort. The quest for more information about our planet, our solar system and the galaxy needs to be continued and receive priority over manned space spectaculars. A well-founded and productive U.S. space program can be designed for a third of what the nation now spends on space. Such a space effort can be pursued without jeopardy to the other national programs that demand critical attention.

In the long run we may expect that man's outward thrust from Earth will redirect his vision, giving him a glimpse of the grand design of things now so imperfectly perceived on his own planet.

The full color of the universe has been shut out by the Earth's gaseous mantle and may now be sensed. The prospect is dazzling to scientists whose instruments alone are sensitive to the full color coming across the vast reaches of space. Instruments capable of probing for life forms on Mars may bring back data of immense interest to bioscientists and of great philosophic and psychological impact to the entire human race.

The heroic aspect of manned space flights has tended to obscure the fundamental values of space science, but as the space effort becomes more rational, and less a frenzied U.S.-Soviet lunge for prestige, we may hope that these basic merits may assert themselves.

Authors to Reader

This book is harshly critical of America's space program. It is an indictment of irresponsibility at many levels, not only within the National Aeronautics and Space Administration, America's civilian space agency, but in the relationships of NASA with the Congress, the Defense Department, the aerospace industry, the scientific community, and the press.

However, we are not against space exploration. Nor do we quixotically propose a halt to the conquest of space. Like millions of others we share the exhilaration of man's reaching out toward the stars. Man shall explore the Moon, the rest of the solar system, and what lies beyond. After reading this book, the reader may decide for himself whether priority should be given to un-manned ("robot") exploration or to manned missions. It is the multibillion-dollar question that now faces the Nixon Adminis-tration and the NASA administrator.

What this nation must not permit again is the adoption of dead-end goals. Only the most Neanderthal anti-space critic would argue that the goal of putting men on the Moon—sometime—is not worth the money and effort. But after the Moon, it would seem, America's civilian space program has no place to go. The Congress is wary about future missions, manned or unmanned, to the planets. A proper base has not been laid. The Apollo program can no longer be considered part of an overall U.S. program. It appears to be a one-night stand, after which the principals will scatter and disappear into the vast maze of the aerospace-defense community. The blame lies only in part with NASA, which per-mitted the entire space program to be "sold" as a one-shot spectacular entitled "Man on the Moon," a dazzling mission that would win the support of the man in the street. The results of this choice have been lamentable; the Moon mission and most other remaining projects have been stripped of much of the scientific value they once had. The Congress, too, is guilty. Spurred by the wide public interest that, despite some ups and downs, has always attended the space race, the Congress has been content largely to limit its support to beating the Russians to the Moon. In the budget-biting year of 1968, the Congress chose not to rein in America's Moon-landing plans, but instead cut back on other NASA programs, such as proposed unmanned interplanetary exploration and support of university education.

As a result, NASA has neither a clearly defined direction nor solidly endorsed goals. The crucial question of whether NASA can maintain its posture as a primarily civilian agency, while not yet resolved, appears to be influenced by a drift toward an increasingly defense-dominated American space establishment under the Nixon Administration. The possible consequences of this trend, the authors believe, require the most thoughtful deliberation now, before the trend becomes irreversible.

In mid-February, 1969, President Nixon's science adviser, Dr. Lee A. DuBridge, announced that his office would oversee a board re-examination of the United States' goals in space. The review and recommendations would be submitted to the President in September, 1969. This move served to underscore the criticisms, fears and hopes of the authors. In his announcement, DuBridge stressed his belief that the space program in the coming decade should be "balanced" in regard to manned lunar exploration, unmanned planetary flight, and manned Earth-orbiting missions—thereby implying that the space program had been "unbalanced" in the previous decade. The Defense Department, DuBridge noted, would play a major part in determining future goals.

Another critical area is that of NASA-industry relationships. Whatever may be said of James Webb (and the authors say much that may seem unfair to his admirers), he was, as head of NASA for seven and a half years, a strong-minded and resourceful administrator, alert to the pitfalls of dealing with an understandably profit-motivated aerospace industry. While he may at times have been the industry's eloquent apologist, Webb also more than once has been its chief whipping boy. The authors hope that NASA under the Nixon administration will prove at least as sensible as Webb in confronting the tremendous pressures the gigantic aerospace complex can exert on important policy decisions. The aerospace industry, as will be shown, is a publicly supported industry, whose ultimate master is the taxpaying American public; but all too often the tail attempts to wag the dog.

It is our hope that this book will inspire fresh thinking about

America's role in space. At any time, Congressional hearings could be convened that would hear out *all* segments of the scientific and technological communities. Such tribunals could explore the many difficult questions that must be faced if future large-scale governmental projects, such as the control of environmental pollution, solutions to the crisis of the cities, and exploration of "inner space"—the oceans—are to avert disaster. Failure in these areas will affect all of us, and future generations, far more than we dare imagine. It is the authors' contention that more could be accomplished by studying NASA's mistakes than by using the space agency as a model for the massive technological endeavors that lie ahead of us.

The nation must also determine the proper level of NASA's long-term budget needs and select realistic space goals for the next twenty-five or more years. Both the budget and the goals will have to stand on their own merits alongside other pressing commitments.

A majority of the nation might well have something to say on these very matters. On February 17, 1969, a syndicated newspaper column, the *Harris Survey*, reported a majority of those polled "opposed" the lunar landing. According to the survey, conducted in 1,544 households between January 21 and 28, 1969, 49 percent were opposed and only 39 percent were in favor of the upcoming extravaganza. Explaining the data, Harris noted that "women, older citizens, and the less well educated are all rather adamantly opposed to the space program. Men, younger people, and the college educated are the ones who tend to favor space exploration." Reminded of the multi-billion dollar price tag of the program, national opposition rose to "55 percent as against 34 percent who are willing to spend that much." If it were not for the specter of Russian competition, opposition would rise to 59 percent as against the support of 30 percent. In general the eastern U.S. was the only sector of the country to give overall endorsement of a Moon landing.

At a time when the "101-percent-perfect" Apollo 7 mission and the spectacular Moon-circling Apollo 8 flight have bedazzled much of the world, and the crowning achievement of a manned Moon landing may be only months or weeks away, the authors run counter to much public enthusiasm for manned exploration of the Moon and planets. Why, the reader may ask, should he read about the past mistakes and deficiencies of NASA, when the space agency is almost daily demonstrating its marvelous engineering and technological prowess? Why, more specifically, should the reader feel compelled to relive the horror of a two-year-old tragedy—the Apollo 204 fire—and the incredible series of derelict decisions that led up to it? The authors answer: Because it took the deaths of five men to make NASA even reconsider its course; because, ironically, America's haste to achieve a single goal, to beat the Russians to the Moon, almost dealt a death blow to America's entire space program; because such things are threatening to happen again.

In building our case against the ineptness and confusion that have marked America's space program since its birth in the late 1950's, we have uncovered material that should surprise and shock every American citizen. However, no surreptitious sources were employed to obtain this material. Such methods were unnecessary. The record is available to any person willing to make diligent search and inquiry. It is contained in the numerous volumes of NASA documentation and Congressional testimony issued by the U.S. Government Printing Office. It is all the more shocking that this story has not previously been told by those members of the press who have privately regarded it as a scandal.

In the more than two years following the Apollo 204 fire that killed astronauts Grissom, White, and Chaffee, many officials and authorities have invoked the three astronauts' names in championing the direction of America's present space program. It is, so the invocation goes, "what the three dead astronauts would have wanted." With profound respect and humility, we believe that we have written what Grissom, White, and Chaffee—and all the American people—would have wished to hear, and should have been hearing, all through a decade and more of space exploration.

Erlend A. Kennan
Edmund H. Harvey, Jr.

MISSION TO THE MOON: A Critical Examination of NASA and the Space Program

■ First I believe that this Nation should commit itself to achieving the goal, before this decade is out, of landing a man on the moon and returning him safely to earth . . . It will not be one man going to the moon . . . it will be an entire nation . . .

PRESIDENT JOHN F. KENNEDY,
Special Message to Congress,
May 25, 1961

Chapter 1 ■ "One Sharp Cry of Pain"

Just after dawn on the morning of Friday, January 27, 1967, a full-scale dress rehearsal of the maiden launching of America's Apollo "Moon ship" was about to get under way. As the sun climbed the Atlantic horizon, Cape Kennedy's massive space-age structures cast long shadows westward. Hours before the actual tests began at 7:55 A.M., members of the ground crew had been arriving at launch pad 34. There an Apollo spacecraft was perched two hundred and eighteen feet above ground. It sat atop the most powerful Saturn rocket then developed. Ground support crews had already started cranking up equipment that would be used in an all-day ground test of the Apollo spacecraft's systems. The three astronauts were not due for several more hours. Meanwhile, their spacecraft, the Apollo 012, would be groomed for their arrival.

The job at hand for the astronauts and the ground teams, this January day, was a "plugs-out" test. The spacecraft would undergo a countdown leading to a simulated launch, at which point the capsule would be disconnected, or "unplugged," from external power sources. This test was a significant stepping stone toward the first manned Apollo flight, scheduled for "no earlier than February 21," a mere three and a half weeks away. On that date, if all went well, the manned Apollo ship would be launched, not yet toward the Moon, but simply into Earth orbit. The Earth-orbital trial would give the astronauts experience in handling the new three-man spacecraft, as well as test the spaceworthiness of the ship itself. That pre-Moon flight, and the series of ground tests leading up to it, had been designated Apollo Mission AS–204,* or simply Apollo 204.**

But no spectacular fiery launch was scheduled for this day. The plugs-out test was later described as "routine" and as a "standard procedure . . . we have been through . . . several times before." Indeed, the first manned Apollo launch, three and a half weeks away, had already been labeled a "bland mission" by a spokesman for the National Aeronautics and Space Administration (NASA). So, the plugs-out test meant, to most of the engineers and technicians of the ground support crews, just another long day of electronic nit-picking.

The astronauts, like the ground crews, began their day in the early dawn hours. Before breakfast, there were brief medical examinations. Each man received a shot of prophylactic penicillin because a nasty streptococcus infection had been making the rounds at the Cape.

By mid-morning, the meticulous suit-donning procedure had begun; and the various sensors, which would relay data to the test monitors, were being attached to the three men. The astronauts were then hooked into their portable oxygen supplies to begin the pre-breathing of the pure-oxygen atmosphere that would exist in Apollo 012's cabin. At about 12:30 P.M., the three astronauts were dressed in space suits and helmets. Lugging their portable oxygen tanks, they left the Operations Support Building and began the drive over to the foot of the umbilical tower at pad 34. (See Fig. 1.)

At about 12:55 P.M., the three astronauts took an elevator up

* "A" standing for the Apollo spacecraft, and "S" for the Saturn 1B rocket that would launch it.
** Possible confusion may arise for the reader from the use of the two designations "Apollo 012" and "Apollo 204." Apollo 012 applies only to the *spacecraft* portion (launch escape system, LES; command module, CM; and service module, SM) of the Apollo-Saturn rig designated to carry out the *mission* known as Apollo 204. Thus, the two designations are often used interchangeably: i.e., "the Apollo 204 command module (or cabin, capsule, or spacecraft)" refers to the command module (012) associated with Apollo mission 204. Several spacecraft similar to the 012 were built (e.g., 008 and 017); some of these were scheduled to be used on later (and newly numbered) Apollo missions following the Apollo 204 mission, in which case they would have borne their own number and the new mission number. In all, fifteen spacecraft were on order.

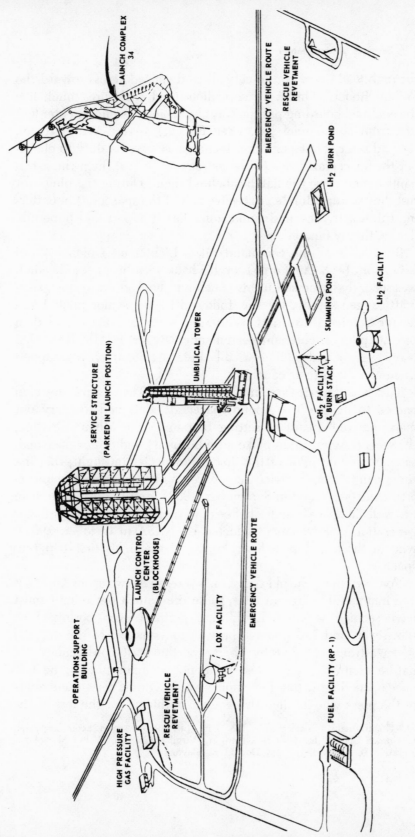

Fig. 1: Aerial Drawing of Launch Complex 34

LAUNCH COMPLEX 34

EMERGENCY VEHICLE ROUTE

RESCUE VEHICLE REVETMENT

LH$_2$ BURN POND

LH$_2$ FACILITY

SKIMMING POND

GH$_2$ FACILITY & BURN STACK

FUEL FACILITY (RP-1)

EMERGENCY VEHICLE ROUTE

LOX FACILITY

RESCUE VEHICLE REVETMENT

HIGH PRESSURE GAS FACILITY

OPERATIONS SUPPORT BUILDING

LAUNCH CONTROL CENTER (BLOCKHOUSE)

SERVICE STRUCTURE (PARKED IN LAUNCH POSITION)

UMBILICAL TOWER

the umbilical tower to the catwalk and started across toward the "White Room." This is an accordion-sided enclosure, much like the enclosed boarding passageways by which passengers enter and exit from commercial jets. (See Fig. 2.) In the White Room, the pad safety crew and other technicians were on duty to check-out the spacecraft prior to the astronauts' arrival, help the astronauts in and close the hatches behind them. During the plugs-out test they were within ten to twelve feet of the spacecraft, monitoring cabin activities, and could immediately report and hopefully deal with any emergencies.

By 1:05 P.M., the command pilot, Lieutenant Colonel Virgil I. Grissom (U.S. Air Force), on his back with his knees elevated, was securely harnessed in his couch and hooked up to the spacecraft oxygen supply. He was followed by the senior pilot, Lieutenant Colonel Edward H. White II (U.S. Air Force), and then by the pilot, Lieutenant Commander Roger B. Chaffee (U.S. Navy). By about 1:20 P.M. all three astronauts had strapped themselves into their couches.

This was America's prime Apollo crew. These were the men named to fly the first Apollo spacecraft, designed to carry out man's age-old dream of setting foot upon the Moon: Grissom, the second American to make a (suborbital) flight into space and, as commanding pilot of the first manned Gemini flight, the first American to journey twice into space; White, a second-generation astronaut (he joined in September, 1962), and the first American to "walk in space"; and Chaffee, the rookie, one of the younger generation of astronauts (selected by NASA in October, 1963), who in three and a half weeks would make his first trip into space.

For forty-one-year-old Grissom, a veteran of two space launches and innumerable ground tests, these pre-launch procedures must have seemed very much old hat, perhaps even boring. Five foot seven and 150 pounds, he was the smallest of the original seven astronauts,* but by no means the least conspicuous. By nature taciturn ("I'm a test pilot, not a philosopher"), he had once opened up with a few choice words against certain members of the press who implied that he was to blame for the loss of the

* The original seven selected by NASA in April, 1959, were M. Scott Carpenter; L. Gordon Cooper, Jr.; John H. Glenn, Jr.; Virgil I. Grissom; Walter M. Schirra, Jr.; Alan B. Shepard, Jr.; and Donald K. Slayton.

beneath his couch.* At about the same ⟨...⟩, the doctors who were monitoring biomedical data noted ⟨...⟩ncrease in White's heart rate. A scant second or two later, the ⟨...⟩ial platform within the capsule rocked slightly, indicating mo⟨...⟩nt by at least one of the crew. Another cry came from the ⟨...⟩ecraft, believed to be from Chaffee: "I've [or "we've"] got ⟨...⟩e in the cockpit!" Cabin temperature was rising.

By this time the cabin pressure, too, ⟨...⟩ beginning to rise, and the inertial platform was rocking cr⟨...⟩ Inside the spacecraft, if the astronauts were following ⟨...⟩correct procedure, White would have been reaching back ⟨...⟩is left shoulder to grab the inner hatch release handle. Griss⟨...⟩ould have lowered the center headrest in order to help Wh⟨...⟩ft down the inner hatch and drop it on the floor of the c⟨...⟩ Chaffee's job was to stay put in his couch and keep up co⟨...⟩cations with those outside the capsule; only if Grissom a⟨...⟩White were having trouble unsealing the inner hatch would ⟨...⟩ to their aid.

About twelve seconds after Grissom'⟨s⟩ first cry, a voice believed to be that of Chaffee yelled ⟨...⟩ something to the effect that there was a "bad fire" in the ⟨...⟩. The temperature within the command module was now r⟨...⟩ rapidly. After this, according to an official memorandum, "N⟨...⟩er intelligible communications were received although som⟨...⟩ners believed there was one sharp cry of pain. Loss of radi⟨...⟩al occurred a few seconds later."**

Although nothing more was heard fro⟨m the⟩ astronauts, it was evident that they were still conscious ⟨s⟩truggling with the hatch for at least a few more seconds: N⟨ASA⟩ medical spokesmen estimated that loss of consciousness wo⟨uld n⟩ot have come until fifteen to thirty seconds "after the firs⟨t sui⟩t failed" (i.e., was burned through).

Meanwhile, at about 6:31:19, or appr⟨oxima⟩tely fifteen seconds after the first cry of "Fire"(?), the cabi⟨n⟩ ruptured, pouring

---

* NASA's version of the sequence of events ⟨...⟩llowed was included in an official NASA release, dated February 3, 196⟨7...⟩as the twenty-sixth in a series used to inform the public in the wake of t⟨...⟩ster. This release, which included only a part of the astronauts' last ⟨...⟩was in the form of a memorandum from Robert C. Seamans, Jr., dep⟨...⟩inistrator, to James E. Webb, administrator of NASA. See Appendix A.

** This preliminary statement conflicted with ⟨...⟩ tape analysis included in the Report of the Apollo Review Board. See ⟨...⟩A.

out flames and great billows of black and acrid smoke. The official death certificates for all three crew members, according to the official NASA memorandum, list the cause of death as "asphyxiation due to smoke inhalation due to fire."*

Outside the spacecraft, in their frantic efforts to remove the hatches and assist the astronauts, twenty-seven pad crewmen were felled by the dense fumes and smoke. Two were hospitalized overnight.

Thus, in less than half a minute, a flash fire, initiated by an unknown cause and supported by the 100-percent-oxygen atmosphere in the cabin, took the lives of the prime space crew of the United States. Valiant rescue efforts by the support crew members were hampered and finally rendered hopeless by the dense smoke, intense heat, and flames that engulfed the White Room and access arm.

When, about five minutes after detection of the fire, the hatches were successfully removed, smoke, fumes, and heat from within the spacecraft prevented immediate removal of the astronauts' remains. The director of flight crew operations, chief astronaut Donald K. Slayton, assisting in removal of the crew, recalled that on peering through the hatch he noted the suits of the astronauts were so entangled and fused with couch materials that he could not identify the individual bodies. It appeared that no mortal could have survived within the fiery furnace. Indeed, it seemed remarkable that the astronauts' bodies had not been entirely consumed in the conflagration. Only the task of removing their bodies remained. There seemed to be no question that the astronauts were dead. According to the summary report of the subsequent investigation: "The Pad Leader . . . reported over the headset that he could not describe the situation in the Command Module. In this manner he attempted to convey the fact that the crew was dead to the Test Conductor without informing the many people monitoring the communication channels . . ."

The bodies of the astronauts were not removed immediately, "in the interest of accident investigation and to photograph the Command Module with the crew in place before evidence was disarranged. Photographs were taken, and the removal efforts resumed at approximately 5:30 GMT (12:30 A.M. EST) on

* See Appendix A.

January 28. Removal of the crew took approximately ninety minutes and was completed about seven and one-half hours after the accident."

And so, at 2:08 A.M., the last of the bodies, that of Roger Chaffee, was recovered. At the foot of pad 34, Chaffee's body was placed in an ambulance and followed the others to the Pan American Dispensary—Cape Kennedy's privately contracted medical facility. From there, at a little after 4:00 A.M., EST, the bodies were transferred to the Bioastronautics Operational Support Unit for autopsies.

From the start, there was no question who would take charge of an investigation of the fire. Within twenty-one minutes after the first cry of fire, NASA officials forbade all outside telephone calls from the blockhouse that served as mission control center. Within an hour, all data and equipment had been impounded. Strict personnel security measures were enforced so that no pertinent information would leak out before an official investigation of the accident was initiated.

At 11:15 P.M. that night, less than five hours after the fire, a delegation of NASA's top brass* from the Washington meeting arrived at the Cape. Very quickly, an investigation team—the Apollo 204 Review Board—was established according to a standard NASA procedure. Official analysis of the tragedy could begin. NASA, through its appointed Review Board, was in complete control.

Just as quickly, an official attitude took shape. NASA officials expressed the view that "it is conceivable that we will never know what initiated the fire . . . or pinpoint the single source of ignition involved with the 204 fire." The flash fire had occurred in spite of the best efforts to avoid such tragedies, and while everything had been done that could have been done to save the crew, Grissom, White, and Chaffee perished on the ground during a simulated launch. It was the last place that such an accident might have been expected. Had the fire occurred in space, during an actual flight, NASA pointed out, the danger would have been considerably less. The fire could have been controlled by venting

---

* The delegation included Major General Samuel C. Phillips, director of the Apollo program at NASA's Washington headquarters; Dr. Robert R. Gilruth, director of NASA's Manned Spacecraft Center, Houston, Texas; and Dr. Kurt H. Debus, director of the Kennedy Space Center at the Cape.

the cabin atmosphere—in other words, by simply opening the windows.

Official shock did not prevent NASA from responding, before the fact, to any insinuation that the three deaths might serve to cast doubt upon America's space program. To the contrary, according to a NASA press release less than twenty-four hours after the fire:

> We know that the space program must go forward and indeed it will. We know and we trust the American people will understand that adventuring into new frontiers always entails some hazard. That is the creed of the astronaut.

NASA officials, in the days and weeks after the fire, spoke often for the three dead men. On February 7, Dr. George E. Mueller (pronounced "Miller"), NASA associate administrator, before the Senate Committee on Aeronautical and Space Sciences, affirmed the theme of the early NASA release: "Individually, and as an organization, we are dedicated to taking every step humanly possible to maintain the safety of the flight crews. But, having taken every precaution, we feel we must proceed with the program."

A Conflicting—and Disturbing—View

NASA should have known it could not make its official version of the fire stand. It could not because of these facts, which will be fully documented in the chapters that follow:

■ The astronauts were not burned to death.

■ Although there can be no doubt that the astronauts were dead when the doctors arrived, there is no certainty that they were beyond medical assistance when rescuers opened the hatches minutes earlier.*

■ The plugs-out test was hazardous and NASA, as will be shown, should have known it. The fact that it was not "classified" as hazardous cannot be passed off, as NASA and many in the Congress have since attempted, as a sort of typographical error.

* However, had the unconscious astronauts somehow been saved from death at this point the possibility of massive lung and brain damage remained.

■ In spite of countless assertions to the contrary, NASA simply did not take "every step humanly possible to maintain the safety" of the astronauts, either in space or on the ground.

The courage and devotion of three dead men are not at issue here. Rather, the issue is NASA's technical and managerial ability —not only at the time of the accident, but from the day in 1958 when NASA was created until the present moment. It is an issue that has been approached by some members of appropriate committees in the Congress, but never met head-on. It is an issue that was assiduously avoided by the special NASA-appointed, NASA-manned Apollo 204 Review Board. It is an issue that must be answered, in part, by reexamining the decisions that led up to the fire, as well as the way the fire itself was "handled" by NASA.

A Moon landing may, as some voices have sung, contribute to an uplifting of the human spirit. At the least, it may temporarily elevate a national "image." But has the effort of meeting an arbitrary deadline, of "beating the Russians," at the expense of potentially far more rewarding space projects really ever made sense? Despite its inexorable momentum, does it make sense now?

In this book the space agency's mistakes will be studied in detail. An examination will be made of NASA's blind belief that its "systems" of management and technology would, by a kind of charmed-life philosophy, eliminate human error and undue hazard.

Has not a contrite NASA redeemed itself in the period after the fire? The answer, quite simply, is No. Beginning with the "101-percent-perfect" Apollo 7 mission (whose goals, incidentally, were almost identical to those programmed for the abortive Apollo 204 mission twenty months before), the same old pre-fire mentality began to assert itself. Planned missions were canceled; schedules were squeezed; the possibility of Russia's beating America to a Moon landing was again posed as an unthinkable national disgrace. And NASA officials and astronauts to the contrary, incredible risks are once more being taken.

This, then, is the story of the Apollo 204 fire and its national implications, past and future, and of the still critical need for reexamination of goals and techniques. Hard questions will be asked. What, precisely, has America's stupendous space program done for the American people? What has been its effect on American science and the scientific community? Has the Congress really, ever, performed its duty to supervise the multibillion-dollar expenditures of NASA? Has the aerospace industry, swollen in size by federal funds, acted in the best interests of the nation? How can the Defense Department justify its own space efforts, which, in many cases, nearly duplicate NASA's projects? Where have the members of the press been who, for over a decade, should have been asking these same questions? As the answers to such questions are reached, a story of great contrasts will unfold, contrasts of honesty and deceit, of unmitigated blarney and challenging criticism, of impassioned naiveté and the most calculating cynicism.

It is the story of a project christened, in some inspired flash of Madison Avenue wit, "Apollo." Apollo—he who was born ahead of his time, "a seven-months' child," ancient god of light, of prophecy and truth, of explorers and colonizers, of manly beauty, wielder of the lyre and the bow. The promise of our twentieth-century Apollo is of soaring heavenward, of breaking our ties with Earth, of transcending, at last, a mortal limitation.

The goal has been to walk upon the surface of the Moon, as President Kennedy urged, within the decade—before the stroke of midnight, December 31, 1969.

Chapter 2 ■ Premonitions of Disaster

NASA's claim that everything possible had been done to protect the Apollo 204 astronauts was based on the assumption that the fatal plugs-out test was nonhazardous. That is, since it was not a hazardous test, or at least had not been classified as such, special precautions were neither required nor expected. The fact is that any test or procedure involving pure oxygen is extremely hazardous. NASA's outright failure to face this reality, according to one scientist, represented "an inexcusable casualness about a hazard that was well known to any technician who ever handled pure oxygen . . . a hazard that keeps industry and hospital officials in a constant state of the jitters." According to another authority: "Change the atmosphere of a sealed chamber from a mixture of gases to pure oxygen, pressurize the oxygen and introduce foreign substance into the chamber. You have created a bomb, waiting only for the spark to set off the inferno."

NASA's complacency regarding oxygen bordered on the incredible, since several fires had already occurred in pure-oxygen or oxygen-enriched tests linked to America's space effort.* Early in their space program the Russians had rejected pure oxygen for their cosmonauts. The United States' own Department of Defense has also indicted oxygen as too risky for its manned space projects. A vessel filled with pure oxygen is called by chemists, most re-

* See Chapter 8.

spectfully, an "oxygen bomb." The Apollo 204 astronauts were sealed in a high-pressure oxygen bomb.

According to NASA's associate administrator, Dr. George E. Mueller, in testimony before a Senate investigating committee, "There was not anything really new that day." This assumption shatters when matched against not less than seven "firsts" that occurred, simultaneously, that afternoon on pad 34. Not all these firsts, perhaps, directly contributed to the fire; but they did represent seven good reasons why the test should not have been considered "not . . . really new," or, in the words of another NASA official, "standard procedure":

■ It was the *first* and only use of a new three-piece spacecraft hatch. A new, unified, much safer hatch, designed for the next generation of Apollo spacecraft, was already under testing. The complexity of the three-piece hatch was such that under ideal conditions (i.e., with pressure equal on both sides of the hatch) the astronauts would have needed at least a minute to a minute and a half to remove the three sections and complete their exit. In the case of the fire, with the tremendous build-up of pressure against the inner hatch, it could not be removed at all from inside the spacecraft.

■ It was the *first* plugs-out test in which as many as three hatches were closed on a crew in an oxygen atmosphere at a pressure of sixteen pounds per square inch, that is, pressure greater than that of ordinary air at sea level, which contains only about 20 percent oxygen.

■ It was the *first* occasion of the Apollo emergency escape drill under all-out pre-launch conditions.

■ It was the *first* occasion when certain nonflight flammable materials, such as two foam rubber cushions—to protect the detached hatches during the "egress" (escape) drill—were placed in the spacecraft.

■ It was the very *first* Apollo test with the entire communications system (ground support, launch vehicle, and spacecraft) installed. Nearly two years after the fire, NASA was still experiencing difficulties and failures with this network.

■ Plugs-out was the *first* all-out testing in preparation for the *first* manned flight of an uprated Saturn rocket assembly, that is, the *first* manned flight of the Apollo program.*

■ It was the *first* fully integrated testing of a Block 1 spacecraft that had been "man-rated," that is, judged ready for manned tests. (Block 1 spacecraft were for Earth-orbital flights with the uprated Saturn 1B, whereas Block 2 spacecraft were scheduled for Saturn 5 flights—those, such as Apollo 8 and succeeding missions, destined to make the actual lunar orbits and landings.)

NASA's main line of defense for the poor judgment exhibited in failing to label the plugs-out test as hazardous was that the spacecraft that bore the three astronauts had been put through six and a quarter hours of successful simulated flight tests, prior to the fatal fire. In these tests, an altitude chamber reproduces, as closely as possible, the effects of reduced atmospheric pressure after a spacecraft is launched. As the spacecraft gains altitude, the atmospheric pressure decreases, until eventually, beyond the practical limits of the Earth's atmosphere, the near-vacuum of space is reached.

Unlike the fatal plugs-out test, altitude tests seem always to have been classified, "routinely," as hazardous. The recognized hazard, however, was not fire, but rather that a spacesuit or cabin leak in these "vacuum" conditions could well exhaust the oxygen supply—resulting in suffocation due to lack of oxygen (anoxia) for the astronauts within. In such an emergency, because of an air lock, the crew would have two sets of escape hatches to cope with—those leading from the spacecraft, and those sealing the altitude chamber from the outside air. The main protection provided the astronauts, in the event of such an emergency, was to have a TV camera in the spacecraft, monitoring their activity at all times. Rescue personnel were available outside with breathing apparatus, if needed.

The day of the plugs-out test, the TV camera inside the spacecraft, which was an important piece of flight and test equipment,

* Walter M. Schirra, Jr., R. Walter Cunningham, and Donn F. Eisele ultimately became the first astronauts to fly an Apollo spacecraft. Apollo 7 (October 11–22, 1968) carried a new Block 2 spacecraft that had been completely overhauled following the accident that killed Grissom, White, and Chaffee.

was absent; its retaining brackets had somehow been bent during installation. Instead, the test support personnel had to rely on a camera that was pressed against the spacecraft and pointed through a small window. This camera viewed only the back of the helmet of the center astronaut (White), portions of his lower body, and very little of the cabin interior. White's arms could be observed only when he raised them. Since the cabin was small and poorly illuminated, the TV image obtained was poor at best.

Without a doubt, another element in the tragedy on pad 34 was a "significant policy change"—a change that resulted from the astronauts' request for an emergency escape drill.

In retrospect, it seems almost unbelievable that this emergency exit drill *had been added to the test procedure at the request of the astronauts themselves*—not by NASA planners or any of their contractors. According to the Apollo 204 Review Board:

> The preliminary outline for this test procedure was written by North American Aviation, Inc. (NAA) in July 1966. The test procedure was reviewed and revised periodically over the next few months. In September the flight crew requested that emergency egress practice which was not in the original test outline be added.

In other words, those who were responsible for the safety of the astronauts, and their supporting personnel, saw no need for the prime crew to practice what was essentially a safety drill— even once. As it turned out, it didn't really matter, as far as the future safety of Grissom, White, and Chaffee was concerned. Long before the escape drill was scheduled to begin at T plus three hours (that is, three hours after the point—"T"—of simulated launch), the three astronauts had already been pronounced dead within their capsule.

The real significance of the addition of the escape drill was that it forced a change in the test procedure as originally written by North American Aviation. A simulated trial of the parachute system in the earth landing system (ELS) had to be canceled. The ELS could be tested, on the ground, only by means of electronic sensors whose bulky cables would have made it impossible to conduct the emergency escape drill. It was either one or the other; both tests could not be conducted at the same time.

Thus, by substituting the escape practice for the ELS test, the astronauts introduced a critical change, apparently without precedent, in the test procedure. They sealed themselves behind three hatches—hatches that were far more complex and unfamiliar than had ever been used before; hatches whose three components were installed for the very first time under live conditions with pure oxygen at high pressure; hatches that were so awkward that a new, quick-opening, "unified" hatch had already been designed for the Block 2 spacecraft. This three-piece hatch had been used in the previous altitude test, but the outer (Boost Protective Cover) hatch had not been installed. Ironically, only two hatches sealed the capsule during a hazardous test, but *three* were required to be installed during the plugs-out test, a test which was not regarded as hazardous, but which proved to be disastrous.

Typically, not everyone present during the plugs-out test was informed of this "significant policy change." Moreover, after the astronauts had entered their spacecraft, the support crew was not able to get the outer hatch fully installed.* Members of the crew that tried to remove the outer hatch from the smoking spacecraft found that the hatch had become "distorted." The men needed to locate and insert a special tool in order to get a hand hold on the outer hatch. The distortion might not have occurred if the hatch had been fully installed—the ground crew had no difficulty in removing the inner two, properly installed hatches.

Out of successful completion of the simulated altitude tests grew yet another assumption, symptomatic of poor judgment and overconfidence. Since the spacecraft had passed earlier altitude tests without incident, NASA permitted certain luxury items, conveniences for the astronauts, to be placed in the cabin during the plugs-out procedure. These items—most of them inflammable—included two foam rubber pads provided to cushion the hatches during the egress drill. Also included were additional Velcro pads, nylon netting, and insulating material. Velcro pads are space-age devices designed to enable the astronauts to keep track of paraphernalia such as pencils and other small hand-held

* An appropriate "squawk sheet" (minor defect list) was filled out, reporting this discrepancy. But, according to set procedures, corrective measures would not be taken until after completion of the test.

items. Velcro is a self-adhesive, nylon—and inflammable—material that was applied to the walls of the cabin. Hooks or clamps, built into the pads, held the desired items within arm's reach until they were needed.

The idea, of course, was that with enough of these hooks scattered about, there was less chance of the astronauts' dropping things or wasting time doing housekeeping chores. The additional nylon netting, also inflammable, served a similar purpose. Since the prime crew were strapped on their backs during the pre-launch simulation, anything they dropped would fall to the floor and out of sight. The netting served, therefore, as a "debris net." Draped beneath and around the three couches, it also helped insure that nothing would become lodged behind an instrument panel during the test period—only to emerge as flotsam during the period of "weightlessness" during an actual flight.

There were also a number of "open" (i.e., incomplete) work items that should have been dealt with before the plugs-out test began. Yet even though the test was five days ahead of schedule, it was decided that these details were not essential and could wait until the next test—the final dress rehearsal of the fully fueled rocket. Of the open items, fifty-six were significant procedural changes in the test operations handbook. Those that specifically involved the astronauts may be considered minor— such as a change in the sequence of activities, or a numbering of paragraphs—but the fact remains that neither the astronauts nor the ground crew had had time to familiarize themselves with the changes.

A most significant "open" item was the recommendation by the ground check-out crew (composed of both North American and NASA personnel) that the amount of polyurethane and uralane insulation and couch material be reduced or be replaced. All of these materials—Velcro, foam rubber, nylon netting, polyurethane and uralane plastics—were the very substances that provided the abundant fuel, and whose strategic location provided the path of propagation, required to transform a flash fire into the holocaust that ultimately occurred. In a very real sense, then, from the standpoint of fire potential, this was *not* the same spacecraft that had passed its altitude tests with flying colors.

NASA Administrator James Webb once likened the Apollo command module to "putting an aircraft carrier or nuclear submarine into a package about three or four times as big as [a conference] table." Yet the plugs-out test, involving check-out of this "most complex machine," was considered "standard."

"An Opportunity to Improve"

There was something drastically wrong with the communications systems in spacecraft 012 on Friday, January 27, 1967. Not long after entering the spacecraft, at 1:00 P.M. (about two hours late, due to delays), Gus Grissom is reported to have muttered, "they want to send us to the Moon but they can't establish communications three buildings away [between the cabin and the blockhouse]."

Attempts to improve communications continued after the three astronauts were securely harnessed inside the command module and the hatches had been sealed behind them. The existing communication problems, hazily defined even now, were further compounded by the fact that the command pilot's (Grissom's) microphone, located inside his space helmet, could not be turned off. It remained "live," or keyed.

NASA's corrective measures for this "minor" problem consisted of random switching of channels in the various monitoring centers. An adequate picture of these chaotic hours can best be gained by reviewing some excerpts from the testimony of eyewitness members of the ground support crew. An entry made at 3:13 P.M. in the log book of the test supervisor reads:

1513—Complete Part A—Astronaut Communications all Screwed Up.

One witness later reported on this problem less colorfully but equally emphatically: "The overall communications problem was so bad at times that we could not even understand what the crew was saying."

The communications problem was so overwhelmingly apparent that it infected test activities at another site, where North American technicians were busy monitoring the exercises of a similar, but unmanned command module, spacecraft 017. What happened there, according to the North American personnel, was this:

Shortly before the accident, we were working our spacecraft and all communications were wiped out in our system, due to somebody shouting very loudly and unintelligibly to us and interfering with our conversation.

NASA's thoughtful view of this period in the plugs-out test is, by contrast, a study in Olympian detachment. NASA Deputy Administrator Dr. Robert C. Seamans, Jr., in a memo to Administrator Webb, summed it up this way:

. . . Up to this time there had been only minor difficulties with the equipment. The purpose of the hold [on the countdown] was to provide *an opportunity* to improve communications between the spacecraft and the ground crew.* [Italics added.]

The fact that the ground crew could not communicate effectively with the astronauts, who were completely isolated and sealed in an extremely hazardous environment, seems not to have penetrated NASA's air of constructive hindsight. Evidently, the switching of channels and flipping of switches was largely unauthorized, uncoordinated and almost completely unsupervised. When at last the communications were such that at least garbled voices could be heard, the problem was considered to have been "worked around" and the test was allowed to proceed. Chief astronaut Donald Slayton (one of the seven original astronauts) put it this way: "We finally agreed to pick up the count in spite of the relatively bad communications . . ."

Thus, the "opportunity to improve communications" was finally judged to be a waste of time.

"A Buttermilk Odor"

The communications problem was not the only problem that got "worked around" that day. At 1:03 P.M., seven minutes after entering the spacecraft, Grissom noticed something "funny," according to the log books of two test monitors. His and the other crew members' oxygen supply (provided through a suit loop which connected them to one another) had picked up a peculiar

* Included as part of testimony before the Senate on February 7, 1967.

and unwelcome odor. The supply was supposed to be pure, color-less, odorless oxygen. But somehow it smelled of buttermilk. Since the cause of this "anomaly" (as unexpected phenomena are termed) was not readily discernible, a hold in the countdown was ordered, to permit a semiquantitative analysis of the astronauts' oxygen supply.

The analysis, like the communications hold, ultimately became a waste of time. Two or three spurts, or "purges," of fresh new oxygen gradually got rid of the smell, and further tests were judged unnecessary. So, one hour and twenty-two minutes after Grissom's complaint, the countdown was resumed—without the cause of the "buttermilk" odor having been found. This incident, after the fire, came under careful examination by NASA's Review Board. It remained unexplained, yet was eliminated as a possible cause of the fire. Why then, is it worth mentioning? Simply because it was never explained.

Nor was anyone bothered, at the time, by a "significant" elec-trical surge, picked up at one of the blockhouse monitors just moments before the fire was detected. This surge, an abrupt in-crease in electrical output from the spacecraft, was observed—and that is all. The Review Board investigators were eventually to link it to six other transient anomalies, and in fact its occurrence probably marks the time at which the fire, otherwise undetected, began.[*]

It is apparent that "working around" the anomalous "butter-milk" odor and the communications problem, as well as letting the electrical surge pass, constituted a drastic break with earlier test-operation philosophy. In the volume entitled *Gemini Midpro-gram Conference* (1967) NASA engineers state very clearly, un-der the heading "No Unexplained Transient Malfunctions Per-mitted":

A ground rule of the Gemini Program has been that a transient malfunction represented a nonconformance which would prob-ably recur during countdown or flight at the worst possible time. Experience has shown that failure analysis of a transient in almost every case did uncover a latent defect.

[*] For a minute-by-minute description of events leading up to and through the fire, see Appendices B1 and B2.

The Gemini task force took great pride in the thoroughness of its approach. But then, the Gemini program was a pioneering effort. Its activities could never have been described as "routine" in nature. The conference report elaborates in this way:

... No failure, malfunction, or anomaly is considered to be a random failure. All possible effort is expended to determine the cause of the anomaly to permit immediate corrective action.

The diligent air of those lines, however, belies the thoroughly practical attitude of the entire space program—or any specific NASA project—be it Mercury, Gemini, or Apollo. Within the pages of this same *Gemini Midprogram Conference* volume, the basic NASA philosophy is spelled out:

Mission Success and Crew Safety

A numerical design goal was established to represent the *probability* of the spacecraft performing satisfactorily for the accomplishment of all primary mission objectives. The *arbitrary* value of 0.95, which recognizes a risk of failing to meet 1 primary objective out of 20 on each mission was selected. The 0.95 mission-success goal was included in the prime contract as a *design goal* rather than a *firm requirement*, which would have required demonstration ... Crew safety design goals were also established, but for a much higher value of 0.995 for all missions. *Crew safety is defined as having the flight crew survive all missions or all mission attempts.* [Italics added.]

Interpreted, this seems to indicate that NASA realized that the chances of total success in a given mission were unlikely. Failure of one out of twenty objectives on an individual mission seemed to represent a reasonable working criterion. Contractors and schedulers, however, do not like rigid requirements. There must be some leeway. And so this "success ratio" was recommended as a goal, not a requirement. Manned flights, of course, demand a considerably greater promise of success—and so the goal was "upped" a bit for those missions. However, it must be stressed that the crew-safety goal was not defined in terms of injury or incapacitation, but simply in terms of *survival*.

Thus, it is not surprising that anomalous problems were

window, of the senior pilot Edward White. Donald K. Slayton, an observer in the blockhouse at the time, later testified to the Review Board:

Somewhere about this time it appeared it was a fairly serious situation, and I think I went over and talked to the medics. I recommended that they get on out to the pad area because they were probably going to be needed up there. The Spacecraft Test Conductor cleared them to go, and they left the Blockhouse. After they had been gone three or four minutes, I had a conversation with the, I believe, the Pad Safety Officer. He indicated things looked pretty bad from his communications.

Meanwhile, the pad crew had been busy passing the word along, looking for fire extinguishers, and fumbling with gas masks that wouldn't work. They ran back and forth between the White Room, the umbilical tower, and the service structure. During the frenzy, some of the crew were inadvertently locked out of the White Room. (Its door was designed to open only one way. The reason for the one-way door was that after the moment of T-0 in the plugs-out test, when the umbilicals would be disconnected and the access arm, of which the White Room is a part, swung away, anyone going through that door the wrong way would face a 218-foot drop.) Other rescuers, almost blinded by smoke, searched for the hatch release tool—buried "in a tool-box with 34 other tools." About this time, the Pan American fire department was sending one of its men all the way back down the gantry because nobody had brought up the right equipment. While all this was going on, a grim sequence of events was unfolding within the spacecraft:

At 6:30:22 P.M., some change in the heart rate of Edward White, the astronaut being telemetered for biomedical measurements at the time, was registered. Shortly after, White's heart rate seems to have returned to normal. However, forty-two seconds later, there was a "marked increase" in his heart rate, at about the same time Grissom (?) shouted, "Fire!" (?). Within eight seconds, fire flared near the ceiling. This flash fire (which alone was not lethal) was caused by volatile gases produced by the burning of plastics and insulation near the sources of ignition.

The gases rose in the cabin, reached the point of flammability—the flash point—and were consumed, but not, perhaps, before igniting some of the plentiful Velcro pads along the cabin walls.

At about the same time, the intense local fire beneath Grissom's couch (since aluminum drippings were later found on the floor, it is evident that the temperature was greater than 1241°F., the melting point of aluminum) ignited the nylon net beneath and surrounding the other astronauts' couches. Flames spread rapidly over and beneath the couches, hampering the astronauts' attempts to escape. Their couches and insulation materials, made of polyurethane foam, ignited, as did the numerous remaining Velcro pads that were scattered around the walls of the interior.

However, throughout this period of less than ten seconds—the time it took to start everything burning including the men's nylon (Nomex)-covered suits—the fire was a very special kind of fire. In pure oxygen, combustion is nearly complete; there is little "left over" to form smoke, the visible produce of incomplete combustion. Yet, in the unique environment of the space cabin, noxious substances, including cyanide, acetylene, butane, methane, and especially carbon monoxide, were rapidly building up. Within seconds, these would render all three men unconscious.

Why would all three have lost consciousness almost simultaneously? The answer is, the oxygen that the astronauts breathed, distinct from the oxygen that pressurized the cabin, was provided them through a common set of hoses. Some time after the fire became so intense, eight to ten seconds after Grissom's (?) cry, the flames ate through one or more of the crew's suits. Since the cabin was then an inferno filled with toxic gases, all three were exposed to the now lethal atmosphere within the cabin. Seven seconds later, the build-up of pressure was so great that the capsule ruptured. At this point a fragment of one of the suits was blown out of the cabin, indicating that the suits had been breached before the rupture occurred. Moments after, the differential in pressure between the cabin atmosphere and the outside was equalized. Now the great billows of smoke began. The plastics and nylon in the cabin produced overwhelming quantities of black, sooty smoke as they smoldered in the oxygen-depleted cabin.

Approximately eleven seconds after the flames are presumed to have eaten through one or more of the suits, the last garbled and unidentified utterance was heard from one of the victims. After this it is assumed that all three astronauts were unconscious. They were still alive and breathing during this phase of smoke production, however, for autopsies revealed "soot within nose, oral cavity, trachea, and bronchi." By about 6:36 P.M., a little less than four and a half minutes after the last cry from the astronauts, the support crew managed at last to open the hatches. Because of the heat, smoke, and apparent futility of the situation, no attempt at removal or resuscitation was made by the support crew.

The astronauts' flight manual contained no instructions on how to deal with a fire on the ground. (There were, in fact, no fire extinguishers within the cabin.) On page 6–6 of their handbook, however, were the following directions concerning a suspected inflight fire:

6–21 Smoke or annoying odors in suit circuit—*Continue Mission* open direct O_2 to purge suits.
6–22 Smoke in cabin—*Continue Mission*—Turn off cabin fan. Crew may elect to abort if source of smoke cannot be located and contained—Crew may elect to decompress cabin.

Purging the oxygen system seems to have eliminated the "buttermilk" odor, but the directive to *continue mission* in case of "smoke . . . in suit circuit . . . [or] in cabin"—with an option to decompress—certainly did not save, and could never have saved, any lives that day.

Early NASA releases concerning the fire said that medical personnel arrived "as soon as conditions permitted." They arrived fourteen to eighteen minutes after the fire was discovered. Two NASA physicians who were in the blockhouse monitoring the senior pilot's (White's) physiological condition by means of a biomedical console, set out for pad 34 after being alerted by chief astronaut Donald Slayton. A third medical officer, a Pan American physician, came in the Pan American ambulance— about the same time as the two NASA physicians. Here, where an unexpected catastrophe was an ever-present threat, NASA did not have its own ambulance available for such contingencies. Nor

were physicians near at hand for more common medical emergencies such as a broken arm or leg, a fall from a gantry, or a
heart attack.

When the physicians did reach the White Room, they were
told by those who had been fighting the blaze that the crew was
dead. The smoke was too dense for the doctors to see clearly,
and so they surmised, "After a quick evaluation, it was decided
that nothing could be gained by attempting immediate egress
and resuscitation . . . It was evident that the crew had not survived the heat, smoke, and thermal burns." The physicians then
returned to ground level to await the clearing of the White Room
area of smoke.

NASA's initial reaction to the fire on the ground was shocked
disbelief. It just could not have happened. (The astronauts' space
suits were later turned over to the FBI to ascertain whether sabotage might have been involved. Nothing was found to confirm
this suspicion.)

Slayton's testimony shows how the full horror began to dawn
on Apollo personnel:

> . . . I elected to call Houston immediately [three or four minutes
> after he had conferred with the medics and the pad safety
> officer] and get things cranked up back there just in case they
> were as bad as we thought they were. They did set up a com-
> mand post immediately and got prepared to notify the families.
> I think it was about ten minutes later before we finally got
> positive confirmation. We did get a call right after the hatch
> was off that it looked very bad up there which is something
> like five minutes after the fire started. We could not confirm
> positively that the crew was dead. As soon as we did confirm
> that, I called Houston; and I went up to the Pad area sometime
> after completing my calls to Houston. I don't remember the
> exact time . . . [It would have been approximately between
> 6:50 and 6:55 P.M., since Slayton next testified he was the first
> to leave the blockhouse after the doctors. When he arrived, the
> doctors had left to await the clearing of the area of smoke.]

Dr. Charles A. Berry, Chief of Center Medical Operations,
Manned Spacecraft Center at Houston, later testified that the
astronauts would have lost consciousness some twenty-five to

thirty seconds after the first of their suits had been breached. All hope of resuscitation would have been lost about four minutes after unconsciousness. Dr. Berry's *post facto* testimony indicates that there would have been slim hope of resuscitation only during the passage of four and a half minutes' time. The hatches, according to the Review Board testimony, "were off at 6:36 P.M.," or about five minutes after the fire was detected.

However, the physicians arrived eight and a half minutes later and *no one* knew, at that time, how the astronauts had died. The exact cause of death was not determined until autopsies the next day. Implicit, therefore, is the fact that no one actually then knew if the astronauts were dead. L. D. Reece, North American Aviation Systems technician, assisted in removing the hatches and thought he heard the crew. He even called several times into the cabin, but got no response. No one had yet touched the crew. It was too dark and smoky to see what the cabin contained.

Thus, while the outside world was led to believe that the astronauts had been incinerated in the fire, the support people knew otherwise. One of the support crew, peering through the smoke-shrouded hatch, had seen an astronaut's naked, uncharred leg through a shredded space suit. The doctors made the same assumption: the crew could not have survived the intense heat, smoke, and thermal burns. The official autopsy examination reports clearly state: "Cause of death: asphyxia due to inhalation of toxic gases due to fire—Contributory cause of death: thermal burns." Subsequent medical reports later added that the first-, second-, and third-degree burns suffered by the astronauts were not so extensive as to have caused death. Moreover, it was not known what portion of these burns had been sustained after death had occurred.* Dr. Berry, before the Senate, corrected the agency's "preliminary" pronouncement on February 27—twenty days later. (The autopsies were performed on Saturday, January 28. The death certificates were signed on January 29.) When Dr. Berry updated NASA's version of the cause of death, his remarks were prefaced by:

> Mr. Chairman, and committee, the death certificates stated the cause of death to be: asphyxiation due to smoke inhalation due

* See Appendix C for official autopsy reports.

to fire.* Our continuing medical analysis of this accident, including the toxicology studies also confirm smoke inhalation. The crew did have some thermal burns of second and third degree (involving all layers of the skin but without charring), but these were not of sufficient magnitude to cause death.

Clinton Anderson, chairman of the Senate Committee investigating the death of the three astronauts, responded to Dr. Berry's updated autopsy findings as follows:

I appreciate that statement because people are asking many questions about what you achieved as the final result. I think that is a good statement.

Nevertheless, the general public was left with the impression that the astronauts had died of burns.

It was the kind of confusion that a great journalistic crusade begins with, the kind of officially sanctioned misunderstanding that attracts an alert and fearless reporter. But there was no crusade.

There had, in fact, been countless opportunities to alert the American public to the waywardness of its massive space program. But NASA's public information staff, and the general press as well, seemed to have decided that the public was not really interested in being informed about the continuing flood of failures that were being reported in the Apollo system, an average of fifty to seventy-five per week since the project had gotten under way in 1961. In its December 26, 1966 issue, *Aviation Week*, the acknowledged leader among aerospace trade magazines, reported, rather blandly, just a month before the astronauts' deaths: "the Apollo hardware is slowly maturing into a qualified manned lunar landing system . . . but . . . command module [spacecraft] development history bulges with more than 20,000 separate failures logged, and officials are critically concerned with establishing an order of importance in rejecting suspect components." Such failures had already demanded more than one hundred important design changes in the spacecraft.

* The original (February 3) pronouncement, made by Deputy Administrator Seamans, used the expression "smoke inhalation," and the later one (February 27) used the same expression. The reason for this minor obfuscation, misquoting of the official autopsy reports, is not clear. Perhaps smoke inhalation sounds more humane than "death due to toxic [poisonous] gases."

In what will undoubtedly remain one of the most candid press briefings in NASA's history, Dr. Joseph F. Shea, the pre-fire Apollo spacecraft manager, had said, "we have been trying to take an approach in the program that in effect says, run the program in a balanced way, don't try to make everything too complex, or you'll never get the job done." Shea pointed, by way of example, to 220 failures in the environmental control system, the life support system for the Apollo spacecraft. In December this vital unit was still in a "rebuild and retest cycle." Shortly after the fire, Shea was replaced as program manager and reassigned to Washington. He soon left NASA for a job at Polaroid.

Evidence of slipshod workmanship and faulty inspection was nothing new in America's space program. It had occurred during the Mercury (one-man) and the Gemini (two-man) projects, and was simply being carried over to the Apollo (three-man) program. William Hines, in a post-mortem *Nation* article of April 24, 1967, recalls one of the astronauts' in-jokes of the period:

. . . an astronaut paying a triumphal post-flight visit to the factory where his spacecraft was built, [is] asked if there is any particular individual he would care to meet. "Yes," says the fictitious astronaut, "I'd like to meet the son of a bitch who welded his lunch box to the left yaw thruster."

The Mercury program provided many actual incidents that underscore the irony of the joke. Loose wires, dust and other debris were left in the Mercury spacecraft by careless workmen. In the *Mercury Project Summary*, published by NASA in October, 1963, the following comment appears under the heading "cleanliness":

Early in the Mercury program motion pictures of the inside of a spacecraft in orbit showed washers, wire cuttings, bolts, and alligator clips floating in the cabin. The cabin fan became plugged on an unmanned flight with similar free-floating debris . . .

At one point even the oxygen and water supplies were found to have been contaminated in a Mercury spacecraft—a case of being first in space with water and atmospheric pollution. Such reports provoked a Congressional committee to call James E. Webb, NASA administrator, on the carpet. Webb, cited by

Fortune magazine for "his skill in Washington infighting," came out unmarked. The only apparent casualty was Walter C. Williams, operations director for Project Mercury and a bold critic of industry performance in both Mercury and Gemini. Williams left NASA.

Nevertheless, Mercury's sanitation deficiencies apparently did not lead to greater "cleanliness" in the next manned space flights, the Gemini series. When Walter Schirra's Gemini 6 was about to lift off to rendezvous with the already orbiting Gemini 7, his Titan 2 booster cut off just after ignition, and the eleven-story rocket remained on the pad. Insulated in the capsule, Schirra knew that there had been a definite indication of ignition; but he "felt" he was not lifting off. He could either abort the mission, or do nothing. He chose to do nothing, thereby saving the rocket, the spacecraft, and probably himself and his copilot Stafford as well. (Three days later, the two astronauts and their Gemini 6 rendezvoused successfully with Borman's Gemini 7.) Why had the Titan 2 fiizzled? According to Mark Bloom, *New York Daily News* science editor, an "electrical ignition plug" fell out an instant before blast-off. Furthermore, a mechanic had left a dust cap in the pressurizing line of one of the engines. If the ignition plug had not fallen out, the dust cap would have caused a faulty pressure reading and might well have caused a major disaster. A quality-control inspector had checked off the work as properly done.

Of the Apollo astronauts, Grissom was particularly outspoken on the subject of sloppy workmanship and slipshod quality control. It was hardly gratitude that prompted him, in one of his last exclusive interviews under a contract with World Book Science Service, to characterize the Apollo spacecraft as "a bucket of bolts." Earlier, in dissatisfaction with the Apollo simulator, he had playfully "hung a lemon on it." Even Grissom was finally satisfied, however, that his complaints had been heeded. He was wrong.

Chapter 3 ■ The Failure of the Press and TV

In cooperation with the National Parks Service, NASA has established a permanent visitors' building at the John F. Kennedy Space Center, America's "springboard to the Moon." Guided bus tours, operated by Trans World Airlines under a NASA contract, are also available (Tour A, an hour and a half, $1.75; Tour B, two and a half hours, $2.50; no charge for children under two, student group rates available). The buses, bearing the proud and curious, roam among the giant shadows cast upon the Florida sand by this awesome space-age Stonehenge, described one observer as a "monument to man's questing spirit."

On the morning of January 28, less than eighteen hours after the accident, the Cape Kennedy tourist buses continued to run right on schedule. One of the tour buses carried an enterprising local reporter, who knew that the $2.50 route would bring him within one mile of launch pad 34—two miles closer than any other newsmen could get that morning. Indeed, the rest of the press was being kept some miles away from pad 34, waiting for NASA to release information.

But as the bus driver pointed out the Cape's newest attraction —the soot-ringed top of the launch complex—this reporter was busy taking notes on the shock and sadness of his fellow passengers for the edification of the readers of Brevard County's *Today,* "Florida's Space-Age Newspaper."

In a strangely specific way, the episode illustrates the relationship that has always existed between NASA, the news media and the public. The bus tours went on—just as NASA's public relations machine, after a disastrous fire, seemed unable to stop itself and change direction. The space program had always been "open" to the space buffs and the tourists—the uncritical, the people who wished to be awed. So many times before, the space program had teetered on the edge of a disaster, and always, before, things had turned miraculously into another public relations triumph, another "success."* Once more, a stray reporter came within calling distance of a big story—and turned away. And, once more, the majority of the press was some distance removed, clustered together as if to gain confidence by their numbers, awaiting NASA handouts and press kits.

The question must be asked: Where have responsible space and science reporters been during a decade and more of American space efforts? Where, specifically, was the press on the night of January 27, 1967?

Not one single reporter of any public media was on hand at Cape Kennedy to cover the plugs-out test. *Editor and Publisher,* a trade magazine for the newspaper publishing industry, felt compelled to print an article by Frank Murray eight days after the fire, pointing out that up to fifteen hundred newsmen had covered earlier manned launches. On these previous occasions, too, a small advance guard of aerospace reporters had always been present to cover final pre-launch tests such as the Apollo 204 plugs-out test.

Undoubtedly, the experience of the Mercury and Gemini missions had taught NASA that interest in the space program could not be kept at fever-pitch forever. After two or three launches, the hoopla, no matter how loud or sustained or varied, began to lose its public impact. NASA's problem: How could the reporters be kept happy, interested and quiet—all at the same time?

NASA's solution was to call a press conference for December 15 and 16, 1966, at the Manned Spacecraft Center in Houston,

* "For instance, in all of the Mercury flights, there is only one flight that would have been concluded successfully, had it not been for the pilot. And had it not been for their own efforts, we would have lost at least two pilots." H. A. Kuehnel, then chief of the Spaceflights Operations Branch, NASA, quoted in Shirley Thomas, *Men of Space* (Philadelphia: Chilton Company, 1965), Vol. VII, p. 107.

Texas. This "Apollo News Media Conference" was no ordinary press conference. NASA poured on the charm. Astronauts Grissom, White and Chaffee (the prime Apollo crew) were there, and so was the back-up crew of Schirra, Eisele and Cunningham (who became the prime crew of Apollo 7, October 11-22, 1968), as well as chief astronaut Slayton. Much of their talk-on-record with the newsmen centered on the problem of how the astronauts would react to "suit-donning and -doffing" during the planned inside-the-capsule TV coverage of their flight. Grissom said he was "very bashful." White said, "Would you believe helmets and gloves?" The newsmen laughed; funny heroes made good copy. So did Houston's Apollo spacecraft program manager, Joseph Shea, punster and poet, who composed a seasonal space poem based upon "The Night Before Christmas." It began:

It was the night before launching
    and all through the center
Everyone wondered how soon they'd reenter.
    The Spacecraft atop of the Saturn stood bare
In hopes that the last black box spare was soon there.
    The NASA's were nestled all snug in their beds
Convinced that we finally had beaten the Reds . . .

It was a gala occasion, but the message came through loud and clear: Don't waste too much time on this first Apollo mission. Bigger and better things were to come. As Shea put it, after softening up the reporters with his verse, "It's almost a bland mission to describe because it's not spectacular."

The newsmen were assured, as usual, that first-hand reporting would be more than adequately handled by NASA itself. For example, Jack King, NASA's chief public information officer at Cape Kennedy, would be in the blockhouse monitoring during the final testing, producing copy for news bulletins.*

* The reputation of NASA's public information staff had not been unsullied. It is an old Washington joke that the letters N. A. S. A. stand for "Never A Straight Answer." One particularly memorable example of the space agency's curious decisions regarding news management occurred at the end of Lieutenant Commander M. Scott Carpenter's Mercury-Atlas 7 flight in May, 1962. For almost an hour, the public was led to believe that nobody knew where Carpenter's capsule had splashed down or whether, indeed, the astronaut was dead or alive. The outspoken Walter M. Schirra said of this incident: "I think people who were relaying information out of Mercury control center boo-booed in not saying that we knew where Scott was."

In short, NASA told the press not to be too awed by the first "bland" manned Apollo mission. And the press was not.

Such behavior was hardly new. Almost from its formation in 1958, NASA had enjoyed a very special relationship with both the aerospace industry press and the public media of print and electronics. Reporters realized that space exploration was quite simply the greatest "science story" of all time. It was also a lot easier, and more fun, to cover than most "science stories." It had just about everything: elements of patriotism and a challenge to American know-how, gee-whiz machines, honest-to-goodness space ships, a new breed of instant hero in the astronauts, the promise of mankind's wildest dreams fulfilled, and the ever-present threat of tragedy. Science fiction had leaped out of the comics into the American mainstream. Many of the larger newspapers, the radio and television networks, and both wire services, had set up permanent facilities at Houston and Cape Kennedy.

In such an atmosphere, the press hardly needed wooing, but it was wooed nevertheless by the aerospace industry and NASA alike. Reporters flew to one burgeoning facility after another, were introduced to the esteemed Wernher von Braun, obtained interviews with space-age luminaries. They learned the new jargon of the space age: to use "mated" or "wedded" to describe the joining of rocket and spacecraft; to call engineers "scientists"; that verbs such as "enhance" and "uprate" were space-age verbs for "improve"; that "integrity" was mechanical, not moral. They learned, too, to call Virgil Grissom "Gus" and Walter Schirra "Wally," and to enjoy Joseph Shea's poetry and puns. It was, in a way, like belonging to an exclusive space-age club, the very same club to which the celebrated astronauts belonged. And there was always a stream of small, thoughtful forget-me-nots: leather-bound books on space exploration, cigarette lighters and jumbo-sized old-fashioned glasses embossed with the name of this or that NASA contractor.

It was all very euphoric, a time of camaraderie and mutual back-rubbing. When criticism was presented, it tended to be passed off as reactionary old-fogeyism. John Lear has described this pre-fire period in the *Saturday Review*:

> . . . the vigorous discussion [of the Moon goal] that had been invited never occurred. A few eminent men . . . trumpeted pro-

test. But their voices, and those of a handful of courageous colleagues, were soon drowned by a ceaseless propaganda barrage from the National Aeronautics and Space Administration and from lobbyists for moonship-makers with fat advertising contracts to stimulate the receptiveness of communications media . . .

Originally, intelligent people everywhere feared the undefined hazards of voyaging a mean distance of 238,000-odd miles across poorly charted seas in the face of the solar wind; but on the promise that it would give candid reports of all that happened on the suborbital and then on the orbital flights of the Mercury (one-man crew) and Gemini (two-man crew) spacecraft, NASA finally established the impression in the minds of most people that the dangers had been exaggerated and that all reasonable precautions were being taken.

The long NASA-press courtship was interrupted abruptly on the evening of January 27, 1967. As might be expected, there were recriminations, hurt feelings, and the baring of old wounds on both sides. Oddly, with only a few exceptions, the press remained silent as NASA accused newsmen (rather than NASA's own public information staff) of consistently misinforming the public.

At approximately 7:00 P.M., on the evening of the tragedy, about a half hour after the fire began, AP reporter Jim Strothman had first word of an accident from a "reliable source." At 7:55 P.M., a bulletin, released by AP's Miami office, indicated that there had been an accidental fire at launch pad 34, killing at least one person, who might have been an astronaut. This vague and uncertain news was promptly broadcast over radio and television.

At about 8:05 P.M., Gordon Harris, NASA public affairs officer at the Cape, told both AP and UPI, in separate telephone conversations, that there had been "a fatality," and suggested that the fatality had been an astronaut who had died in an explosion or fire on the launch pad. Finally, at about 8:32 P.M., a full two hours after the fire, NASA announced that all three of the prime crew had been killed.

The official NASA justification for delaying the news was that time was needed to inform the next of kin. This motive cannot be questioned, and is not. But are we expected to believe that the "a fatality" phrase was designed to spare the next of kin? An "a fatality" release came an hour and a half after it was known that all three had died. Apparently, NASA had decided on a common news-management stratagem: the deliberate release of piecemeal information, presumably to soften the nation's shock. Perhaps, also, NASA was hoping for time—time to reorganize, time to decide how to handle the worst disaster of the space age.*

Sometime after 8:05 P.M., NASA officials began to control the news with a firmer hand. All the initial news releases were carefully reexamined, numbered, and re-released. The original 8:05 release, for instance, read:

Release #1

Cape Kennedy

Released Shortly After Accident at 6:31 p.m. EST 1/27/67

There has been an accidental fire at Launch Complex 34 during the plug-out test of the Apollo-Saturn 204 involving a fatality. More will be announced after next of kin are notified. The prime crew was in the spacecraft.

This release was then retyped and labeled "A/S 204 Release #1." Significantly, the word "a" was dropped—so that the revised "first release" then read, "There has been fatality." The original release was conveniently disavowed by the disclaimer that it had been "unauthorized."

There are several possible explanations for this obvious indiscretion. The editorial change from the specific mention of "a [singular] fatality" to the less specific and very vague "fatality," which can be taken to mean one or several persons, seems to have been an attempt to cover the first release—a statement that included a deliberate deceit. NASA's best information officers, in their noble attempt to save the agency's image, had gone on record as having said, either as a fact or as an implication, that at least one person was dead. But of course it had been known

---

* Very nearly the same reaction occurred when aquanaut Berry L. Cannon, a civilian electronics engineer died on February 17, 1969 while with the Navy Project Sealab 3, at a depth of 600 feet in the Pacific. First news releases said he had died of an apparent heart attack. When an autopsy revealed no signs of cardiac arrest, it was learned that he had died of carbon dioxide poisoning. It was then learned that "personal failure" had resulted in one of the crews' breathing canisters not being supplied with the chemical required to remove carbon dioxide. The Navy at first refused to identify whose canister had been empty. The Sealab 3 project commander hinted that "sabotage might have been involved."

all this time that three victims had died, and that the three were astronauts, not some anonymous members of the support crew. Once the immediate shocked disbelief had subsided, the public information staff must have realized that the error would have to be corrected, or else additional discrepancies were likely to become necessary. Therefore, they simply rewrote the news release, an act that suggests NASA may have actually believed that public reaction could be contained.

Subsequent releases identified the accident as a "flash" fire. This proved, as we shall see, to be a persistent myth. It enabled everyone, including most members of the press and of the Congress, to believe that the astronauts had died quickly, before they were really aware of what was happening to them. This myth also suggested that rescue was doomed from the start.

At the Cape the next morning, Saturday, the press got its first taste of what was to come. The newsmen knew that NASA public information officer Jack King had been in the blockhouse Friday night monitoring the test at the time of the accident. But King proved no help at all. He had been instructed to "save his eyewitness reports" for the official inquiry.

NASA chose as its official spokesman Major General Samuel C. Phillips, director of the Apollo program at NASA's Washington headquarters. He had been flown hastily to the Cape the night before. The major general, presiding at a press conference, stated that the spacecraft had been on "internal" power at the time of the accident. By that time at least some reporters had determined that the spacecraft might have been on external power (which was the case). The same error was made the previous night at about 11:05 P.M. by Paul Haney, public affairs officer at the Manned Spacecraft Center in Houston, Texas. Subsequently, Phillips' and Haney's relatively insignificant misunderstanding was corrected, presumably at the Cape. In any event, the two space centers could not agree when the newsmen later inquired about the inconsistency. Attempts to settle the point with Julian Scheer, Chief, Public Affairs, NASA headquarters in Washington, D.C., drew "no comment."

By Sunday, the newsmen, tired of being restricted to the monitoring blockhouse miles from pad 34 and frustrated by lack of information and pictures, were clamoring to send at least some representatives up the service structure for first-hand observations and pictures of the burned-out spacecraft. NASA countered with a suggestion that a still photographer and a newsreel photographer might go to the scene and report their observations to the rest upon their return. The reporters balked, insisting that a qualified newsman should represent them. George Alexander, then with *Aviation Week* and an experienced hand on the NASA beat, was unanimously selected by the impatient reporters. After an hour of close-at-hand observation of the scene of the accident, Alexander reported back that the interior of the cabin was gutted, debris-strewn, and covered with gray ash and soot. He had also observed melted hoses and insulation and a "still recognizable" flight plan book.

Thus, two days after the fire, newsmen finally had some hard copy. But it was only a glimpse into the full story. NASA again pulled down the shades as its Review Board went to work in earnest.

By then, a distorted version of the fire, based on NASA information, was already being imprinted on the public consciousness. There were two main elements of distortion. The first was the notion that the astronauts had been literally cremated, as shown by the use of such phrases as "incineration" (*Newsweek*, February 6, 1967) and "charred bodies" (*Time*, February 3, 1967). The second was that it had been a flash fire that "was over in an instant" (*Newsweek*), and that the astronauts had died "as soon as they noticed the fire" (*Time*).

The persistence of these misconceptions, long after even NASA itself had been forced to correct them, is powerful testimony to the authority of first impressions. And persist they did, in the most influential circles:

■ Over a month after the accident, John Lear, in a *Saturday Review* article that was highly critical of the events surrounding the fire, spoke of "three charred skeletons."

■ Almost three months after the accident on ABC's "Issues and Answers," ABC Science Editor Jules Bergman had to be dispossessed of his belief in the astronauts' cremation. In a brief pre-program discussion, he apparently mentioned that the astronauts had been "instantly cremated." Later, on the live portion of the program, NASA's Colonel Frank Borman, astronaut and Review Board member, felt compelled to correct Bergman.

■ A year to the day after the fire—January 27, 1968—in a memorial tribute by *Today*, "Florida's Space-Age Newspaper," a front-page editorial recalled: "one year ago the men, their faith, their hopes turned to charred embers in seconds." On page 2, a *Today* reporter reflected on that day the astronauts had "burned to death."

■ Not only newspapers and magazines but some of the most reputable source and reference books have accepted the notion that the astronauts "burned to death." The phrase appears, for example, in the 1968 McGraw-Hill *Encyclopedia of Space*.

■ Even the astronauts themselves perpetuate the myth. Commander Wally Schirra in *Life* magazine, December 6, 1968, said: "Ever since Gus Grissom, Ed White and Roger Chaffee . . . were incinerated during a routine test."

The persistence of the myth of instant death in a flash fire reflects, in large part, NASA's own persistence in shaping the facts in the first few emotional days after the fire. Administrator Webb, asked by Olin Teague of Texas, of the House Subcommittee on NASA Oversight, to describe NASA's control of information after the fire, revealed that on January 31, 1967, a telegram had been sent to Apollo contractors by Mr. John G. McClintock, chief of the program control division, in Houston. It said, in part: "As a result of the recent accident involving spacecraft 012 and in the interest of the Apollo program, contractors are asked to have their personnel refrain from participating in any of the following activities pertaining to the Apollo program: Speeches (except currently scheduled courses of instruction or familiarization); Presentation of technical papers; Publication of articles in periodicals or technical journals; Holding of news conferences; and News releases."

McClintock's telegram then gave a clear warning to all contractors and subcontractors to guard against "pressure from news media" which might "lead towards speculative conclusions concerning the accident." The message ended with the admonition to tell reporters nothing but what they could find "in the public domain."

Webb then went on to explain to Teague that a second telegram, sent on February 2, 1967, to the Manned Spacecraft Center, Kennedy Space Center and the Marshall Space Flight Center, served to lessen (but only partially) NASA's stranglehold on the news.*

This second missive, prepared by George Mueller, NASA associate administrator, and Julian Scheer, assistant administrator for public affairs, pointed out that "this matter is in the hands of the Review Board and no speculation on causes or probable cause is proper." Speeches *per se* were not forbidden. However, "the speaker must stay away from those areas about the accident which speculate on causes or probable causes . . . Discretion must always be exercised, but there is no blanket embargo."

While the Mueller-Scheer directive did not expressly forbid technical papers, articles in journals or periodicals, or news conferences, it did insist that all such information be cleared with NASA. It was particularly insistent on two points: first, that personnel refrain from all "speculation" ("such as on one-gas versus mixed-gas atmospheres"); second, that "contractors understand their responsibility to the Review Board. The desire is not to hamper the Board in its work . . ."

Faced during these days with an almost total vacuum of hard, reliable news, many publications sought to feed the public's concern by printing emotional first-hand reminiscences about the astronauts. UPI went so far as to cable a reporter, reassigned in Saigon, for his personal memories of the dead astronauts. The effect of such remembrances, John Lear has noted, was that:

> A notable period of time elapsed before any major detail of the tragedy was released, and then the story was funneled through reporters closely associated with the dead men. Being human, these commentators were deeply involved emotionally, and allowed themselves to become vehicles for a propaganda campaign to support the 1970 deadline as a memorial to the sacrificed heroes.

* See Appendix D for both NASA communications regarding release of news.

Eventually, certain newsmen—for example, John Noble Wilford of *The New York Times*—began to see weaknesses in NASA's official fire story. Five days after the fire, Wilford received information from some talkative engineers before NASA's embargo could be rigorously enforced. They relayed the distinct impression that at least two of the astronauts had gotten free of their couches and had attempted to remove the hatches. This story reported anguished cries from the crew and other unpleasant details. While some elements of Wilford's story later proved exaggerated,* NASA was forced to correct earlier statements that the astronauts had died quickly, silently and painlessly. Subsequently, it was learned that Senior Pilot White had indeed gotten partially out of his couch, and may well have begun attempts to remove the hatch before he was overcome by the poisonous gases. The myth that "everything was done that could have been done" began to crumble.

Like Wilford, a few other reporters began to reassess the meager information NASA had been feeding them. It became clear that NASA's first two, and only, informal briefings immediately following release of news of the fire had been, to say the least, disorganized. In Houston, the evening of January 27, Haney had been asked, "Paul, other than the environmental control system—oxygen—were there any other critical substances on board?"—and again later, "Is there anything combustible in the command module? Other than oxygen?"

Haney's reply was: "No, but that in itself, of course, saturates all the insulation and all the other surfaces that it sees in the spacecraft."

Neither Haney nor the newsmen, at this point, appeared to remember much about the inside of the spacecraft. The Review Board later identified 1,412 nonmetallics or combustibles—and oxygen was not one of them. The information officer and press could have been corrected by any eighth grade general science student, who knows that oxygen does not burn. It *supports* combustion. Haney later inserted the comment that oxygen burned explosively, that it was a burning agent.

* Wilford's story, which spoke of charred skin and other grisly details, must have contributed to the myth that the astronauts had been burned to death.

Haney was obviously confused. Asked if the hatch was pressurized at the time of the accident, he replied, "No, the spacecraft itself was not pressurized. It was sealed."

One newsman at Haney's briefing must have really thought he was on to something. When he learned that the suits were on pure oxygen, and at least "partially pressurized," he asked a series of questions geared at establishing that the astronauts had burned within their suits, and that the rescuers, upon opening the hatches of the smoldering furnace, had found empty suits with bits of ashes inside. A *Time* reporter must have been listening. *Time* reported, on February 3, that "the flames were apparently sucked into the astronauts' space suits, killing them . . ."

When Major General Phillips was questioned the next morning at the Cape, a newsman inquired about previous fires "in the history of Mercury, Gemini, and Apollo . . . manned or unmanned." Phillips replied: "Has there ever been a fire in the previous manned spaceflight program? To the best of my knowledge there has not."

The harassed Paul Haney was almost—but not quite—as positive. His response to the same question the night before had been: "You might recall, we were doing a chamber run—the Navy was doing it for NASA about four years ago . . . and they had a flash fire in the chamber . . . They were burned, but they managed to get the fire out. It was in a regular—it wasn't a spacecraft exactly, it was a room. There were several bad burns but there was no loss of life. That's the only thing of this kind that I can recall.*

Both NASA officials were either very poorly informed or had suffered lapses of memory comparable to total amnesia. Most of the press remained unperturbed, however, until a few days later, when an altitude chamber test at Brooks Air Force Base in Texas claimed the lives of two more men—only this time at a much lower cabin pressure than had existed in the Apollo 012. At last, reporters started digging, and came up with the information that there had been at least some previous fires** in NASA test-

---

* Haney seems to have been referring to a fire that occurred November 17, 1962, in the U.S. Navy's Aircrew Equipment Laboratory. Test conditions were 100 percent oxygen at 5 p.s.i.

** The history of NASA's oxygen fires is fully discussed in Chapter 8, supplemented by Appendix G.

ing programs involving pure-oxygen and oxygen-enriched environments. But nobody seemed to know just how many and how
similar these fires had been.

By and large, however, the press proved to be very cooperative
during this trying time in NASA's career. How could a reporter
be critical in a time of national loss? In a talk before the American Institute of Aeronautics and Astronautics, in Cocoa Beach,
Florida, on February 6, 1967, Dr. Kurt H. Debus, director of
Kennedy Space Center, once more reiterated the proper and
patriotic attitude:

> . . . we will go forward with Apollo, with the unmanned
> scientific spacecraft launch programs, and whatever future
> missions are entrusted to us, forever mindful that this is what
> Virgil Grissom, Edward White and Roger Chaffee would want
> us to do.

> And so we are working, as Gus Grissom, Ed White and Roger
> Chaffee would want us to do, at the Apollo launch complexes
> which will be seen on your tour.

It can hardly be argued that NASA was not aware of the tremendous public relations value of its astronauts. NASA's popu-
larity in large part was built upon the astronauts' super-hero
image—the public is not likely to fall head over heels in love
with a rocket assembly. America's space effort, quite obviously,
owed much to the astronauts. NASA and the aerospace industry,
aided by a cooperative press, posthumously repaid Grissom,
White, and Chaffee by pushing the theme that they had been
simply test pilots doing their job, fully conscious of the hazards,
in full knowledge of the death risk. Continued concern over
their deaths, it was suggested, did a disservice to the astronauts'
memory and also prevented "getting on with the job"—something the three dead astronauts "would want us to do," as Kurt
Debus put it. This approach, not surprisingly, proved especially
appealing to the aerospace industry. A mere ten days after the
accident, an editorial in *Technology Week*, one of the industry's influential spokesmen and apologists, urged, "Let's knock it
off!" by which was meant the "maudlin, saccharine concern" for
the astronauts.

It was apparent that NASA concurred—but with more reserve.

The argument that Grissom, White and Chaffee were nothing but overglamorized pilots had many things to recommend it, not the least of which were the cold facts. It was not "the press," alone, however, who in the past had turned the astronauts into larger-than-life scientist-athletes, Buck Rogers, Jack Armstrong, and the Hardy Boys rolled into one. NASA had exuberantly contributed to the image-building. NASA had spent hundreds of thousands of dollars on publicity, public relations, personal appearances designed to "sell" the astronauts as anything but re-treaded test pilots, as the following table displayed by NASA at the December 15–16, 1966 Houston "Apollo News Media Conference" shows:

ASTRONAUT PUBLIC AFFAIRS ACTIVITIES
1966
Jan. thru Nov.

Public Appearances (Includes overseas tours)	810
Formal Presentations	314
PAO Input (Friday Interviews)	137
Correspondence Processed	73,360
Controlled VIP Items	2,001
Appearance requests (exclusive of telephone requests)	1,592

It all served a highly useful purpose, offering a means by which the public could identify with America's space program: human interest. And human interest means popular support; popular support means money from the Congress. So, as long as it worked, NASA and the aerospace industry were very willing to have heroes as astronauts.

Then on January 27, 1967, the hero image suddenly became a liability, and the astronauts, by a wave of NASA's wand, were turned back into test pilots. NASA blamed the press for creating the super-hero image.

The jilted press suffered indignity after indignity. What is surprising is how placidly the newsmen took this abuse from NASA. Joseph Shea, who a little over a month before had been entertaining reporters with puns and doggerel at Houston, proved a bit less than the newsmen's trusted ally. Four days after the fire, on January 31, he was telling Review Board members at the Cape how his experience could help them "to control the release of all information" and guard against the "amplification of inconsequentials" by the press. "We're trying to give you," Shea told the Review Board, "at least the ability to tap our background of experience here, and what the reporters are like and what they might resonate on and what they might not resonate on."

All through the winter and spring of 1967, the press continued to take abuse. A congressman-friend of NASA, George P. Miller of California, chairman of the House Science and Astronautics Committee, commiserating with Administrator Webb, spoke of "the very gratuitous and generous build-up that was given NASA through the public media." Administrator Webb himself showed a strange kind of gratitude. In a speech to members of the House Science and Astronautics Committee, in which he asked "for whom the Apollo bell tolls," Webb commented:

It tolls for an open program continuously evaluated by opinion-makers with little time for sober second thought—operating in the brilliant color and brutal glare of a real-time, world-wide mass media that moves with the speed of a TV camera from euphoria to exaggerated detail.

The public media, of course, were not entirely innocent of hero-making. The astronauts make good copy. A nation has a hunger for heroes. This need was filled, but other important responsibilities were slighted.

If, instead, the press and other media had been on guard for problems, for the failures that were so very numerous, had looked into earlier fires, had cared to search out the glaring discrepancies everywhere in the space record, NASA might not have stuck to its hastily made decisions, such as the highly prejudicial choice of pure oxygen as a cabin atmosphere. NASA, after all, must report to the Congress, and congressmen are very sensitive to what the public media are saying back home. Newspapermen and TV commentators could have done their job. There were many clear and ominous warnings of imminent tragedy. *Aviation Week, Aerospace Technology,* and other aerospace publications such as *Space Business Daily* all reported the events, good and bad, as they occurred. Seldom, it is true, do any aerospace reporters go crusading, but they report the news. It was there for any responsible, general newspaperman to pick up, if he had simply looked

As James A. Skardon has pointed out in the *Columbia Journalism Review:*

> Through 1966—and up to the time of the Apollo fire—there was a series of accidents which, if viewed as a pattern, could have alerted the press to a need for a thorough re-examination of the Apollo program.

> These mishaps were reported as individual events. There were stories to the effect that they would slow up the moon schedule, which was (and remains) an ever-present preoccupation of the press. Apparently no space writer or publication considered them as a pattern nor did any extensive looking into the quality and safety aspects of Apollo.

Back in mid-1964, for example, the American Institute of Aeronautics and Astronautics (AIAA) *Journal of Spacecraft and Rockets* carried a feature article by F. J. Hendel, of North American Aviation, the Apollo prime contractor. In his article, Hendel noted:

> Oxygen is more important to the survival of man than water or food. Man can survive for as long as two weeks without water or food, but without oxygen he can live for only a few minutes . . . On the other hand, it presents a fire hazard, which is especially great on the launching pad, when the cabin is purged with oxygen at 14.7 pounds per square inch [the pressure of air at sea level] . . .

> Even a small fire creates toxic products of combustion; hence fire prevention measures and/or fire-fighting methods are mandatory. However, no fire-fighting methods have yet been developed that can cope with a fire in pure oxygen.

Thus, more than two years before the fire, Dr. Hendel set out clear guidelines for the need to provide fire-fighting equipment and breathing apparatus—as protection against fire "in the pre-launch period," a period of *extreme fire hazard.*

On the other hand, someone must have read these documents,

as can be seen from a minor background item included in the final report of the Apollo Review Board. In tracing the development and history of the 012 spacecraft, adequate documentation of the altitude tests was apparently unavailable. The Review Board therefore included the history of a similar spacecraft, command module 008, whose altitude testing was presumed to be typical of all Apollo spacecraft. It is of the greatest significance that two fire extinguishers were located in that (008) spacecraft during its testing. Not only were *fire extinguishers* included, but *fire-resistant* Teflon sheets and *fireproof* Beta-cloth were draped over wire bundles and the astronauts' couches. These particular items, nonflight items, were conspicuously absent in command module 012 during the fatal plugs-out test on January 27, 1967.

The fact is simply that neither North American Aviation, the largest contractor for the Apollo projects, nor NASA was prepared for a fire on the ground. Yet each had previously sponsored studies—available to any reasonably enterprising reporter—that showed extreme fire hazards. Clearly, the "largest and most complex research and development program ever undertaken" was far less than a perfect prototype for large-scale technological projects. Its decay had been spreading, like a slow, systemic cancer, for many years.

■ *If we do not make these efforts, we will not be first on the Moon, we will not be first in space, and one day soon we will not be the first on the Earth.*

D. BRAINERD HOLMES
quoted in Aviation Week,
April 29, 1963

Chapter 4 ■ Sputnik and the Stigma of Second Place

On July 29, 1955, President Dwight D. Eisenhower declared the desire of the United States to make its debut in the beckoning space age. The American space program was to be spearheaded "with the launching of small, unmanned Earth-circling satellites as part of the U.S. participation in the International Geophysical Year (IGY) which [took] place between July, 1957 and December, 1958."

Then, on Friday, October 4, 1957, a mechanical "basketball" called Sputnik let loose a feeble beep that reverbrated around the world—the space age had begun.

The world was overwhelmed by the Soviet accomplishment. In America, the realization that Buck Rogers might prove to be a Russian peasant* stunned citizens in all walks of life. Nicholas E. Golovin, President Eisenhower's Special Assistant for Science and Technology, has recalled that "the startling impact . . . of Sputnik 1 . . . penetrated deeply into the substance of public affairs in all countries, but perhaps especially so in the U.S. This was because the . . . posture of general leadership in basic science of the U.S. had led people almost everywhere, and particularly in this country, to believe firmly that it would be ourselves and not

---

* As it happened, Yuri Gagarin, first man in space, was the son of a Russian collective farmer. In a memorial article, *Soviet Life* (July, 1968) described him as "this son of a peasant."

the U.S.S.R. that would first provide so public a demonstration of national technical prowess."

Dr. Wernher von Braun, key figure in the development of our modern liquid-propelled rockets, particularly the giant Saturns, offered an appraisal that is perhaps even more to the point. He reminds us that "overnight, it became popular to question the bulwarks of our society, our public education systems, our industrial strength, international policy, defense strategy and forces, the capability of our science and technology. Even the moral fiber of our people came under scathing examination."

President Eisenhower, in an attempt to soothe the wounded national pride, declared that "the Russians captured all the German scientists at Peenemünde." This was not quite the case, for as *Fortune* magazine has pointed out, the U.S. shared, with Russia and England, the "most significant booty" of World War II—"rocket men." *Fortune* added, "the myth that Soviet space accomplishments were German, not Russian, still persists in some quarters. But it was established long ago that, with the exception of an electronics expert named Helmut Gröttrup, the U.S. Army transported the brains of Peenemünde to Huntsville, Alabama." The big lift, known as "Operation Paperclip," included, besides von Braun, one hundred and twenty-seven other German rocketeers and three hundred and forty-one box cars of V-2's, equipment and records. Wernher von Braun, leader of the German team that developed the V-2 rocket for Hitler, was to become director of the Marshall Space Flight Center (MSFC) at Huntsville— the center that fashioned the Saturn 5 to carry our first astronauts to the Moon.

Just a little more than a decade after Sputnik, General Bernard A. Schriever, retired commander of the U.S. Air Force Systems Command, told the National Space Club on March 4, 1968:

We . . . have every right to feel deep satisfaction at the expansion of man's knowledge that has resulted from ten years of space research and development. And yet, the nation's space program is being reviewed, questioned, and even criticized.

Thus, in the short span of ten years, the U.S. space establishment had gone from hysterical reaction to the Russians in the late

1950's, to enthusiastic self- and public awe in the mid-1960's. Then came a period of defensive introspection following the Apollo 204 fire. With the "perfect missions" of the manned Apollos 7 and 8 in the last months of 1968, America's space program once again felt a spine-tingling euphoria as it stood on the threshold of its most spectacular triumph—the lunar landing. What were the dynamics of these erratic turnabouts? We should turn back to the last days of the World War II.

The devastation of Hiroshima on August 6, 1945—and then of Nagasaki on August 9, 1945—cast mankind, traumatically, into the atomic age. The Frankenstein monster of instantaneous and world-wide self-destruction had been let loose among us. For Americans it was the beginning of a national neurosis. The "new priesthood" of scientists, as described by Dr. Ralph E. Lapp, had suddenly come down from their ivory towers, taken off their sterile white suits, and handed mankind weapons capable of wiping out whole civilizations. This in itself represented a major readjustment of the national psyche, but the confusion was compounded by the presence within American shores of repatriated German V-2 specialists. The rockets of these now honorable men —the same men who had sent terror screaming down on London —could be used to transport nuclear warheads, developed by American atom-splitters, across oceans, from continent to continent, at the press of a button. The Intercontinental Ballistic Missile (ICBM) build-up of the late 1950's engulfed us in a frightening game of international brinkmanship—a missile race between the Soviet Union and the United States.

A lone glimmer of hope was the International Geophysical Year, the eighteen-month period (1957–58) of scientific international cooperation focusing on polar exploration, geodetic surveys, and solar observation. For a time it seemed that IGY might engender an enduring spirit of cooperation, might somehow reduce the fierce and wasteful military and technological competition between the two great opposing ideologies. But IGY alone could not save mankind from itself. The space age, ushered in by Sputnik when IGY was a little over three months old, promised far more. It offered the conviction that science and technology, seeing the error of their ways, could transform our destructive capacity into a new and exciting journey to the stars.

Yet the snowballing competition of the nuclear age had so infected the American national consciousness that the longed-for fruits of the newborn space age already seemed, for some Americans, beyond reach. Thus, Sputnik, with its implied missile superiority, nearly spoiled the dream of peaceful cooperation—simply by upstaging the U.S. America's humiliation by Sputnik was, in fact, so steeped in military implications that it was difficult, at the time, to think of anything else. The conquest of space—the *last* frontier—somehow promised to the pioneers a total control over the world and all its activities. Since the United States saw itself standing alone as preserver of the Free World, abdication of leadership—in any realm—meant slavery for all of mankind.

The launching of Sputnik 1 was unquestionably of tremendous significance as an historic "first." However, the public and official hysteria that followed in its wake was irrational and uncalled for. The fact is that the United States had been discussing—openly, for the most part—its own plans for space shots for at least two years prior to the launching of Sputnik 1. Project Vanguard, designed to place America's first artificial satellite in orbit, was proceeding through a painfully difficult development and testing history that had put it many months behind schedule. Vanguard, carrying a scientific payload for various atmospheric measurements, was to be lofted by a military rocket. For that matter, the Vanguard project had been preceded by plans for a purely military venture—Project Orbiter—a joint Army-Navy project conceived in 1954. This highly classified project, using the Army-proven Redstone missile as launch vehicle, was linked with the development of new missiles, as well as with the potential of using satellites for military surveillance and reconnaissance. It was set aside, however, by Eisenhower because of the possible criticism such a military achievement might evoke on the international scene.* Project Orbiter was expected to have placed its first object in orbit during the summer of 1956. Project

* Throughout his two Administrations, President Eisenhower was extremely careful to make a distinction between military and civilian space ventures. For example, a rocket that launched a scientific payload was termed a "launch vehicle," even though it might be exactly the same as a rocket that launched a warhead or military payload, in which case the identical rocket was called a "missile."

Vanguard, involving the design and development of a new three-stage launch vehicle, was expected to reach this same goal by the fall of 1957.

While these projects were being discussed in the various news media, and, of course, in Washington, the activities of the Soviets were also sufficiently known. So much emphasis has been laid, in recent years, on the "secrecy" of the Russian program—as opposed to the "open" program of the U.S.—that it is apparently forgotten that the July, 1955, announcement of Project Vanguard was followed three months later by the first of several Soviet statements that served as very clear signposts of Russian activities. As Willy Ley has noted, an article in *Aviation Week* (October 31, 1955) reported on a Soviet announcement by Professor Kyrill Stanyukovitch, stating: "Russian engineers believe it is possible to build larger satellites than those now being discussed in the Western press." *Aviation Week* followed, on October 29, 1956, with a report on some basic data gleaned from *The Moscow News* about the planned Russian satellite (its approximate size, weight, and orbital characteristics). The following year *The New York Times* of June 2, 1957, reported to the nation that *Pravda* had declared, in effect, that the Russians had created the rockets and all the instruments necessary to solve the problem of the artificial earth satellite. Simultaneously, in a document which summarized Soviet activity, the U.S. Air Force predicted a Russian launch, commemorative in nature, by September, 1957. Finally, the Russians delivered an official report to the headquarters for the IGY on June 10, 1957, declaring the readiness of their satellite program. This was four months before Sputnik 1. They even announced the frequency on which it was to transmit.

Thus, in spite of ample warning, which included the date of launching (missed by a few weeks because of delays) and the approximate size, weight, and orbital characteristics, Americans still reacted to Sputnik 1 with shocked disbelief. It was as if no one had ever heard of a satellite program—Russian or American. Sputnik 1 (described by Eisenhower's Defense Secretary, Charles E. Wilson, as "a useless hunk of iron") was followed, on November 3, 1957, by Sputnik 2—a larger and heavier satellite further embellished by a payload that contained the Russian dog Laika, the first Earth creature to orbit in space.

While the American public was fretting over these demonstrations of Russian technological talent, the Congress responded with an investigation. In fact, both the Senate, headed by Lyndon B. Johnson, and the House, headed by John W. McCormack, had separate hearings, with a total of 108 witnesses, aimed at understanding the problems of space that confronted the nation. The Congress, like the general public, was most concerned with assaying just how far ahead of us the Russians really were. Actually, there was little cause for alarm at this stage of the space age. Scientifically and technically, the United States was not very far behind the Soviets. However, the exaggerated responses of the Congress, the press, and the lay public produced inevitable results, some of which, at least, were clearly beneficial. Efforts were made immediately to get the separate space activities of various American agencies all under one roof, with one budget and one broad mission.

Despite these efforts, the Air Force Committee on Space Technology, on December 6, 1957, urged an increase in military space activities with a prime goal of achieving lunar landings because "Sputnik and the Russian ICBM capability [had] created a national emergency." Shortly thereafter, the Department of Defense created the Advanced Research Projects Agency (ARPA) to initiate Earth satellite and lunar probe activities. ARPA served to coordinate the independent activities of the Army, Navy, and Air Force. Interagency rivalry and repeated failures to get Vanguard off the launch pad worked to slow the U.S. space program, but the all-too-visible fact that Russia had its Sputnik forced the Defense Department to persist.

By January of 1958, the American Rocket Society, with the Rocket and Satellite Panel of the National Academy of Sciences, called for a national space establishment—one which "excluded weapon development and military operations." The statement indicated that an American rocket could be crash-landed on the Moon by 1959, with an instrumented soft landing to follow in 1960. It was felt that a manned Moon landing could be accomplished by 1968.

Then, one hundred and nineteen days after Sputnik 1, on January 31, 1958, the United States, with a sigh of relief, officially joined the space age. Its entry was Explorer 1, launched by a

Jupiter-C rocket. (The ill-starred Vanguard project finally produced a successful flight on March 17, 1958.) The Explorer, carrying an experimental payload devised by a group under the direction of Dr. James Van Allen at the State University of Iowa, confirmed the existence of one of the Earth's radiation belts. The "belt" was then named after Dr. Van Allen; this was the most celebrated contribution of the International Geophysical Year, proclaimed as a scientific and technological triumph.

Yet Americans could not forget that Explorer 1's launching, historically almost simultaneous with that of Sputnik, was not "first" in space. The American public did not then understand that it took many years to develop rockets ("launch vehicles") that could put even a small payload in orbit, months and even years to design and build satellites such as Sputnik and Explorer 1. Nor did anyone seem to appreciate the fact that America could not be far behind Russia if it had been possible to follow the Sputniks so rapidly, even allowing for the far heavier Soviet payloads. U.S. citizens had not been sufficiently informed about the significance of the various delays that had prevented the U.S. from meeting its intended launch schedule. The assurances of men like von Braun and Van Allen that the U.S. could have beaten Sputnik by many months, if it had wished, fell on deaf ears. The very fact that a Russian satellite was whirling above American soil had tremendous psychological impact, and it produced a predictable reaction: *Americans must catch up and beat the Russians.*

The compulsion of Yankee ingenuity to be the "firstest," the "biggest," and the "bestest" had already begun to warp the future of America's space program.

In keeping with his Administration's foreign policy goals of disarmament, nuclear test bans, and the outlawing of weapons in outer space, President Eisenhower had already proclaimed that "outer space should be used only for peaceful purposes." On March 5, 1958, the President approved the recommendation for a civilian space agency. Three weeks later, the national interests in space were outlined as to their importance, urgency, and inevitability in the history-making report of the President's Science Advisory Committee. Four factors were cited as underlying America's space program: man's thrust of curiosity; the defense objective (i.e., "peaceful" defense against alien space powers); national prestige; and opportunities to add to our scientific knowledge of the Earth, the solar system, and the universe. The National Aeronautics and Space Act, authored primarily by Senator Lyndon B. Johnson and his staff, was signed into law on July 29, 1958. By October 1, three days short of the first anniversary of Sputnik, NASA was open for business.*

The Congress, on the basis of its post-Sputnik investigations, had assumed that the United States was about two years behind Russia. The "gap" was primarily in large booster development. It was not a gap in scientific talent or the ability to utilize that talent. More than anything else, it was a gap in policy. For about five years, the United States had failed to mobilize its space hardware and engineering facilities. Dr. Van Allen, as well as a number of other spokesmen, advised that an annual budget of about $500 million would be required to conduct an adequate program, one that could be geared to closing the gap.**

The charter approved by the Congress for the new space agency, usually referred to as "the Space Act," was largely patterned after NASA's predecessor, the National Advisory Committee for Aeronautics (NACA).*** It provided for an administrative director, appointed by, and directly responsible to, the President. NASA was to be supervised by an advisory board, the Space Council, whose members would include the Vice-President, who would be chairman of the Council; the Secretary of State; the

* Looking back, on March 1, 1968, President Johnson remarked during a two-hour visit at the NASA Manned Spacecraft Flight Center, at Houston, Texas: "I spent almost thirty-eight years in the Nation's capital. In all of that period of time, I have voted for thousands of bills and I have written a few. But the one legislative enactment that I suppose I am proudest of is the bill that I wrote and introduced that made possible NASA, that brought into existence this great facility, and others in the program throughout this nation."

** NASA's budget did not reach that mark until 1960, but from the very beginning it had the habit of doubling every year through 1965. In 1966 it began tapering off from about $5.5 billion—a level that NASA had hoped would continue indefinitely. The Apollo disaster and the conduct of the Vietnam War, however, resulted in a further cutback in 1968.

*** The National Advisory Committee for Aeronautics was established in 1915 by an act of Congress. It was the first U.S. government agency set up to oversee and direct aeronautical research. NACA, too, was created in an atmosphere of national urgency: On February 1, 1915, the Smithsonian Institution advised the House of Representatives (63rd Congress, 3rd session), "This country led in the development of heavier-than-air machines. Today it is far behind."

Secretary of Defense; the administrator of NASA; and the chairman of the Atomic Energy Commission. The Space Council was provided a staff headed by an executive secretary.

The NASA charter directs the agency to adhere to "the policy of the United States that activities in space should be devoted to peaceful purposes for the benefit of all mankind . . . The Congress further declares that such activities . . . peculiar to or primarily associated with the development of weapons systems, military operations, or the defense of the United States (including the research and development necessary to make effective provision for the defense of the United States)* *shall be the responsibility of, and shall be directed by, the Department of Defense."* (Italics added.)

In section 203(a) of the charter, NASA is charged with the responsibility to "provide for the widest practicable and appropriate dissemination of information concerning its activities and the results thereof."

The question of military space activities was a bit more difficult. The opening charge of the Space Act clearly assigned all military activities, their "research and development," to the Department of Defense. However, in order to insure maximum national security, a military liaison committee was formed. Thus all findings of NASA relevant to national security were readily available to the Defense Department.

The Space Act had not indicated whether NASA or the Defense Department would direct manned space flight. The Moon missions of the Army, the Navy, and particularly the Air Force, were treading water, waiting for the "go-ahead" from the President and the Defense Department's Advanced Research Projects Agency (ARPA). Then, in August of 1958, to the dismay of all the military services, the first manned satellite program, christened Project Mercury, was assigned to NASA. Its goal was to "demonstrate, soon and safely, man's capacity for space flight."

The task was not an easy one. Under the Eisenhower Administration, NASA was largely confined to a science-oriented pro-

---

* This parenthetical phrase attained great significance in the late 1960's when NASA was attempting to justify its involvement with defense-oriented projects by declaring that its research stopped short of actual *application* of weapons and other military operations. The subject will be dealt with more fully in Chapter 10.

gram of space exploration. President Eisenhower himself had never been an all-out champion of spending money for manned space flight and it was uncertain whether any "demonstration" could convince the dubious President of the value of man in space. NASA's first order of business, therefore, was to recast and face-lift the agency so that it would then be allowed to go on to pursue the higher goals of a man-in-space program. The management core of the National Aeronautics and Space Agency (later changed to "Administration") was derived mainly from the predecessor agency, the National Advisory Committee for Aeronautics (NACA). "The alumni of NACA have retained a dominating influence, commanding eight of NASA's field facilities," observed *Fortune* magazine in August, 1967.

NASA acquired its first administrator, T. Keith Glennan, whose task it was to integrate the existing space objectives of the military (ARPA) with the personnel, funds, and facilities of the defunct NACA. Included were the manpower and hardware of the IGY Vanguard project. Glennan also inherited the recommendations of the NACA Special Committee on Space Technology, set up in early 1958. Headed by H. Guyford Stever, and including James A. Van Allen and Wernher von Braun, this committee urged the development of large boosters and emphasized the need for a manned lunar landing "within the next ten years." It concluded that a manned landing on the Moon could be achieved by March, 1967. The final report of von Braun's group revised that estimate, suggesting a manned landing might come even sooner: "There is a possibility that a manned lunar landing, on an emergency basis without a backup vehicle, could be accomplished as early as July, 1966."

In January of 1959, NASA signed a formal contract with the Rocketdyne Division of North American Aviation for the development of a million-pounds-plus, liquid-propellant rocket engine (the F-1). This rocket had been designated, at its inception, as military hardware, but had not been assigned to any specific military mission.

The military, meanwhile, had not been idle. The Army Ordnance Missile Command (AOMC) submitted to the Pentagon's ARPA in March, 1959, their "Saturn Systems Study," which included fourteen of the most promising designs selected from 1,372 possible adaptations of an eight-engine cluster, then known officially as the Saturn.* The eight-engine unit was conceived for a monstrous one-stage Nova rocket that was never built (see Chapter 5). Instead, a cluster of five of these same (F-1) engines was adapted for a three-stage rocket, which became the Saturn 5 of the Apollo program.

By September of 1959, a Saturn cluster-engine was judged to be "the quickest and surest way to attain a large space booster capability in the million-pound class." On November 8, 1959, the Saturn project was placed under the technical supervision of NASA. President Eisenhower made it known (subject to the approval of the Congress) that von Braun, now a U.S. citizen, and the Saturn team, at Huntsville, Alabama, would also fall to NASA, "in accord with the national policy of the scientific and peaceful uses of outer space." By December, 1959, the entire Saturn project and the Moon mission had been given over to NASA.

Thus, although NASA was born out of the peaceful and civilian spirit of the old NACA, it acquired most of its muscle from strictly military projects.

Clearly, the space age did not abruptly and unexpectedly loom before us from over the Russian horizon. It is equally obvious that the great "quest" of the two rival atom powers was military rather than scientific.

The current global deployment of supersonic military aircraft, from all indications, marks the end of a great era. It is a simple fact that modern aircraft can be modified only so much before they reach the practical limits of aerodynamic inventiveness. Air forces of the future will require preeminence in the infinitely broader and more hostile arena of space. This need for mobility

---

* A Moon landing mission was studied briefly by Army Ordnance Missile Command, which formed a "Project Horizon" study for the purpose of establishing a military requirement of achieving a "lunar outpost" at the earliest possible date. The first phase of the "Project Horizon" report was completed in May, 1959. It pointed, with dogged determination, to a manned lunar landing by 1965, with an operational "lunar outpost" in 1966. A budget of about $670 million per year through 1968 was suggested. The proposal was not well received by the Department of Defense, on the grounds that it had no military justification. The project was not abandoned, however, since NASA became the new patron of nonmilitary space. In a very real sense, then, Project Apollo is the same mission (with a somewhat less ambitious timetable) as Project Horizon, proposed by the military in 1959.

in space has long been urged by military strategists as a logical and necessary extension of military powers.

Thus it was that the "scientific" achievements of Sputnik and Explorer came to be regarded as a measure of the opposing nations' military capabilities. And how did such a metamorphosis occur? The transition was really quite effortless. In the late 1950's, both the United States and Russia were engaged in the expensive game of missile stockpiling, out of which grew the modern concept of survival through nuclear deterrence. At the time, neither power had yet evolved a sufficiently "clean" and light-weight nuclear bomb that could be laid on target by then-existing missiles. The United States chose to wait until it had a compact nuclear warhead before committing itself to a launch vehicle for its nuclear missiles. In September, 1956, the Atomic Energy Commission announced that it could deliver a compact, small-yield, nuclear warhead "by 1965 at the latest." This meant, to the U.S. military, that relatively small launch vehicles would be required to keep pace in the arms race. The development of Inter-Continental Ballistic Missiles (ICBM's) would not need to await the development of bigger boosters. As it happened, the AEC had made a very conservative estimate: small-size, high-yield nuclear warheads were ready in 1960.

Under Secretary of Defense Charles E. Wilson, the Department of Defense allowed development of larger missiles to lag, while the Atomic Energy Commission worked diligently toward a smaller nuclear warhead. In contrast, the Soviet Union (significantly behind the U.S. in nuclear technology) boldly opted for bigger and heavier launch vehicles. Russia used the principle of several small boosters, or "strap-ons," clustered together to provide the thrust required to launch their nuclear payloads that weighed in at about ten thousand pounds.

Both camps achieved their selected goals—to the eventual and everlasting chagrin of the United States. According to Wernher von Braun: "The Soviets were far behind the U.S. in nuclear technology, and the Russian nuclear weapons were clumsy and bulky. U.S. planners decided to wait until smaller warheads were available to build ICBM's. The Soviets went ahead with the massive rockets needed to hoist their primitive bombs. The decision not only gave them a significant edge in ballistic missile technology, for years, but also was a great factor in their leadership in space exploration."

By 1960, the United States had developed and multiplied its "family" of ICBM's, designed for the compact nuclear warheads that had been promised. The space age, however, had already arrived—and the U.S. was caught with no large boosters. The Russians, too, eventually developed light-weight nuclear warheads, but only *after* their big-booster homework was done.* Their zealous attention to big boosters, designed for their big and primitive warheads, reaped historic dividends: Soviet engineers simply substituted large and impressive satellites for the obsolete warheads. With the big rockets, developed for military purposes, they achieved a seemingly endless series of space spectaculars— each of which added to the frustration of America's missilemen, most of whom had opposed from the start the Department of Defense decision to shelve development of big boosters.

While most Americans had become resigned to being second in space—at least for a few uncomfortable years—the public was confident that it was just a matter of time and money before the United States, too, would have the large-booster capability. To those in positions of power, however, the development of larger boosters and more elegant satellites did not look quite so effortless. A major shift in space policy was required; so was a readjustment of America's space image.

Almost overnight the entire national space program was shorn of its military objectives and relabeled "civilian" and "peaceful in nature." In late 1959, it will be recalled, the Army Ballistic Missile Agency (ABMA) and its Saturn team had been assigned to NASA. The Army's Jet Propulsion Laboratory, in California, was similarly handed over, along with the former Air Force-Air Corps and NACA research facilities at Langley.

However, even before this name-swapping had occurred, the image-building of space activities as predominantly "peaceful" had begun. The flight of America's maiden entry in the space arena, Explorer 1, provides adequate testimony to the desire of the U.S. to portray its space efforts as exclusively peaceful in

---

* Obviously, the weight of a satellite (manned or unmanned) is an indicator of the weight-lifing potential of its booster. At the time of the first Sputnik, weighing in at 184 pounds, and then Sputnik 2, at nearly a ton, the best the United States was able to orbit was the tiny eighteen-pound Explorer 1.

nature. The prime objective of that historic flight, conducted by a hard-nosed, security-conscious Army-Navy coalition, had really little to do with Explorer 1's precious scientific payload and the discovery of the Van Allen belts. The rocket that launched Explorer 1, the "Jupiter-C" (Jupiter Composite Reentry Test Vehicle), was geared to test experimental materials for the nose cone of forthcoming IRBM's (Intermediate Range Ballistic Missiles).

The masquerade of "peaceful space research" has continued through the decade of the 1960's. A starry-eyed American public, taught to associate space activity with manned flights, lunar exploration, and a possible landing on Mars or Venus, may choose to ignore the harsh military undertones of the space-age dream. But the defense strategy of stockpiling military ballistic missiles, on which both the United States and the Soviet Union depend, is the critical part of each nations' space program. Each of the thousands of ballistic missiles to be launched in the event of World War III would send a nuclear payload five hundred to eight hundred miles out into space. This warhead then would face the same searing reentry that has provided the heart-stopping climax of NASA's Mercury, Gemini, and Apollo flights. In like manner, most "peaceful" launches—Soviet and U.S.—serve various military roles, not the least of which is the testing of new nose-cone materials.*

When development of Project Mercury (one-man space capsules) was handed over to NASA in 1959, Eisenhower accomplished two ends. First, he redefined manned space flight as civilian and peaceful in nature and began to tap effectively the ground swell of public support that reached its peak during the Gemini flights of the mid-1960's. (Eisenhower's motives were probably much less ambitious; they reflected both the intent of the NASA charter and the failure on the part of the military to articulate a clear and present need for a lunar landing.) Second, Eisenhower avoided a serious conflict with the diplomatic commitments of his own Administration. At the time, disarmament and nuclear nonproliferation talks were beginning to make some

---

* The Soviets have been more secretive about their space program, not necessarily because it is more advanced, but because they seem to fear, perhaps even more than the United States, the stigma of losing any event in the space race.

headway. The United States had thus far held on to the reins of leadership in efforts towards world peace. It would have been most difficult to explain the accelerated space activities if they were not executed in the open by a civilian agency and for peaceful purposes.

As already noted, when proposals for the creation of a civilian space agency were drawn up by PSAC in March, 1958, the justifications for a national space program were:

1. man's thrust of curiosity
2. national defense
3. national prestige
4. scientific growth

The last of these points, the "scientific," has frequently been cited by NASA and the Congress as *the* motivation for the entire program. The result is that America's space program has been thought, by most people, to be proof of U.S. scientific and technological) superiority among the family of nations. If for some reason the astronauts failed to reach the Moon before the Soviet cosmonauts, America's scientific rating would fall to a dismal and humiliating last place "in a race run by two horses."

NASA, with considerable success, designed its "open" program, with its countless press releases, extensive television coverage, magazine contracts with astronauts, and many, many speeches, to drum up popular support for the tremendous expense of going to the Moon. The alternative, NASA implied, was almost too terrible to contemplate: the eternal stigma of America's being "second on the Moon"—Sputnik all over again. The level of space activity required to catch up with and surpass the Russians, after Sputnik, called for increased funding, greatly increased launch activity, and monopolizing of priority materials and labor. It was decided, and wisely so, that this sudden drain on the nation might not stand the test of secrecy, inevitable news leaks, and consequent public controversy. A wide-open crash program was the United States' only choice if it hoped to beat the Russians to the Moon. The open space program was also part of modern defense strategy, known as saber rattling, by which the U.S. advertises its weapons and space capabilities for everyone to see. The Soviets naturally rattle their weapons.

Meanwhile, in 1959, the Russians appeared to be lengthening their lead in space. Soviet achievements included three Luniks (Moon probes) and the first crude view of the Moon's far side. The Congress and the public media became ever more concerned about the East-West space race. The following year produced two of America's most significant successes—the interplanetary probe Pioneer 5, and the highly successful weather satellite Tiros 1. However, it was the U-2, piloted by Gary Powers, that created the headline-grabbing crisis of the year, even though a new species of "spy-in-the-sky" satellites was by then beginning to render the U-2 spy plane obsolete.

With the solid successes of Pioneer 5 and Tiros 1 thus muted, Americans remained uncertain when, or if, the time would ever come when their nation would no longer be a shameful second in space. The period of national frustration which had begun with the beeping of Sputnik on an October day in 1957, persisted—not quite so gloomily, not quite so desperately—but persisted nevertheless.

The foundation was laid for two stirring issues of the 1960 Presidential election: the missile gap and the space race. This was the year that NASA's Space Task Group at Langley selected tentative plans for a fourteen-day Earth-orbital manned mission, leading to the lunar landing. The name "Apollo" was proposed for the project in May, and on July 29, 1960, the chief of manned space flight at NASA headquarters, George M. Low (a former NACA employee), announced publicly, for the first time, that the long-term flight plans to succeed Project Mercury were officially called Project Apollo. NASA Administrator T. Keith Glennan indicated that a strapping and unprecedented $2 billion annual NASA budget would be required by the mid-1960's toward the fulfillment of these goals.

It remained for a man then campaigning vigorously for the Presidency of the United States, John F. Kennedy, to pass judgment on these lofty proposals.

> ■ *Control of space will be decided in the next*
> *decade. If the Soviets control space they can*
> *control earth, as in past centuries the nation that*
> *controlled the seas dominated the continents.*
>   SENATOR JOHN F. KENNEDY,
>   in Missiles and Rockets,
>   October 10, 1960

Chapter 5 ■ Safety vs. the Race Against the Russians

John F. Kennedy managed, where others had failed, to fan the
political fires of the space program. His preelection view was
blunt: "If man orbits earth this year his name will be Ivan."
In a campaign statement that was prepared with the aid of
Edward C. Welsh, executive secretary to the Space Council, and
that appeared in *Missiles and Rockets,* Kennedy made the most
of the highly emotional climate surrounding the space race: "We
are in a strategic space race with the Russians, and we have been
losing . . . But we cannot run second in this vital race. To insure
peace and freedom, we must be first." Kennedy declared that
target dates for the lunar landing and a space platform should be
"elastic." He added, however, "All these things and more we
should accomplish as swiftly as possible."

The much-touted U.S. ratings in space provided Kennedy with
a campaign theme—a lasting theme of his Administration: "This
is the new age of exploration; space is our great new frontier."
It was an irresistible slogan. The U.S. lag in space was, once
again, equated with a "gap" between the Soviets' big boosters
and the smaller ones of the United States. Vice-President Richard
M. Nixon, defending the Eisenhower Administration, insisted that
there was no missile gap. It was not until after Kennedy had

assumed office and was privileged with the classified information of the Presidency that the new Secretary of Defense, Robert S. McNamara, let slip that indeed there was no missile gap. U.S. missiles, despite their lower lift-off thrust, were as capable of raining devastation on the U.S.S.R. as the Soviet missiles were of devastating the U.S.—and the U.S. had more of them.

The Eisenhower Administration, in its last days, took a firm stand on the issues of space exploration. The Eisenhower-appointed Commission on National Goals submitted its report on November 27, 1960, stating:

The United States should be highly selective in our space objectives and unexcelled in their pursuit. Prestige arises from sound accomplishment, not from the purely spectacular, and we must not be driven by nationalistic competition into programs so extravagant as to divert funds and talents from programs of equal or greater importance.

Eisenhower could not have agreed more. He reportedly snapped: "The Moon has been up there a hell of a long time. If we don't get there tomorrow, it won't go away." In fact, according to a paper delivered at the December, 1968 meeting of the revered American Association for the Advancement of Science (AAAS), a former member of the Eisenhower science advisory staff announced that President Eisenhower had fully intended scrubbing any further manned-flight projects after Mercury.

MIT's James R. Killian, appointed by Eisenhower in 1957 to hold the new office of Science Advisor to the President, reacted similarly. He declared that large expenditures on giant boosters and manned flight would be better spent on education. As the year 1960 ended, the Man-in-Space Panel of the President's Science Advisory Committee (PSAC) reportedly indicated that "the cost of a manned lunar landing program would range from $20 to $40 billion." NASA fervently defended itself against all opposition. The appeal of the space program to President-elect Kennedy was well known. NASA steadfastly held out for a lunar landing, before 1970, as a desired national goal. Plans for the mission were drawn up during the summer of 1960. NASA Administrator Glennan, adroitly side-stepping the outgoing Eisenhower, indicated the decision on these plans would be made in the White House by the new Administration.

As the President-elect, John F. Kennedy was already marshaling his forces—the "new intellectuals." His Vice-President, Lyndon B. Johnson, would serve as chairman of NASA and would have the task of naming the new NASA administrator. On January 11, 1961, nine days before his inauguration, Kennedy named his new Science Advisor, Jerome B. Wiesner, who, like his predecessor Killian, was from MIT. The following day the President-elect released a brief report prepared by a nine-man ad hoc committee on space, headed by Wiesner. The Wiesner report is of considerable significance because it was not well publicized. Its criticism of NASA was devastating, and yet, historically, it was largely ignored.

The Wiesner report spoke in broad, sweeping terms, stating that the second-rate posture of the U.S. space effort had stemmed from "organization and management deficiencies." Criticism was aimed at the "executive and other policy-making levels of government," as well as at NASA and the Department of Defense. The Wiesner report "virtually challenged the very existence of the civilian space agency." It described the Mercury program (which was later to launch Alan Shepard and Virgil Grissom on suborbital shots, and finally which made John Glenn America's first man to orbit in space) as "marginal" and recommended that after inauguration President Kennedy should "not endorse the present program and take the blame for its possible failures."

Furthermore, according to Eugene M. Emme, NASA historian, the report "seemed satisfied only with the scientific portions of the NASA program, and recommended that NASA should have a vigorous, imaginative, and technically competent top management, meaning that all, including departing NASA Administrator T. Keith Glennan, were less than competent."

Wiesner's recommendations for manned space flight were as follows:

We should stop advertising Mercury as our major objective in space activities. Indeed, we should make an effort to diminish the significance of this program to its proper proportion before the public, both at home and abroad. We should find effective means to make people appreciate the cultural, public service, and military importance of space activities—other than space travel.

Finally, the Wiesner report proposed a new set of five goals,* superseding the four proposed by the President's Science Advisory Committee (PSAC) in 1958. "National prestige" led off the Wiesner list, replacing the rather nebulous "man's thrust of curiosity" on the PSAC list. PSAC had placed "national prestige" third. Both placed "national defense (security)" second. The Wiesner report substituted two goals ("scientific opportunities" and "practical applications") for PSAC's, again, rather vague "scientific growth." A significant addition made by Wiesner was "international cooperation."

On Inauguration Day, Glennan vacated NASA headquarters, leaving the space agency without an administrator. These were dark days for NASA morale, with its personnel branded, by implication, as second-string; but perserverance paid off. (A glance down the NASA roster, then and in the late 1960's, showed many of the old, familiar names.) The pace of international events was to quicken so that the Wiesner recommendations were all but disregarded.

On January 25, 1961, Deputy Administrator Hugh L. Dryden (whose proffered resignation had been ignored) informed the White House of the possible world-wide implications of a NASA launch, scheduled for the following week, which was to feature a suborbital flight with a passenger—a chimpanzee named "Ham."**

President Kennedy moved quickly—he told a press conference that Vice-President Johnson would name the new NASA administrator. Johnson had bequeathed his Senate majority leadership and his chairmanship of the Aeronautical and Space Sciences Committee to Senator Kerr of Oklahoma. The Vice-President, after consultation with Kerr, nominated James E. Webb, a lawyer then serving as an executive, a director, and assistant to the presi-

---

* (1) national prestige, (2) national security, (3) scientific opportunities, (4) practical applications, and (5) international cooperation.
** "Ham" was originally called "Pat"—after Patrice Lumumba. NASA headquarters insisted the chimp's name be changed.

dent of the Oklahoma-based Kerr-McGee Oil Industries, dominated by Senator Kerr's family.

Having had no previous direct affiliation with the space program, * Webb was considered a safe, even conservative personality to place at the helm of space ship Apollo. At Johnson's request, Wiesner invited Webb to the White House. On February 9, Mr. Webb was confirmed as the new administrator by the Senate. In accepting the position, Webb said that he wished to be free to "recommend the best program in accord with the national interest." With Dr. Dryden, former director of NACA, and Dr. Robert C. Seamans of MIT at his side as highly respected deputy administrators, Webb immediately undertook measures to whip the faltering NASA organization back into shape.

In the meantime, other events were shaping the ultimate stance of the nation's space program. The Russians had let it be known that a manned flight was in the offing. Kennedy responded by announcing that America would not sacrifice an astronaut in an attempt to beat them. Late in February, NASA announced that either Glenn, Grissom, or Shepard would make the first manned Mercury flight. (Almost exactly a year later, on February 20, 1962, John H. Glenn became the first American to orbit the Earth.) In March, President Kennedy met with NASA officials and members of the Space Council. Within a week, the budget inherited from Eisenhower had been increased to provide funds for the acceleration of manned flight—in effect, an effort to move up the lunar landing by two years. Thus, the Apollo project, like its legendary namesake, became "a seven months' child." So lofty a god required less than the normal gestation. But then, "gods grow up swiftly."**

The renewed emphasis on manned space flight, so strongly opposed by Wiesner, the President's Science Advisor, was further bolstered by the Space Science Board of the National Academy of

---

* Webb, however, was no stranger to Washington. He had served as director of the Bureau of the Budget and as Undersecretary of State during the Truman Administration. In announcing his resignation as head of NASA on September 16, 1968 (effective October 7, 1968), he recalled that twenty-five of his forty working years had been spent in government service.

** Robert Graves, The Greek Myths (New York: George Braziller, 1957), Vol. I, p. 76.

Sciences. Its report, "Man's Role in the National Space Program," recommended:

> Scientific exploration of the Moon and the planets should be clearly stated as the ultimate objective of the U.S. space program for the foreseeable future.

The same report, however, reminded all that manned space flight was a high point in space exploration, and one "in which the entire world can share." Thus, man in space remained the symbol of national leadership in "bold and imaginative U.S. space activity." The National Academy of Sciences accentuated the fact that "inherent here are great and fundamental philosophical and spiritual values which find a response to man's questioning spirit and his intellectual self-realization."

So earnest a plea did not elicit the desired and expected response from other scientists—at least not immediately. The National Academy of Sciences found itself in sharp conflict with the loosely organized but influential members of the scientific community at large, who had voiced strong opposition to the entire subject of manned space exploration. It was obvious to these "outside" scientists that manned flight would be tremendously more expensive than the scientifically more rewarding, but less glamorous, remote-controlled unmanned flight program. Consequently, any sweeping decision was temporarily postponed by the Kennedy Administration.

On April 12, 1961, the Soviet cosmonaut Yuri Gagarin became the first human being to orbit the Earth. This was the second most significant turning point in the space age, but the shock was somewhat less than that caused by Sputnik. The American public was better informed by 1961, and had learned to heed the little warnings that occasionally found their way from the Soviet Academy of Arts and Sciences into the pages of aerospace journals and, less frequently, into the public press. Still, the impact of Gagarin's flight—and the breed of giant boosters required for its accomplishment—was sufficient to set off another wave of controversy in the United States.

The earliest rumors of Gagarin's 108-minute flight were viewed skeptically—until the announcement three days later that he had been recovered safely. Politically, these were trying days for the new President. Congress was up in arms, tired that we were "second" once again. Kennedy responded with the following cryptic remark, made at a press conference held on the day of the Moscow confirmation: ". . . No one is more tired than I am . . . the news will be worse before it is better . . . We are, I hope, going to go in other areas where we can be first, and which will bring perhaps more long-range benefits to mankind. But we are behind." Kennedy had been President less than three months before being confronted by Gagarin's space spectacular and, five days later, by the Bay of Pigs fiasco.

Rallying to the rescue, Administrator Webb indicated that it would be possible "to proceed faster than the funds recommended by President Kennedy." It was a question of "whether we expect to proceed as we did in connection with the atomic bomb." A crash program involving a commitment of as much as $40 billion (a figure arrived at by the President's Science Advisory Committee) would be required to land an American on the Moon. Unlike Eisenhower, Kennedy was always moved by the adventure of space exploration. But the young and disillusioned President might have wished to postpone a major commitment to manned space flight, if he could have afforded to ignore pressing political expediencies. Gagarin's flight occurred while NASA officials and witnesses were testifying before the Congress, urging a larger budget. It was not long before NASA established the insinuation that the Soviets were fond of staging their space extravaganzas on commemorative occasions. One ominously momentous occasion preyed on everyone's mind: the fiftieth anniversary of the Bolshevik Revolution in October, 1967.

On March 14, 1961, the question was put to NASA Deputy Administrator Robert C. Seamans, Jr.: Could additional funds, as requested, get an American on the Moon by 1967 before the Russian anniversary? He replied thoughtfully:

This is really a very major undertaking. To compress the program by three years means that greatly increased funding would be required for the interval of time between now and 1967. I certainly cannot state that this is an impossible objective. If it comes down to a matter of national policy, I would be the first to review it wholeheartedly and see what it would take to do the job. My estimate at this moment is that the goal may well be achievable.

Seamans cautioned that it was only speculation that the Russians would attempt a landing in 1967, but the Congress and the Administration had the fever. The feeling grew that if there were any chance—any chance at all—that the Soviets would try a Moon landing in 1967, America ignored that chance at its peril. How could the United States of America, the most powerful and advanced country in the world, forfeit the great prize of the Moon landing to the Russians?

Two other considerations—one scientific, the other political— made the 1967 target date particularly appealing to the Kennedy Administration. Scientists knew that, beginning in 1968, a period of intense solar flare activity would occur; and while it was unclear just how space flight and space communications might be affected, it seemed wise to try to get under the wire before the Sun put on its big show.* The second, political, consideration was simply that 1968 was an election year. Gambling just a little on his reelection in 1964, Kennedy saw, perhaps, that no President could be ungrateful for the opportunity to claim, for his Administration and his party, the responsibility for a successful Moon landing.

At President Kennedy's request, the weeks following Gagarin's flight were filled with running consultations. Vice-President Johnson and Edward C. Welsh were frequently in contact with various key space figures, such as NASA Administrator Webb, his Deputy Administrator Dryden, Secretary of Defense McNamara, General Bernard Schriever, Dr. von Braun, General James M. Gavin, and Admiral William F. Raborn. They were charged with answering the great questions posed by Kennedy: Can we go to the Moon as proposed? What will it cost? What technological problems and risks will we face? Johnson and Welsh made their optimistic recommendations by early May, 1961. Faced

---

* In early July, 1968, large solar flares, emitting "plasma clouds" made up mainly of electrons and causing "magnetic storms" around the Earth, disrupted short-wave radio communications for periods up to eighteen hours. And after Soviet cosmonaut Colonel Georgi T. Beregovoi's Earth-orbiting Soyuz 3 flight of October 26–30, 1968, there was speculation that fear of radiation from solar activity had caused the Soviets to bring Beregovoi down sooner than planned.

with these pragmatic questions, even the President's Science Advisor, Dr. Jerome B. Wiesner, stern critic of Project Mercury, chose to comply with the Johnson-Welsh position. President Kennedy held back decision until the final hectic weekend of May 20–21. The President then responded by saying simply, "Nothing is more important!"

On May 25, just over six weeks after Gagarin's flight, the historic decision was revealed. In a special message before Congress, in what the President termed his second State of the Union message, Kennedy spoke the words that since have become the holy scripture of NASA and a most grateful aerospace community:

> I believe that this nation should commit itself to achieving the goal, before this decade is out, of landing a man on the Moon and returning him safely to Earth. No single space project in this period will be more exciting or more impressive to mankind, or more important for the long-range exploration of space; and none will be so difficult or expensive to accomplish . . . In a very real sense, it will not just be one man going to the Moon . . . it will be an entire nation . . . I am asking Congress and the country to accept a firm commitment to a new course of action—a course which will last for many years and carry very heavy costs . . . If we were only to go half way, or reduce our sights in the face of difficulty, it would be better not to go at all.

Looking back, it is not surprising that Kennedy found himself speaking these words. He was surrounded by an awesome army of NASA and aerospace industry scientists, engineers, politicians, and lobbyists who had coveted for years the goal of a manned lunar landing in the 1960's. Their plans were well laid—so well that there were even those who felt that the "lunar landing within this decade" could be accomplished without additional funds.

Two aspects of Kennedy's 1961 pronouncement bear reexamination, now, at the end of that decade, in another period of debate over America's space goals. In his special message before Congress of May 25, Kennedy urged the nation, the Congress, and the scientific community to discuss and to weigh his challenge. This reasonable suggestion was the only means by which the President could be sure of sound justification for his majestic commitment. No such period of examination occurred, for critics were overwhelmed by a now familiar barrage from NASA spokesmen and their industrial allies.

The burgeoning space program was viewed as a means of keeping the aerospace-defense industry growing at a rate to which it had become accustomed. The Kennedy commitment was a major shot in the arm for a defense-oriented economy that was threatening to sag. It meant thousands of new jobs for technicians and other skilled laborers who would be idled if disarmament efforts were to prove effective.

Secondly, as if to imply that the actual words of his "commitment" were to be taken as a metaphor, rather than literally, Kennedy pointed the way to his ultimate purpose. In his Inaugural Address he had said:

> Let both sides seek to invoke the wonders of science instead of its terror. Together let us explore the stars.

In his first State of the Union message, Kennedy enlarged on this ideal, "I now invite all nations—including the Soviet Union—to join with us in developing a weather-predicting program, in a new communication-satellite program and in preparations for probing the distant planets . . . today this country is ahead in the science and technology of space, while the Soviet Union is ahead in the capacity to lift large vehicles into orbit. Both nations would help themselves as well as other nations by removing these endeavors from the bitter and wasteful competition of the 'cold war.'"

In the final major address before his death, President Kennedy made a last attempt to denationalize the space monster that had been unleashed by his premature commitment. In a speech before the United Nations General Assembly on September 20, 1963, he said: "Why should man's first flight to the Moon be a matter of national competition? Surely we should explore whether the scientists and astronauts of our two countries—indeed of all the world—cannot work together in the conquest of space, sending someday in this decade to the Moon not the representatives of a single nation, but of all our countries."

Again and again, President Kennedy championed this theme.

It was, however, the one aspect of space exploration that NASA and the aerospace industry liked least to hear. He reportedly did not even brief NASA officials about his extemporaneous remarks before the U.N. He appealed to the nations of the world to join together, as an alternative to warfare, in the common good that could be derived through cooperative efforts in space.

NASA, however, chose to take the executive endorsement quite literally. The task of managing the mammoth complexities of the mushrooming space establishment required enlarged facilities, and, with them, new blood. But first, since the Moon mission now had highest priority, it required a major decision on the part of NASA officials—a decision whose previous postponement was symptomatic of the aura of unreality that enveloped "going to the Moon." NASA had not yet even selected a "mode" (engineerese for "method") for the lunar landing. The decision to make the landing by a prescribed date was made before government and industry had decided how to make the trip.

Two systems had been proposed. The original and boldest plan was called Nova. The Nova mission would have required a giant launch vehicle, using tremendous booster force to make a direct Earth-Moon rendezvous with all three astronauts aboard. The second proposal was an Earth-orbital method, in which a small lunar landing craft would be launched from a mother ship in orbit around Earth.

The Earth-Orbital Rendezvous (EOR) had two obvious advantages over the rather stupendous Nova concept. EOR required no more than the smaller, second-stage Saturn (J–2) engines already being developed by von Braun's team at Huntsville, Alabama. Secondly, even though the EOR technique was more complicated in execution, it could easily shave as many as fourteen months off the Moon-landing time limit that had been based on the proposed Nova. The space maneuvers required by the Earth-orbital method, while somewhat complex, were viewed as an area of some risk, but they would have to be faced one day on any account. EOR is the technique required for any future missions to the planets and the rest of space beyond the Moon—better to get the experience now. This rationale was particularly favored by Dr. Jerome Wiesner, Kennedy's Science Advisor.

Late in 1961, Dr. John C. Houbolt, then head of the Theoretical

Mechanics Division of NASA's Langley Research Center, in Virginia, introduced a third and new concept. He suggested that NASA was going about things the wrong way, since a Lunar-Orbital Rendezvous (LOR) technique was easier, cheaper, and involved specific design requirements that could be handled separately but simultaneously by different contractors. The LOR technique was further enhanced by the fact that it promised to cut "from six to fifteen months" from the proposed EOR method. In the LOR technique, the spacecraft from which the lunar landing craft (the "LM," or Lunar Module) would depart for the Moon's surface is placed in orbit around the Moon, rather than in orbit around the Earth, as in the EOR plan. Two astronauts would make the journey to the Moon, while the third astronaut stayed in the command module, remaining in lunar orbit, awaiting their return. The three would then eject their craft out of lunar orbit and head back to Earth.

Heated debate ensued within NASA over the selection between these two techniques. The firm commitment, now endorsed publicly by the President, required a timely decision. Von Braun was persuaded to join Administrator Webb and others within NASA in pushing for the lunar-orbital approach. The reasons were obvious. Wiesner, however, ardently defended the Earth-orbital technique which in the long run seemed to provide the U.S. space program with training needed for future missions aimed at Mars that were already on the drawing board. In many ways the Earth-Orbital Rendezvous method was also less risky than the Lunar-Orbital Rendezvous. Since a mission meeting with a failure on or in orbit around the Moon had almost no chance of rescue and meant almost certain death for the astronauts, the EOR was preferable; reentry from Earth orbit would be, in contrast, a relatively short and simple matter.

The debate seemed irreconcilable, and Webb took the problem to President Kennedy. Faced with the choice of vetoing his Science Advisor or hamstringing a new and plainly very determined NASA administrator, Kennedy sided with Webb.

Thus, by the end of 1961, the United States had committed itself to the lunar-orbital approach. (On the other hand, Russia seemed to prefer the Earth-orbital technique.) At last, then, the U.S. could begin building the hardware, systems, and all the other paraphernalia required for the Moon landing. Apollo, which would take man to the Moon, sprang from the drawing board to the aerospace factories, and from there into the minds of the nation.

Project Apollo was placed in the charge of D. Brainerd Holmes. The new director of manned space flight, an experienced RCA electrical engineer, responsible for the successful construction of the Ballistic Missile Early Warning System (BMEWS), met the challenge squarely. Thoroughly committed to beating the 1967 Bolshevik anniversary, he ran the program on a "go-for-broke" basis. With the motivation of a true zealot, he brushed aside criticism of the pell-mell pace of the Apollo project by pointing out in the spring of 1963: "If we do not make these efforts we will not be first on the Moon, we will not be first in space, and one day soon we will not be the first on Earth."

James E. Webb, NASA administrator, concurred: "Were we, as the symbol of democratic government, to surrender this opportunity to the leading advocate of the Communist ideology, we could no longer stand large in our own image, or in the image that other nations have of us and of the free society we represent."

Holmes and Webb were not merely talking to themselves; they were both acutely aware that the strains created by the Apollo crash program were already becoming apparent. In February, 1963, George M. Low, NASA's director of Spacecraft and Flight Missions, Office of Manned Space Flight, told a NASA-industry conference: ". . . a number of specific problems have arisen for which we would welcome solutions. . . . However, many of these existing solutions may have to suffice. Our time scales may just be too short . . . to permit major design changes in Apollo."

NASA officials, however, remained confident. Four months after George Low's rather pessimistic appraisal of NASA's ability to solve certain technical problems, Administrator Webb addressed a major conference on space-age planning. As keynote speaker, he thanked the House of Representatives for its "unanimous support given in the NASA Authorization Bill for Fiscal Year 1963." He then went on to assure his listeners: "The goal of lunar exploration is feasible from an engineering standpoint. No great new technological breakthroughs are required. The timetable set by the President gave us nine years to carry out the project in a prudent, step-by-step manner."

The "unanimous support" that Webb found in the Congress was not so evident elsewhere, in spite of Webb's glowing appraisal. The voice of opposition was growing—especially among previously quiescent scientists who had, by now, studied the evidence carefully. There were those who feared that NASA's rapid expansion was draining the nation's science and engineering talent, creating a disastrous technological imbalance. With each passing month, the program became less and less a "scientific" venture and more of a gigantic, government-sponsored industry, a kind of aerospace version of the Depression's WPA. In such an atmosphere, scientific goals became secondary and suspect. Furthermore, NASA, with Congressional assistance, had managed to snare the lion's share of America's research dollars for Project Apollo. Apollo accounted for three-fifths of NASA's budget, and NASA claimed about a third of the entire national research budget. Researchers in countless other fields of endeavor complained futilely that NASA was swallowing their dollars as well.

Administrator Webb had derived traditional support from the National Academy of Sciences, but many of its members, individually, were considerably less enthusiastic. Dr. George B. Kistiakowsky, for example, when asked in 1963 about the more earthly rewards of space research, replied, "Hogwash." Other critics recalled that the Apollo commitment had been made while the nation's morale was at a very, very low ebb. Oddly, too, the very success of the manned Mercury flight had seemed partly to sate the public appetite for space flight. Indeed, in the span of two short years, the U.S. seemed to have "caught up with the Russians" in manned flight—and had actually surged ahead in scientific adventures.

The year 1963, then, marked the first of several periods of widespread reconsideration of space goals by the Congress and the people. Funds formerly so readily handed to NASA now seemed to be needed elsewhere. The validity of NASA's goals and its reputation for genius came under examination. It occurred to many congressmen and scientists, debating the new budget for fiscal 1964, that the commitment to the lunar landing was being taken altogether too literally. Brainerd Holmes, still working with all stops out for a landing in 1967, had lost the support of his chief, Webb, and other less single-minded managers. Administrator Webb, knowing full well that the Congress would cut the 1964 budget, sought to quell this in-house dissent by reducing Holmes's autonomy.

Threatened cuts in the succeeding years were regarded as doom for the Moon deadline. A frequently repeated refrain was: "Lack of Congressional support in funding seriously hampers NASA's ability to reach the Moon within the decade."

The critics, however, were swept over by the then almost unstoppable NASA-aerospace industry juggernaut, which gained momentum and employees month by month. Robert Hotz, giving voice to the aerospace industry's unquenchable thirst for a brimming space budget, editorialized in *Aviation Week*, on April 29, 1963:

> This anti-Apollo chorus usually reaches its crescendo in the spring, when the National Aeronautics and Space Administration budget is facing significant Congressional decisions, and dwindles to a barely perceptible pianissimo after every successful U.S. and Russian manned space flight.

Aviation Week noted, rather cynically, that "the scientific community has traditionally provided the most solid opposition to the manned space flight programs," even though manned space flight was presented to the public as America's supreme "scientific" effort. Hotz added: "There has been a steady rate of conversion from critics to supporters during the Mercury years. This has been helped by the fact that it has become obvious that NASA does not intend to neglect scientific exploration because of the Apollo priority."

To the critics, Hotz's observation meant simply that some of their numbers had defected, having been won over by NASA grants; but, in any case, Hotz felt James Webb's missionary work was going well. This period marked the falling-out of much of the scientific community with NASA and the Congress over the Moon goal. Each succeeding year saw further cuts in other areas of research and development; the gap between NASA and the scientific community merely widened.

In January, 1964, with budget time coming up, NASA was once again under fire. NASA's Dr. Robert Seamans remonstrated the Congress on the grave consequences of penny-pinching: "We are now at the point where we have to admit that we will not make it [the manned lunar landing] in this decade unless we get the full appropriation and the supplemental as soon as we can get them." Seamans and other NASA officials were somewhat overstating the case. The Apollo target date, threatened by a budget cut and "unexpected technical troubles," had apparently slipped from 1967 into 1969—certainly still within the decade.*

That same week, Administrator Webb first brandished what was to prove his most effective verbal weapon. Senator Clinton P. Anderson of New Mexico, alarmed at reports that the manned lunar landing would now coincide with the peak period (1969–70) of unusually intense solar radiation, dared to question NASA's Apollo timetable. Webb was said to retort, "if the space agency misses its goal of landing men on the Moon before 1970, it will be because of funding and not radiation problems." He described Senator Anderson's sources as "inaccurate."** The "expected level of radiation," according to Webb, was safely below that found acceptable by the Space Science Board of the National Academy of Sciences. Senator Anderson's data was based on a model "more severe than the present picture being accepted by NASA."

As a result of the new "austerity" forced upon NASA for upcoming 1964, Brainerd Holmes, the Apollo manager, at complete odds with Webb over NASA policy, was all but ignored, since his public statements had helped to tarnish NASA's public image. He resigned "to take a $90,000 job as a senior vice-president at Raytheon."

* Public statements seldom agree with private commitments. For, as we shall see, the 1967–68 target date was considered within reach until January 27, 1967, when the Apollo astronauts died and the entire program came to an immediate halt.

** The "inaccurate" sources were previous studies conducted by NASA researchers (NASA Technical Note TN D–2125). As the lunar target date drew near, in mid-1968, talk of radiation hazards was heard once again. Officials were surprisingly mute on the subject. The foreword to a more recent NASA publication (NASA SP–169), however, ends with this statement: "Relatively speaking, shielding [against radiation] is in good shape. At this time it appears that unknowns in the space radiation environment and in the effects of radiation on man remain the largest uncertainty in the problem of protection against space radiation."

By mid-year, however, the round of debates, so typical of the budget-planning season, had noticeably subsided. The two-man Gemini project, which followed the Mercury one-man flights, was beginning to show promise—without direct challenge of further Soviet space spectaculars. There was renewed emphasis on the unmanned "advance party" projects—projects like Ranger and Surveyor, designed to probe the Moon's surface in preparation for the ultimate manned landing. However, technical difficulties, and a string of failures in the Ranger series, brought charges from the Congress that NASA had adopted a policy of "shoot and hope." NASA, and Webb in particular, made new overtures to the scientists who remained the space program's most outspoken critics.

Yet NASA was not without allies in this campaign. President Johnson, "author of the Space Act," and NASA's patron and godfather from its inception, had a hand in rebuilding public confidence in NASA. When finally, on July 28, 1964, Ranger 7 returned the first close-up television pictures of the Moon, he made a notable attempt to nullify the Apollo critics once and for all. President Johnson, at a White House meeting, cornered NASA's associate administrator and sometime spokesman for the science community, Dr. Homer E. Newell. The following transcript, described by William Gilman in *Science: U.S.A.* as a "unique catechism," is a portion of their conversation:

JOHNSON: Are you satisfied? [i.e., with the space program's progress]

NEWELL: I am. In fact, I am delighted.

JOHNSON: Elated?

NEWELL: Elated . . .

JOHNSON: Is it desirable to get there [the Moon] as soon as you can?

NEWELL: In my opinion, yes.

JOHNSON: As quickly as possible?

NEWELL: As quickly as possible, yes, Mr. President.

JOHNSON: What do you lose by backing down?

NEWELL: You lose leadership.

JOHNSON: Leadership in what?

NEWELL: Leadership in world science and technology, in achieve-
ment and accomplishment.
JOHNSON: Leadership in the world?
NEWELL: Leadership in the world . . .
JOHNSON: Do you have any comments?
NEWELL: I agree completely.

Such idyllic togetherness could not help but warm the hearts of
NASA and the aerospace industry. Then, on October 12, 1964,
the Russians launched Voskhod 1, carrying a doctor, an engineer,
and a cosmonaut, on a twenty-four-hour space journey. Within a
week, *Aviation Week* manned the ramparts: "The U.S. space
medicine program has long been the weakest link in our national
space program and still suffers from loose organization and in-
different support at the top levels of NASA and the Pentagon
. . . His technical timidity on the potential of military manned
space operations may rank in history as one of Mr. McNamara's
biggest blunders."

For *Aviation Week*, as well as for many others in the aerospace
industry and in Washington, Voshkod 1's feat was humiliating—
a challenge, once again, to the United States' space ego. This
time, Robert McNamara made an easy target: Why had he always
withheld his all-out backing for "the potential of military manned
space operations"? Didn't he understand what the Russians were
up to? The setting was perfect to give a big push to NASA's
Gemini series, America's two-man space project.

Gemini had been designed to explore the problems of man's
survival for long periods in the hostile environment of space—
precisely the problems with which the military would have to
deal before embarking upon large-scale manned space operations.
Besides, Gemini would be good for NASA's nonmilitary sector
of space exploration. The span between the end of the Mercury
flights, in 1963, to the beginning of the Apollo flights, late in the
decade, was patently too long. Gemini could keep NASA in high
gear during this five-year interval.

Whereas Mercury had been charged with merely putting a
man in orbit, Gemini had broader purposes, designed to answer
the questions that arose from those first manned Mercury space

flights. Its role was twofold: to determine what activities man could perform in space; and to practice, in mid-flight, the rendezvous and docking exercises which would be required to accomplish the Apollo lunar landing and the construction of post-Apollo space platforms. Gemini's achievements, to be discussed shortly, were to prove more useful, in many ways, to the Pentagon than to NASA.

The Gemini flights, conceived as a kind of intermission performance between the big-name acts, turned out to be the public relations hit of the mid-1960's. Until Apollos 7 and 8, they were NASA's greatest spectaculars: color photographs of the Earth taken with hand-held cameras; the first American "walk" in space; and hundreds of hours in space flight, loudly applauded across the land.

The first Gemini flight, one of two unmanned launches, took place on April 8, 1964—twenty-two months behind the original schedule. Finally, on March 23, 1965, the first of ten scheduled manned flights began. Gemini 3 astronauts Grissom and Young had the privilege and the responsibility of demonstrating that men could be more than just passengers. Although the Gemini spacecraft were little more than modified Mercury capsules— "two-seaters" using the same basic life-support systems, the same atmosphere, and the same basic hardware—they did have one unique feature. Their mission was to demonstrate that the astronauts could control, that is, "steer" the spacecraft in flight. The ability to pilot manually was essential to the later rendezvous and docking missions. Gemini 3 was a success.

Public and political reaction was immediate, and it grew in intensity. NASA was absolved of charges that the Gemini program was an ill-conceived and badly managed bit of grandstanding. An approving Congress and an admiring nation followed the Gemini exploits with fervor. NASA lobbed the USAF Titans, modified ICBM's, with their Gemini payloads, one after another into space. The Soviets had never done anything like it.

On March 16, 1966, Gemini 8 provided the first opportunity to attempt an actual docking exercise in space. Astronauts Armstrong and Scott, during a projected three-day flight, were to maneuver their spacecraft, high over Brazil, to lock onto an

Agena payload launched on the same day. The docking was successfully completed, but a short circuit in the control system of one thruster resulted in a bumpy ride. As the spacecraft rolled and pitched uncontrollably through space during the next orbit, a separation was executed. While it later proved to have been unnecessary (the short circuit was subsequently overcome by radio command from the ground), the mission was hastily cut off. In the seventh orbit, sixty hours earlier than planned, the two astronauts returned for a safe splashdown.

The remaining four Gemini flights were considerably more "routine," and provided an opportunity for other astronauts to gain experience in piloting the spacecraft. Minor problems occurred, of course, but the astronauts, with remarkable confidence in the spaceworthiness of their ship, were able to work around them. On Gemini 10, for instance, having performed the more important duties of the mission, copilot Collins opened the hatch to take some "scientific" pictures. After forty-five minutes of picture-taking, he closed the hatch. The two astronauts' suits had filled with fumes from rocket exhaust and the ablation heat shield,* and they had to open their faceplates to take eyedrops.

Gemini 12, the last flight in the two-man series, was launched on November 11, 1966. Astronauts Lovell and Aldrin further advanced the art of manned space flight. The docking guidance computer failed, but they were able to accomplish the rendezvous under manual control. Aldrin, the copilot, successfully demonstrated that short "space walks," separated by periods of rest, need not be exhausting. He returned still fresh from five and a half hours of exposure to the vacuum of space.

In addition to winning the hearts of a nation, the Gemini successes did a great service to the U.S. military space program. To Presidents Eisenhower and Kennedy, NASA's "peaceful" charter meant that the civilian space agency must strive to keep clear of military entanglements. However, a separate manned military space project known as Manned Orbiting Laboratory (MOL) had been under study for some years before the Gemini flights. Behind its austere title, MOL was a highly classified project, designed to utilize man's role in space (*if* Gemini and

---

* The problem of leaking suits continually crops up. See Chapter 7.

Apollo were able to prove that there was one) and to take over where the U-2 plane left off. The declared task of MOL was military reconnaissance.

The successful experiments in docking and rendezvous were considered by the military space planners to be Gemini's most significant contribution. Many of the biomedical experiments conducted by Gemini crews were also geared to help MOL planners in their design requirements. Moreover, a modified Gemini spacecraft (Gemini B) was selected as the "shuttle" between MOL and Earth.

The Gemini series ended on November 15, 1966, with a score of ten out of ten "successful" manned flights. Throughout the nearly twenty months of the Gemini program, there had not been one single Soviet manned flight. Furthermore, having done the military a big favor with its Gemini flights, NASA could style itself as a defender of the nation's security. Now, in the late fall of 1966, an unprecedented, though short-lived, period of chest-swelling self-congratulation ensued within the nation's space program—the wellsprings of the "overconfidence and complacency" that would culminate two months later in the Apollo tragedy. So many things had gone right for Gemini; how could anything go wrong in a mere ground test of Apollo 204? The Moon had never seemed closer.

Immediately after the Apollo 204 disaster, NASA froze all manned flight activities (accounting for the vast majority of the NASA budget) and volunteered to investigate the accident, correct the problems, and absorb the 3-percent annual "cost of living" increase—all within the pre-fire (fiscal 1967) budget. Yet, in spite of clear indications that the fatal fire could delay manned flights by six months to a year (it proved to be nearly two years), NASA continued to wave the banner of "a lunar landing within the decade."

If NASA could offer to absorb these costs, lose nearly two years of operation, and still meet its Moon goal, then the earlier threats about missing the lunar landing deadline were merely used to intimidate the Congress and the public. It becomes all too clear that the "space race" has been used as a fiscal bludgeon for many years. NASA had fully expected to land men on the Moon during the early part of 1968. There may even have been faint hopes, through juggling flight schedules, of making it before the close of 1967. Ambitious and outspoken Holmes was gone, but his goals, more diplomatically handled, remained.

Even after the Apollo tragedy NASA could not speak with one voice. Months before the actual cost and impact of the fire had been fully appraised, Wernher von Braun suggested that we might still make it in 1968.

Dr. Seamans took a more conservative view. He read into the Apollo fire hearings, several times from a prepared statement: "As we have often stated, the Apollo program is predicated on a success schedule and there are no margins of time or money in the program; any failure or accident will have direct impact on schedules and on hardware availability."

The fiftieth anniversary of the Bolshevik Revolution came and went in October, 1967, without any Soviet space spectacular and no indication of one to come. Six months before, on April 24, 1967, the Russian cosmonaut Vladimir Komarov had been killed when the parachute system designed to slow his space capsule's descent apparently fouled. It became evident to Soviet space officials that Komarov's spacecraft, the Soyuz 1, was badly flawed and would require extensive engineering changes, as did the U.S. Apollo. This realization was a severe blow to the Russians' space pride, especially since they had implicated "haste" and "flaws" in the Apollo 204 fire. A period of sober reappraisal and extreme caution ensued in the Soviet space program. To many observers, the U.S.S.R. seemed about to abandon the Moon race—while placing greater emphasis on its equivalent of the U.S. MOL project. This was not an illogical assumption, since such a project would have had at least a psychological value, militarily. Furthermore, the Soviets, who began their designs on the Moon with an Earth-orbital (EOR) technique, seemed always to have focused more directly than the U.S. on grander prizes—the planets Venus and Mars.

Why, then, did the Moon "race"—to beat either the Russians or an arbitrary deadline—go on? Perhaps only because, by the curious logic of inertia, it was too late to stop. As in 1961, NASA and many congressmen used John Kennedy to justify their course. "If we only go halfway," Kennedy had said, "it would be better not to go at all."

But there were voices of dissent, and some balky congressmen suspicious of NASA's plans. Old, tried-and-true budget-inflating techniques were no longer adequate. In good times, NASA officials inflated the space program's monetary needs—in the accumulation of "slush funds." Now, in bad times, these unused funds and deep cuts in almost all non-Moon science and research projects diminished the cost of their blunders. Through a bit of fiscal adjusting, NASA let the public believe that "the Apollo fire cost the taxpaper [about] $100 million." This information, carried by *The New York Times,* February 28, 1968, neglected to point out that the actual cost, due to stretch-out of the Apollo schedule, came to about $700 million. This latter figure—just seven times greater—had been announced by Dr. Mueller at a January 29, 1968, budget press conference. Thus, the Apollo fire cost the American taxpayer a good deal more than the total cost of the seven unmanned flights in the highly successful Surveyor series that actually landed on the Moon, took thousands of close-up pictures of the lunar surface and made chemical analyses of the lunar soil. The total bill, then, of landing Americans on the Moon, had risen from $23.2 billion to $23.9 billion.

The larger price in lives, valuable and irreplaceable scientific projects, and in national prestige was similarly discounted, at least in the view of NASA and the Johnson Administration. For as the opening statement in the *Report to the Congress from the President of the United States, U.S. Aeronautics and Space Activities, 1967,* under "Leadership in Space," reads:

> Both the U.S. and the Soviet Union suffered a space disaster and registered achievements. While the Cape Kennedy fire set the U.S. manned program back by over a year, it did not produce a psychological disaster abroad. The dead astronauts were mourned by the world as a universal loss, and, despite the investigating board's frankness in fixing the blame, the U.S. space image was only temporarily damaged.

Despite so kindly an official endorsement by the President, NASA's golden age of high-handed threats ("if we don't the

Russians will"), schedule-mongering, and blank checks seemed to be drawing to a close. A time of reckoning had come at last, and NASA seemed humbled. So it had been, according to Robert Graves, with the legendary Apollo. "Having earned Zeus's anger once—he learned his lesson and thereafter preached moderation in all things: The phrases 'Know thyself!' and 'Nothing in excess' were always on his lips."

In the Senate Committee's final report (January 30, 1968) on the Apollo 204 accident, the majority of members seemed satisfied that NASA was showing the required humility. The Senate Committee, while urging that NASA still attempt to make the "end-of-the-decade" Moon landing because "the schedule is an essential and significant management tool," advised the space agency to proceed only as fast as safety would allow:

Safety must be considered of paramount importance in the manned space flight program even at the expense of target dates. The earnest declaration that "safety is our prime consideration" must be transfused into watchfulness so that people do not again stumble into the pitfall of complacency.

To some observers, familiar with NASA's long and spotty record on "safety," the Senatorial advice seemed overly forbearing, a bit superfluous. The mildness of Congressional rebuke, however, is better understood in the light of the performance, in the first few months following the fire, of the Apollo 204 Review Board. Among the difficult tasks of the Review Board was the preservation of a close family secret—the lost hope of NASA and Congress for a "miraculous" Moon landing in 1967 or 1968, one or even two years ahead of John F. Kennedy's schedule. The Board also had another unspoken responsibility: the preservation of NASA's good name.

■ *The Board is very concerned that its description of the defects . . . that led to the Apollo 204 accident will be interpreted as an indictment of the entire manned space flight program . . . Nothing is further from the Board's intent.*

Preface to the summary volume of the
Report of Apollo 204 Review Board

Chapter 6 ▪ NASA Investigates Itself

Sixty-eight days after the fatal fire, the Apollo 204 Review Board prepared a letter transmitting "herewith" a bulky, multivolume— but still unfinished—Report to NASA Administrator James E. Webb. Four days later, from 2:00 P.M. to 5:00 P.M. on Sunday, April 9, 1967, copies of the Report were made available to members of the Congress—most of whom had not been forewarned and were absent for the weekend.* Administrator Webb has testified that he, too, received the Report at this time. It was less than twenty-four hours before the House Subcommittee on NASA Oversight met to consider the Report, and less than forty-eight hours before the Senate Committee on Aeronautical and Space Sciences was asked by its chairman, Clinton P. Anderson of New Mexico, to hear members of the Apollo 204 Review Board on their final Report of investigation and to discuss the "Board's findings, determinations, and recommendations."

The House Subcommittee met at 10:15 A.M. Monday. The Senate Committee opened its hearings at 10:05 A.M. the next day.

This case of cliff-hanging timing prevented many members of both committees and their staffs from familiarizing themselves with even the Report's summary volume, not to mention the twelve volumes of appendices that then accompanied the Re-

* Those who read their daily newspapers, however, might have learned that the Report was scheduled to be delivered on Sunday.

port.* Within the next few days, the Report had been labeled both a "whitewash" and a "harsh, scathing report." It deserved neither description. It was, more simply, inadequate. Without acknowledgement of prior research, it resurrected criticisms and warnings that had, in many cases, been made years before. It focused on technical errors rather than on errors of overall judgment and perspective. It completely side-stepped the culpability of high-level NASA management.

The fact that the Report made engineering sense, that it served to pinpoint certain preexisting engineering and technical deficiences can hardly be argued. Could it have done less? Some evidently thought so. Senator Margaret Chase Smith of Maine seemed to be happily surprised to find, two days after receiving it, that the Report was so "complete and wonderful." Over in the House the day before, Representative Ken Hechler, of West Virginia, went on record to the effect that "this report shows great courage and candor on the part of both the Board and NASA . . . The findings brought out in this report show that the members of this Board have approached their task seriously, conscientiously, and objectively. I believe the report is not only a credit to NASA, but it is a symbol of the srength of our form of government that a report like this could come out . . ."

A few members of the Congress were much more skeptical. Administrator Webb and Dr. Seamans, NASA deputy administrator, had barely concluded their opening statements before the House Subcommittee on NASA Oversight, when Representative Donald Rumsfeld of Illinois raised some ugly points:

Many of us have been concerned from the initiation of this investigation that the membership of the Board was such as to

* As Congressman Wydler complained in the House hearings on April 10: "I have a great deal of difficulty understanding just exactly how I could possibly proceed with the Review Board, as such, just directing my attention to that part of the problem. I went back to my office today and I found there a pile of documents called an appendix which was at least a foot high and which have been referred to constantly in the hearings today—panel 6, report No. D, or something of that nature—as answers to questions. It is going to take me time, certainly, to try to evaluate some of that material. I may try to get a hold of particular parts and get some questions concerning it. But that is not going to take place by the end of this evening under any circumstances because I am here to begin with. I don't know what I am supposed to do on questioning the Board."

preclude a true examination of the internal functioning of NASA.

It is inconceivable to me, in view of the scope and magnitude of the conditions found by the Board, that they could exist without their being the direct result of serious and fundamental management defects within NASA . . .

Is it not correct . . . that the members of the Board, in many instances, were the very individuals responsible for such things as quality control, reliability, engineering and development of the spacecraft and for spacecraft operations?

Some minutes later, Representative John W. Wydler of New York expressed particular concern about the "independence" question. He found it "somewhat inconsistent, somewhat conflicting" that NASA's top management should have put subordinates "in the position of investigating their superiors." It was, in Representative Wydler's view, "a very unenviable position for those people to be in."

Such criticism, however muted by the tact and good will of the doubtful congressmen, came very close to undermining both the premises and the performance of the Review Board. Administrator Webb met the challenge with his own superior blend of pique, vigor, and thinly veiled hurt feelings. The NASA administrator's actual view of the Review Board's assignment, it became apparent, was somewhat narrower than (as he himself had put it in his opening statement) "to search for error in the most complex research and development program ever undertaken."

Indeed, from the very start, NASA had carefully prepared the Congress to accept the view that the Review Board's actual role was to get the Apollo program moving again. Eleven days after the disaster, NASA Deputy Administrator Seamans told the opening session of the Senate Committee on Aeronautical and Space Sciences' hearings into the Apollo 204 fire: ". . . It is therefore possible that we may fly the Apollo without having been able to establish the cause of the fire. Even in that case, I believe that the care and skill with which the board and program office are conducting their investigations and reviews will provide the necessary assurance that such an accident cannot be repeated."

The Review Board never did establish the cause of the fire; and Apollo flew again.

As to the independence and make-up of the Board, Webb took the tack that its results should speak for themselves. His central thesis, it became evident, was that the interest of the Congress and the people in the Board's independence was a "technical question" very much beside the point. The important thing, according to Webb, was to accept the Board's Report and let him and his "able-bodied" NASA team get on with the job of "flying again."

"I think," Webb declared, "if we are dependent upon the confidence of this committee or the public on whether or not independent people serve on a board to investigate detailed technical problems, then the system is never going to work and we will never fly. These men [the Review Board members] are the best we have. Let us examine their work rather than debate a technical question as to whether an independent board might have done better."

To at least some objective observers, it was readily apparent that the issue of the Board's independence should not be cast aside as "a technical question." For if a truly independent board had been chosen it would probably not have come up with a report that avoided mentioning any of the basic defects that afflicted the top levels of NASA management.

In such circumstances, then, it came as no surprise that NASA's administrators were delighted with the Report that its own Review Board prepared. Indeed, during the investigation, the Review Board, which should have been investigating NASA's complicity in the Apollo tragedy, went out of its way to inform top NASA administrators what it was doing and turned repeatedly to them for guidance. During the period of the Board's active investigation, which began on January 28, 1967, and lasted just over two months, NASA's top men—Webb, Seamans, and Mueller—had devotedly shepherded its progress. Dr. Seamans visited the Cape on four separate occasions, in the first twenty-five days after the fire, to meet with the Board. Three weeks after the investigation began, the Board held a full-scale, dress-rehearsal "preview" of a briefing that was scheduled for presentation to Dr. Seamans the next day. "Expressly invited" to this preview, and accompanied by key staff personnel, were most of NASA's top brass, including Dr. George E. Mueller, Dr. Wernher von Braun, and Major General Samuel C. Phillips.

Obviously, the Board wished to make sure it would not displease Dr. Seamans. The evidence is it did not, for on February 23, three of the Board members (Chairman Dr. Thompson, astronaut Colonel Borman, and explosives expert Dr. Van Dolah) accompanied Dr. Seamans to Washington for five days "to brief the honorable James E. Webb, Administrator, NASA, on the tentative findings and preliminary recommendations of the Board." The intimacy of the Board and NASA's top men continued right up to the eve of Congressional hearings on the final Report, when Mr. Webb met with the Board members in Washington.

Thus the Review Board did exactly the job NASA had told it to do. It went far enough into specific shortcomings to appear critical, yet not so far into general deficiencies as to be damning. The Review Board allowed NASA to continue practically unscarred, and it allowed James Webb to declare to a committee of Congress investigating the Report: "Whatever our faults, we are today an able-bodied team."

How could it happen that NASA was allowed to investigate itself? At the root is the ability of a quasi-scientific super-agency headed by a Cabinet-level administrator to perpetuate itself, to operate autonomously, almost as a little dictatorship, within the framework of U.S. democracy. (A budget cut from an annual five billion to four billion dollars, such as occurred in 1968, does not represent a diminution of NASA's internal power; and it still leaves NASA the top-moneyed sub-Departmental-level agency in the U.S. government.) The performance of the Review Board, far from damaging NASA's autonomy, simply extended it into the new sphere of "handling" national tragedy.

The Review Board was officially created the day after the fire by a memorandum from NASA's deputy administrator, Dr. Robert Seamans. Named by Seamans to the Board were the following:

Dr. Floyd L. Thompson, Director, Langley Research Center, NASA, Chairman

Lt. Col. Frank Borman, Astronaut, Manned Spacecraft Center, NASA

Maxime Faget, Director, Engineering & Development, Manned Spacecraft Center, NASA

E. Barton Geer, Associate Chief, Flight Vehicles & Systems Division, Langley Research Center, NASA

George Jeffs, Chief Engineer, Apollo, North American Aviation, Inc.

Dr. Franklin A. Long, PSAC Member, Vice-President for Research and Advanced Studies, Cornell University

Col. Charles F. Strang, Chief of Missiles & Space Safety Division Air Force Inspector General Norton Air Force Base, California

George C. White, Jr., Director, Reliability & Quality, Apollo Program Office, Headquarters, NASA

John Williams, Director, Spacecraft Operations, Kennedy Space Center, NASA

In no uncertain terms, Seaman's memorandum made it clear that the Board's responsibility was to James Webb and to nobody else. Board members were to report "their findings relating to the cause of the accident to the Administrator as expeditiously as possible and release such information through the [NASA] Office of Public Affairs." Also, as if to remind the Board where it should look for its "findings," the memorandum concluded with: "The Board may call upon any element of NASA for support, assistance, and information."

The original Apollo 204 Review Board, then, consisted of nine men, six of whom were employed by NASA. Within the next five days, two of the original appointees, Dr. Franklin A. Long, of Cornell and Mr. George Jeffs, North American Aviation's chief engineer for the Apollo project, were no longer members. By February 3, one new member, Dr. Robert W. Van Dolah, had been appointed, and a lawyer, George T. Malley, had been borrowed from NASA's Langley Research Center, to serve as legal counsel for the Board. Thus, the final Board consisted of six NASA men, a U.S. Air Force accident investigator, a Bureau of Mines fire and explosions expert, and a NASA lawyer. Who were these nine men described by Mr. Webb as "the best we have" and by another observer as a "blue-ribbon Board"?

Dr. Floyd L. Thompson, then Director of NASA's Langley Research Center, at Hampton, Virginia, became the chairman of the Apollo 204 Review Board. He had started his career at Langley in 1926 as an employee of the former National Advisory Committee for Aeronautics, which in 1958 provided the nucleus of the staff for the fledgling NASA. In May, 1963, he was awarded a NASA medal "for his outstanding leadership of the scientists and engineers who were responsible for . . . Project Mercury."

Dr. Thompson enjoys the rare position of a "scientist-engineer" who is appreciated by the Congress, NASA administrators, and his professional colleagues alike. In defending the integrity of the Review Board, Mr. Webb said of him: "He is experienced in all of the disciplines involved, and a very wise man." Late in 1967, Dr. Thompson's fellow aerospace engineers demonstrated their respect by nominating him for the presidency of the American Institute of Aeronautics and Astronautics for 1968, and he was duly elected at the AIAA meeting in January, 1968. Perhaps Dr. Thompson's highest accolades, however, were spoken by his fellow Virginian, Representative Thomas N. Downing, who presented him to the House Subcommittee on NASA Oversight on April 10, 1967. "In truth," said Congressman Downing, "he is this nation's senior scientist." Dr. Thompson earned a B.S. in aeronautical engineering from the University of Michigan in 1926.

"We know first he is brilliant," Mr. Downing continued. "We know he is dedicated. He is painstakingly thorough. We know, too, he is one of the most honest men that has ever walked this earth. His integrity, so far as I know has never been questioned.

"Among other qualities," Mr. Downing went on, "he is in truth a modest man . . ." While having earned neither a master's nor a doctor's degree, Dr. Thompson carries the title "Doctor" by virtue of having been awarded two honorary Doctor of Science degrees in June, 1963, in his sixty-fifth year, one from his alma mater, the University of Michigan, the other from the College of William and Mary, Williamsburg, Virginia.

Colonel Charles F. Strang, Chief, Missile and Space Safety Division, Directorate of Aerospace Safety, Deputy Inspector General for Inspection and Safety, Headquarters, U.S. Air Force, acted as chairman of the Review Board when Dr. Thompson was away. An Air Force career man, Colonel Strang entered the Air Force in 1940 at the age of twenty-two and was commissioned a second lieutenant in 1943. He graduated from the Air Force Command and Staff College (Maxwell Air Force Base, Alabama) in 1956, and from the Industrial College of the Armed Forces (Washington, D.C.) in 1965. Among his awards are the Legion of Merit and the Air Force Commendation Medal with Oakleaf cluster.

One of the two non-NASA men on the Review Board, Colonel Strang's value lay in his experience in investigating and handling disastrous accidents. As Dr. Seamans explained: "Colonel Strang was alternate president of the Air Force Board that investigated the Titan 2 missile accident of August, 1965, at Little Rock Air Force Base, Arkansas. It was a serious accident, involving fifty-three deaths." Colonel Strang's successful execution of that investigation led to his being put in charge of all procedures and selection of evidence for the Apollo Review Board.

Mr. E. Barton Geer, Associate Chief of the Flight Vehicle and Systems Division at NASA's Langley Research Center, was, like Dr. Thompson, a carry-over from the old NACA when NASA was formed in 1958. Like Dr. Thompson, he had spent his entire career at Langley, which he joined after graduation from Iowa State College in 1942 with a B.S. in mechanical engineering. Among his recent tasks at Langley had been chairing a committee to review the performance and operation of the Explorer Injun 4 satellite, and participation in design reviews of the lunar-orbital spacecraft. A resident, like Dr. Thompson, of Hampton, Virginia, active in civic affairs in that area, Mr. Geer had been elected to membership of the Engineers' Club of the Virginia Peninsula, of which Dr. Thompson is an honorary life member.

Astronaut and U.S. Air Force Colonel Frank Borman was the command pilot in the fourteen-day Gemini 7 mission (March 16, 1966) and was later to command the Apollo 8 flight. Unlike any other of the NASA representatives to the Board, Colonel Borman holds an advanced degree, Master of Science in aeronautical engineering, which he received from the California Institute of Technology in 1957. Class of 1950 at West Point, Borman graduated from the U.S. Air Force Aerospace Research

Pilots School in 1960 and stayed on there as an instructor until 1962, when he was selected by NASA as an astronaut. He has over five thousand hours of flying time, most of it in jet aircraft.

Mr. George C. White, Jr. began his career in "manufacturing" with Piper Aircraft in 1935. He received a B.S. in aeronautical engineering from Tri-State College, Angola, Indiana, in 1937. By the criterion of different employers, both in the public and private sectors, Mr. White was more experienced than any member of the Review Board. After a stint with Piper, he worked for Curtiss-Wright, then the Dansaire Corporation, and, in October, 1947, joined the NACA Langley Research Center (where fellow Board members Dr. Thompson and Mr. Geer were also then employed) for work in rocket-powered research models and special helicopter and airplane projects. In 1953, it was back to the private sector for Mr. White, this time with Fairchild Aircraft (now Fairchild-Hiller) and its Surveillance Drone and Goose Missile. After ten years at Fairchild, Mr. White was hired by NASA, where he rose from Chief, Command and Service Module Development, to Director, Apollo Reliability and Quality in the Apollo Program Office, NASA Headquarters, at the time of his appointment to the Review Board.

Dr. Robert Wayne Van Dolah is the special fire and explosives man that NASA went "outside" to get from the Bureau of Mines (U.S. Department of Interior). The only Board member to earn a doctorate, Dr. Van Dolah received his Ph.d. in organic chemistry from Ohio State University in 1943. A member of Phi Beta Kappa, he received his B.A. from Whitman College, Walla Walla, Washington in 1940. After jobs with the William S. Merrell Company and the Chemistry Division of the U.S. Naval Ordnance Test Station. Dr. Van Dolah joined the Bureau of Mines in 1954. His fire and explosion credentials were indeed impeccable.

To quote from his brief biography in the Review Board Report: "In his current position he plans and directs research in the fields of combustion, explosions and explosives . . . he directs investigations related to a variety of space, military and private industry problems in the field of combustion and explosions."

Mr. John J. Williams has been a government employee all his working career. Starting as an electronics technician with the U.S. Navy in World War II, then moving up after his discharge through various technical and engineering positions for the U.S. Air Force, he joined NASA in 1959 and subsequently worked on both the Mercury and Gemini programs. He received a B.S. degree in electrical engineering from Louisiana State University in 1949. At the time of the fire, he was Director, Spacecraft Operations, John F. Kennedy Space Center (Cape Kennedy), responsible for the preparation, checkout, and flight readiness of manned spacecraft. In 1966, Williams was presented NASA's Outstanding Leadership Medal by Dr. Seamans for his work in manned space programs.

Dr. Maxime A. Faget, like Mr. Williams, graduated from Louisiana State University, from which he received a B.S. degree in mechanical engineering before serving three years as a U.S. Navy officer in World War II. He, too, was at Langley Research Center (together with Board members Thompson, Geer, and White), beginning in 1946. In February, 1962, he became Director of Engineering and Development at NASA's Manned Spacecraft Center in Houston, Texas. He has been responsible for the design and direction of many aspects of the Mercury, Gemini, and Apollo programs. Dr. Faget is an author (*Manned Space Flight,* Holt, 1965, as well as technical papers and textbooks) and a joint patent holder ("Survival Couch," "Mercury Capsule," etc.). As chief designer and patent holder on the entire Mercury capsule—from which so many of the Apollo engineering concepts were derived—Dr. Faget's presence on the Board was almost mandatory. He received the honorary degree of Doctor of Engineering from the University of Pittsburgh in March, 1966. In 1963, he was awarded the NASA Medal for Outstanding Leadership.

George T. Malley, Counsel to the Board, is a retired Naval Reserve Officer. He had been appointed Chief Counsel at Langley Research Center in 1959, the year before Dr. Floyd L. Thompson became Director at Langley.

What of the two men—Long of Cornell University, a member of the President's Science Advisory Committee, and Jeffs of North American Aviation—who were originally appointed to the Board and then released? Significantly, both were outside the government. Neither had a record as a loyal and dependable government employee nor had spent long years drawing federal pay. Between them and the rest of the Board there were none of the ties— neighborly, professional, college, military service—that bound, for example, Thompson and Geer, or Williams and Faget. They were, quite simply, outsiders, much more so than Colonel Strang, who knew how to handle ugly investigations, or Van Dolah, the fire and explosions man.

Long's release, effective February 1, seems to have been a simple matter of the Cornell scientist deciding he did not have the time to serve on the Board. The case of the North American engineer, George Jeffs, is less clear-cut. When questioned about the removal of Jeffs and Long from the Review Board before the House Subcommittee on NASA Oversight, Dr. Seamans chose conspicuously different language to describe each man. About Long, Dr. Seamans testified:

> Dr. Long was contacted on the twenty-eighth of January and agreed to serve as a member of the Board. He came immediately to the Cape. After several days there, it was apparent to him, as of course, it was apparent to all the members of the Board, that this was going to be an extensive amount of work stretching over at least several months. Because of his responsibilities at Cornell University he could not devote full time to the Board activities for this period. *He therefore requested that he be relieved of the Board responsibility* but continue as a consultant and in this we concurred. [Italics added.]

But about Jeffs, Dr. Seamans said:

> At the first review that we had of the membership of the Board, this was January 28, we felt that this man [Jeffs] had great knowledge of the program and that he could materially assist the Board, so that the first instruction does contain his name. *However, after further discussion we felt that it would be inappropriate to have on the board itself a contractor official* and hence with concurrence of all parties he agreed to serve as a consultant but not as a Board member. [Italics added.]

The clear-cut implication that Long himself asked to be let go, but that Jeffs was fired, was borne out the next day in testimony elicited by Representative Wydler, questioning Jeffs himself. It had been either Thompson or Geer, Jeffs testified, who "suggested that I might be removed from the Board and placed in a different status, still providing maximum support to the objectives of the Board." Wydler pressed for a reason, to which Jeffs responded: "I really don't know the full reasoning for my removal." An intriguing further dimension in the Jeffs case can be found buried in Appendix A of the Review Board Report. It indicates that Jeffs suspected that the Review Board apparatus served to silence minority viewpoints. Appendix A contains the minutes of the Board's meetings in the period from January 31, to March 31, 1967. The following reference to ex-Board member Jeffs was made by Chairman Floyd Thompson on February 13:

In a meeting with the panel members on February 9, 1967, Mr. Jeffs brought up the question about names on panel reports. The Board has decided that Panel reports will be signed by the Panel Chairman only. The administrative procedure involved in putting that matter into our system will be developed by Panel #15. *As regards the concern that may have underlied* [sic] *Mr. Jeffs' suggestion that we need assurance that the Chairmen of panels are not withholding an important minority opinion from proper considerations, we are asking that the Board monitors will assume the responsibility for assuring that minority views are given proper consideration and that serious differences that are not resolved are brought to the attention of the Board.*

Curiously, the passage italicized above is the only testimony in the entire volume of Board minutes that is printed in heavier (boldface) type. It can only be assumed that the Board was extremely sensitive to the charge of muzzling criticism, and hoped, by the inclusion of such a passage, to counter any such charges.

It was hardly a convincing countermeasure. For one, the entire Report may be searched in vain for a transcript of Mr. Jeffs's "meeting with the panel members on February 9, 1967." Doubtless, Jeffs's reservations, expressed in his own words, would make interesting reading. Furthermore, it is clear that Jeffs might just as well have kept his mouth shut: the Board's response is that "serious differences that are not resolved are brought to the attention of the Board"—the very same Board for which Jeffs had been found "inappropriate." Such was the kind of "maximum support" that Jeffs was allowed to give after his removal as a Board member.*

It would not have been surprising if a split had developed early between Jeffs, the North American man, and the other members of the predominantly NASA Board. Again, more than any member of the final Board, Jeffs was outside the government structure. He would not be eager to accept blame in his company's name if he felt the fault lay with NASA, or more generally, with the nature of big government agencies.

Nor, as seems more likely, would the presence of a top North American engineer have fitted in with what must have been, even then, developing as NASA's bold long-term goal—to chastise North American, but finally to forgive, forget, and make up by an across-the-board retroactive renewal of the Apollo contract.

By February 3, then, NASA had its Board. The nine men set up an investigative structure organized into twenty-one panels, each with its own chairman. Each panel handled a specific phase of the investigation (e.g., "Sequence of Events," "Origin and Propagation of the Fire," "Witness Statements," "Security of Operations"). The panel chairman reported directly to a "Board monitor," that is, to one of the nine members of the Review Board. Twenty of these twenty-one panel chairmen were NASA employees. The one exception was Air Force Lieutenant Colonel K. H. Hinchman, Panel 17, reporting to Colonel Strang.

In addition to the panels, an "Apollo 204 Review Board Advisory Group" was set up. It had five classes of membership, in order of influence: (1) representative, (2) consultant, (3) liaison officer, (4) observer, (5) secretariat. The seven representatives consisted of six NASA men, including the amiable Dr. Joseph Shea, the Apollo program manager at Houston Manned Space-

---

* On February 2, Chairman Thompson had explained, cryptically: "There has been a need to change the status of one of our members, because of problems regarding the association of contractors and government workers. In accordance with the requirements of a situation we find ourselves in, Mr. Jeffs is no longer a member. He will act as a consultant."

craft Center, and one Air Force lieutenant colonel. The consultant group of seven was about an equal mix of non-NASA government people and complete outsiders, such as Jeffs and Long. There was one liaison officer: Dr. Duncan Collins from the Secretary of the Air Force's office in the Pentagon.

The observer group was the largest. It was composed entirely of NASA personnel, including all the astronauts and other NASA luminaries, such as Dr. Kurt H. Debus, director of the Kennedy Space Center; NASA Associate Administrator Dr. George Mueller; and Major General Samuel C. Phillips, U.S.A.F. (Retired), from NASA's Washington headquarters. The secretariat did the administrative, clerical and secretarial housekeeping for the Board.

Having fashioned this cohesive and compliant investigating organization, the Review Board went to work with dispatch. Among its more dramatic procedures was the disassembly of a "nearly identical" Apollo capsule (spacecraft 014) before undertaking the piece-by-piece disassembly of the damaged Apollo 012, the object being to establish the conditions in Apollo 012 prior to the accident. Eventually, over a thousand items from Apollo 012 were displayed for the edification of Review Board and panel members. In addition, the Board also interviewed almost six hundred witnesses in an effort to establish a version of the sequence of events during and immediately after the fire, and to evaluate the conditions that led to the accident. In all, according to Dr. Thompson, some fifteen hundred people directly supported the investigation.

So smoothly did the Review Board's work proceed that by March 12, barely seven weeks after the Board had been set up, six of the twenty-one panels had submitted their final reports. The final reports of the other panels, with the exception of Panel 18, "Integration Analysis," followed by March 30, 1967. Disassembly of Apollo 012, in which the three astronauts had died, had been completed only three days before, on March 27, 1967.

The Board made nine principal recommendations,* leading off with what must be the most glaringly obvious statement in the history of American technology: "The amount and location of combustible materials in the Command Module must be severely

---

* The complete summary of the Apollo 204 Review Board's "Findings, Determinations, and Recommendations" is given in Appendix E.

restricted and controlled." The Board then went on to recommend (again, most obviously) that the time and effort required for the astronauts to get out of their capsule should be reduced. Among the more specific recommendations were: a review of emergency procedures and training of support personnel; "a detailed design review . . . on the entire spacecraft communication system"; "an in-depth review of all elements, components and assemblies of the Environmental Control System"; the use of full-scale "mock-ups" to determine fire risks and fire-safety measures in future command modules; and the "timely distribution" of test procedures to insure that all elements of the organization were familiar with any procedural changes. The list of recommendations concluded with this sweeping—but, to some, long overdue—plea: "Every effort must be made to insure the maximum clarification and understanding of the responsibilities of all the organizations involved, the objective being a fully coordinated and efficient program."

To the majority of readers of the Report, however, it was an impressive list of recommendations, dazzling in its apparent completeness—specific, stark, and hard-hitting—and despite the charges of a NASA-controlled puppet Review Board and the conspicuous absence of any general evaluation of either NASA's or North American's top management, the Review Board Report succeeded in getting Webb, North American and NASA through the Congressional hearings of April and May, 1967. NASA, seemingly, was off the carpet, although a hard core of Congressional critics remained.

A happy ending to the Apollo tragedy seemed at hand, and NASA was busy producing the facts and documents to prove it. Reporters at Cape Kennedy covering the first unmanned orbital flight of the Lunar Module (designated as Apollo 5) on January 22 were presented with two thick pamphlets detailing hundreds of design and procedural changes made in the Apollo program as a result of the fire*

These two thick paper volumes represented something of a grand finale in the Review Board's command performance for James Webb and NASA. They were, on the surface, dramatic

---

* The volumes were entitled *Status of Actions Taken on Recommendation of the Apollo 204 Accident Review Board.* See Chapter 9, pp. 186-87.

proof that the Review Board had done an exemplary job; its work had exposed errors and NASA had corrected them. Here was the evidence. Questions of the Board's "independence" were now simply irrelevant.

Thus, the "flying again" pitch seemed to have resulted in an unflawed triumph for NASA—but not quite. The space agency had to wait nine more months, until after the splashdown of the "perfect" Apollo 7 manned mission,* before it appeared to move out completely from the shadow of the Apollo 204 disaster. NASA had to wait because in February, 1967, during the Congressional investigations into the accident, it had made a foolish miscalculation.

During the Congressional hearings, Representative Ryan, Senator Walter F. Mondale of Minnesota of the Committee on Aeronautical and Space Sciences, and other congressmen had learned of the so-called "Phillips Report." This report had been prepared by a staff headed by NASA's Apollo program director, Major General Samuel C. Phillips. It was severely critical of the performance of North American Aviation, the Apollo prime contractor. The Phillips Report had been completed over a year before, in December, 1965, and been forwarded to John Leland Atwood, president of North American Aviation, with a covering letter dated December 19, 1965.

The Phillips Report, as events developed, irked Mondale, Ryan and other congressmen partly because it revealed gross deficiencies in North American's workmanship on the Apollo contract, and partly because Phillips felt North American had overcharged NASA (although such situations have become accepted as commonplace in government-contractor relationships). The suspicion that the program defects delineated in the Phillips Report had not, in many cases, been corrected—and may have played a part in the Apollo disaster—was not overlooked by more critical congressmen.** Worst of all, the congressmen felt that NASA had deliberately tried to conceal the report in order to spare North American.

The aerospace industry seemed well aware, all along, of the

---

* See Chapter 13 for a description of this and other Apollo missions.
** See Appendix F.

good deeds being done in its behalf by James Webb and the Review Board. The aerospace press, expressing its gratitude, spared no effort to defend the Board against its scattered critics. Typical was an editorial by William J. Coughlin in *Technology Week*, March 13, 1967, which ridiculed and chastised *Los Angeles Times* aerospace editor Marvin Miles for having the effrontery to write an article headlined, "NASA Owes Nation the Whole Truth." Coughlin's editorial, entitled, "Where Were You, Marvin?" said in part:

We find many so-called experts willing with full hindsight, to explain that the fire hazard was evident all along and that NASA is trying to cover up its own negligence . . . We think NASA's sincere efforts at investigation can do without newspaper heroics such as this. Hindsight is mighty handy but where were you when we needed you, Marvin?

Yet even in the face of such skillful and inspired defense, a few congressmen remained unconvinced. For them, the Review Board increased, rather than diminished, doubts that NASA's top management had been—or ever could be—capable of leading the space effort of a democratic nation. It had been the Phillips Report affair that had prompted their doubts. The question must be asked: Had there been no Phillips Report, had NASA never been caught in the act of withholding information, had Congressional pride never been insulted, might some congressmen still have found cause for alarm? Perhaps.

Perhaps if a Senator Mondale or a Representative Ryan had laid bare for their colleagues the whole dismaying record of NASA's investigation into the Apollo disaster, the evidence, cumulatively, could have aroused Congressional indignation as much as, or more than, the Phillips Report.

■ For example, why did Chairman of the Review Board Floyd Thompson's view of the "management" question change so radically between his testimony before the Senate space committee on April 11, 1967, and his views stated in a letter to the committee chairman, Clinton Anderson, three days later? On April 11, Senator Smith remarked to Dr. Thompson, "I would like to get on the record your own feelings about whether there is a de-

ficiency or inefficiency in the management of the Space Agency."
This was Dr. Thompson's reply:

Well, I am afraid that my feelings, as far as I feel qualified to
comment at this time, are pretty well expressed in the report . . .

Now, we did not consider ourselves a board of management
experts nor did we employ management experts to try to
analyze the problem in detail, so I would be a little hesitant to
pull off the top of my head at this point, statements beyond
what we have already stated.

Three days later, however, Dr. Thompson had become a sufficiently astute "management expert" to pin blame on the "lower
levels of management" and to suggest that NASA's top management was capable of looking into the situation. He added specifically: "If any management level is to be charged with the
failure to recognize and correct the deficiencies noted in the
Board's Report, it would be the design and layout engineering
level."

In other words, in Dr. Thompson's strange brand of management analysis, top management bears little responsibility for the
lower levels of management.

On February 29, 1968, Dr. Thompson was appointed special
assistant to James Webb, in order to "bring his long service and
experience in science and technology to bear on the NASA program and management matters." Among Thompson's new duties
was to head a "NASA Headquarters Interim Working Group" that
would evaluate future manned flight projects. On March 18,
1968, NASA announced that Dr. Thompson would retire on his
seventieth birthday (November 25, 1968), but would continue to
serve the space agency as "consultant to the administrator on a
part-time basis after retirement."

■ One of the saddest figures in the entire Apollo 204 investigation was Thomas R. Baron, a former North American quality
control inspector (or "missile preflight inspector") and receiving
inspection clerk at Cape Kennedy, whose job had been "ter-
minated" in early January. Physically ill, with a history of ulcer
and diabetes, Baron had not been in good health for some years.
In the first few days after the fire, Baron turned over to the Review

Board a report running to five hundred pages, which was comprised of notes he had taken since joining the Apollo program in September, 1965. The report contained scores of specific criticisms leveled at his former employer, North American Aviation, in the areas of safety, quality control, handling of records, personnel, and operations procedures. Perhaps Baron's most sensational charge, which he alleged to have learned in conversation with another North American employee, Mervin Holmburg, the week after the accident, was that the astronauts had smelled smoke in their suit loops ten or twelve minutes before the fire, and that they had tried for five minutes to get out of the capsule. Baron said he believed Holmburg, even though he was aware that Holmburg had not been near the capsule during the fire and was only repeating hearsay.

The Review Board's response to Baron's allegations was to send one of the Cape Kennedy medical staff to interview him about his "problems." Baron testified: "I took it as a psychiatric examination . . ." Before the House Subcommittee on April 21, Baron suffered further indignities, among them a tirade by Representative Ken Hechler of West Virginia, in which the congressman called Baron "utterly irresponsible" and ridiculed him for misspelling the name "Slayton" in his report. (Hechler did not comment on the lengthy spelling corrections and errata that accompanied the Apollo Review Board Report.)

Later in the same hearing, Mervin Holmburg, who had been waiting to be summoned, was called before the Subcommittee hearing to defend his honor. He testified that he had never told Baron anything about the astronauts' last minutes.

Thus was Baron discredited. The fact that his notes, written before the fire, pointed out, again and again, the same deficiencies "found" by the Review Board—and that he complained, again and again, of an employee's inability to be heard by upper management—were conveniently forgotten. Baron died on April 28, 1967, at dusk with his wife and one of his stepdaughters, when his car apparently stalled at a railroad crossing. The car was demolished by an oncoming train.

■ Baron's allegation that the astronauts had been aware of the fire long before they were "officially" said to be was discredited as the hearsay opinion of a sick, emotionally unstable man. Yet similar testimony by others has never been adequately refuted. Gary W. Propst is an RCA technician who was observing (on a TV monitor) the astronauts inside the capsule the night of the fire. On January 31, 1967, he told the Review Board:

> About 15 seconds after the cry of fire, I saw more arms in addition to White's in front of the porthole seemingly coming from the left. Looking further back into the spacecraft, I could see the legs of the center Astronaut moving about. The movement inside the spacecraft lasted about 2 minutes before the flames began to block the view . . . During the entire time that I watched the Astronaut's [sic] moving, their spacesuits were silver in color with no signs of being burned or charred . . . I know that my times are very near accurate because I remember saying to others that had gathered in the area of the monitor: "Blow the hatch, why don't they blow the hatch?" One person that was near said that the spacesuits would protect them from the heat until they could get out. A short conversation then took place concerning how long and how much the suits could protect them from the fire. Also comment was made on why no one had entered the White Room as yet. During the time of this conversation the White Room was still clear and the Astronaut's [sic] motion still visible.

Apparently, the Review Board decided that Propst's time sense had been distorted by the horror of the scene that he watched on the TV screen. Propst remains certain that he was correct. A year after the fire, the Florida newspaper *Today* sought Propst's version of the fire again. Propst said: "I think NASA convinced themselves of what happened in that spacecraft, but they didn't convince me. It was about three minutes after the fire started that the White Room began to fill with smoke. Prior to that time the air was clear. I saw the astronauts moving inside for at least two minutes before the flames began to block the view."

■ The appointment of U.S. Air Force Colonel Charles F. Strang and Dr. Robert Wayne Van Dolah of the Bureau of Mines to the otherwise wholly NASA-manned Review Board was used by NASA to illustrate its desire for "excellence and independence" of the Board membership. Yet since seven out of nine Board members were NASA men, it must be assumed that Webb, Seamans, and Thompson would not have been bashful about putting two more NASA men on the Board—*if* men of Strang's and Van Dolah's specialties had been available. They were not. In other words, James Webb's "able-bodied team," engaged "in the most complex research and development program ever undertaken," did not have an experienced accident investigator. Even more incredible, NASA—whose daily business is highly explosive rocket fuels, and which had sponsored studies showing the extremely high fire risk in oxygen environments—did not have within its ranks a qualified fire and explosions expert.

■ On December 7, 1967, before either the Senate or the House had said its last word on the Apollo investigation, NASA brazenly signed a new contract with North American Aviation for Apollo command and service modules, a contract that was *retroactive* to December 4, 1966, or over seven weeks before the fatal fire.

■ For many congressmen, NASA's secretive handling of the Phillips Report came as a rude shock. A close reading of the Review Board Report would have shown that secrecy fairly leaps from many of its pages.

In the summary volume, for example, under "Board Proceedings" for January 31, 1967, one finds a strange Alice-in-Wonderland passage stating that while Review Board records will not be classified as confidential, they will be treated as "Confidential": "In lieu of classifying Review Board records as confidential, a special cover sheet will be used to comply with the Chairman's instruction that all Apollo 204 Review Board records and materials be treated as 'Confidential.' A supply of these cover sheets was provided."

Appendix A, one is told in the summary volume, contains "complete transcripts of General Sessions of the Apollo 204 Review Board." A typical "complete transcript" is that of February 1, 1967, in which there are no less than fifteen notations of "off the record discussion." A sample:

CHAIRMAN: Is there discussion?
            (Off the record discussion.)
CHAIRMAN: On the basis of this discussion, Item 4, as proposed,

is approved for action, so we may continue with the presentation.

Appendix B contains the statements of witnesses. Of almost six hundred individuals interviewed, the statements of exactly forty-six are given in Appendix B. The more than five hundred statements that were never generally released were, together with other Review Board reports, files, and working materials, subsequently stored at Langley Research Center. Access to these materials was to be determined by Langley's director, then none other than Dr. Floyd L. Thompson, chairman of the Apollo 204 Review Board.

■ When, on December 29, 1967, NASA Associate Administrator Mueller sent Representative Teague the two-volume *Status of Actions Taken on Recommendation of the Apollo 204 Accident Review Board,* Mueller's letter of transmittal contained the following curious comment:

I am sure you are aware that some actions ensuing from the AS-204 accident cannot be completed until a series of ground qualification and flight tests have been run and their results evaluated. *For example, the new unified hatch will require extensive testing during 1968.* [Italics added.]

Exactly which "unified hatch" was Dr. Mueller talking about? Over seven months before, the following exchange had taken place between astronaut Frank Borman and Senator Stephen M. Young of Ohio, in the Senate space committee:

SENATOR YOUNG: Well, there was no intent, as a matter of fact, to use this new hatch design in the Apollo program, was there?

COLONEL BORMAN: There was, yes sir. It was being designed at the time for incorporation on the Apollo.

SENATOR YOUNG: For the Apollo application program.

COLONEL BORMAN: No, sir; for the Apollo lunar program. But, you see, we had no plan for doing extravehicular activity on the Block I spacecraft. So we felt there was no requirement to incorporate this new hatch design on command module 12 because it would not be actuated on orbit.

A little later in the same hearing, Colonel Borman remarked: "It was my belief that at the time of this accident, a unified hatch was on the design board, but Dr. Mueller said at the time of the accident that there were three different approaches being considered."

Was Dr. Mueller talking, in the Teague letter, about a unified hatch that was *not* being considered *before* the accident? Not likely—seven months is too short a time for an entirely new hatch to develop from a mere idea to "qualification and flight tests." A more likely explanation is that Dr. Mueller thought it wise to give the impression that the unified, quick-opening hatch had been chosen *as a result of* the Review Board's recommendations. The facts seem, on the contrary, to indicate that the "new" unified hatch design had been chosen well *before* the accident. As for Dr. Mueller's "three different approaches," Colonel Borman told the Senate Committee: "I had considered them rapidly and settled on one that I felt was proper."

Why the apparent confusion over the "new" unified hatch? The answer seems to be that, as the potential cost and extent of the Review Board's recommendations became generally known, Borman's early candor was replaced by a somewhat different NASA strategy. The problem was simply this: How could the technical deficiencies detailed by the Review Board be explained? And how had they been permitted to exist in the first place?

NASA evidently realized that it could not give satisfactory answers to such questions. What NASA and the Review Board could do, however, was to try to convince the Congress and the people that "something good" had come out of the Apollo disaster. Thus, Dr. Thompson, who must have been fully aware of the earlier fire studies, and fully aware that NASA had chosen to ignore them, could with apparent sincerity tell the Senate Committee: "I think . . . we have stimulated here a very important advance in the understanding of the risk of fire by this review."

James Webb, too, could not help but put his stamp of approval on the fiction that the Review Board had contributed new and positive findings. As he told Chairman Clinton Anderson of the Senate Committee: "My own estimate is that this team which is a first-class team in industry and our own group and in the universities is going to find in the disassembly of this burned vehicle and the disassembly of the companion vehicle which was not burned a great deal of information that will permit them to have tremendous assurance in the product we put together after that process."

The most damning statement in the whole Review Board story occurs, ironically, at a point in the Report where the Board attempts to express most eloquently its conviction that NASA had been cruelly served by fate. The text of the "Investigation and Analysis" section of the Report concludes with the observation that "in its devotion to the many difficult problems of space travel, the Apollo team failed to give adequate attention to certain mundane but equally vital questions of crew safety."

No statement could better reveal the cruel dichotomy that had always shaped NASA's approach to space travel. Simply stated, it is this: America's space managers had always treated "mission success" and "crew safety" as if they were two separate problems. The rockets that "could do the job" came first, and the men were made to fit them. So deeply had this dichotomy been ingrained in the NASA philosophy that evidently the Board could not grasp that there could be no rational distinction between the "difficult problems of space travel" and the "mundane* . . . questions of crew safety." They are one and the same. If an Apollo capsule, back from the Moon, bore three dead astronauts, would NASA label such a mission a "success"? One can only hope NASA would not.

The Review Board failed, too, because quite plainly it was set up to fail. From its very inception, it was never expected to find a specific cause of the fire—and it did not. Nor was the Review Board charged with finding a point of culpability—and it did not find one. Neither the Congress, nor the press, nor the American public spoke a word. Why? The premise that only NASA could investigate NASA—and the fact that this premise went unchallenged until much too late—reflects a pervasive twentieth-century bent of mind: Scientific and technical efforts are not being

---

* According to the Random House Dictionary, mundane means "earthly, common, ordinary, banal, unimaginative [from the Latin equivalent of mund(us) world + anus-ane]."

judged according to the precepts of ordinary reason, nor within a moral context, nor even within the framework of democratic political institutions. They are autonomous, sacrosanct, a law unto themselves. The observation is hardly new. Never before, however, has the attitude had a bolder expression than in the performance of the Apollo 204 Review Board and its apologists. Administrator Webb, taking his cue from Representative Alphonso Bell of California, gave the standard rationale for appointing an "in-group" to conduct a scientific and technical evaluation.

MR. BELL: Mr. Webb, aren't you really trying to say that it is very difficult to find somebody in some other area that is qualified to know exactly where to go to find the errors, to pinpoint where they are, and what specifically it is? It would take another person—as excellent an engineer as he might be —it would take some time to get acquainted with the process in order to put his finger on the specific discrepancies.

MR. WEBB: Specifically. Also if you take him out of his surroundings where you find him, you take him away from all the strengths that give him his reputation. It takes time to take him out of his surrounding. Very few people are not heavily and deeply involved. Dr. Long [the Cornell scientist who had been named to the original Review Board, but then asked to be relieved] was deeply and heavily involved elsewhere. That was our problem with him. We have done the best job that could be done under the circumstances.

In short, only an insider knows the ropes.

At the heart of Administrator Webb's comment is the implication that there are two breeds of people: those who understand NASA's problems, and laymen. The outsider, or layman, in Mr. Webb's view, has neither the time, the patience, the will, nor the intellectual equipment to evaluate the technical problems of the space age, no matter how great their import for the layman himself.

It is a false and dangerous assumption, and there is no better evidence of just how false, and how dangerous, than in the intriguing history of the "oxygen question."

■ *I do not believe we were going full speed ahead
damn the torpedoes; we have never taken a step
during the course of this program because of
cost or because of schedule or because of any
other pressure that in our judgment had any
effect whatsoever on the safety of the astronauts.*
                    DR. GEORGE E. MUELLER,
               *NASA Associate Administrator for
                Manned Space Flight, April 12, 1967*

■ *. . . Final environments selected for Gemini and
Apollo would not have been 100 percent oxygen
. . . if man's physical capabilities had been of
prime concern . . .*
                    DR. LAWRENCE E. LAMB,
                *Chief, Internal Medicine, School of
                Aerospace Medicine, Brooks Air Force
                Base, Texas, in* Aviation Week,
                        November 23, 1964

Chapter 7 ■ Oxygen: The Most Dangerous Gas

Often an overwhelming sense of absurd and needless waste suf-
fuses our response to great disasters. The thought lurks: *It did
not need to happen.* So it was with Apollo; so it was also with
another disaster of the twentieth century—the sinking of R.M.S.
Titanic. The *Titanic*, the greatest man-made marvel of its time,
sank on its maiden voyage. The Apollo 204 spacecraft, a product
of the "largest and most complex scientific and engineering task"
of our own time, burned while in grooming—just before its
maiden voyage.

On April 12, 1912, the unsinkable pride of the transatlantic
luxury liners struck an iceberg, sustaining a three-hundred-
foot gash. Three hours later, the mighty *Titanic* went under, taking about fifteen hundred souls with her. Even though the *Titanic*
was built with painstaking care and with "foolproof" safety
engineering, its sinking resulted from a series of avoidable and
totally unprofessional decisions stemming from complacency and
overconfidence. Public disbelief gave way to a sense of having

been duped—and a feeling that the "unsinkable" *Titanic* had been sent under by the vindictive hand of fate.

With similar but more kindly fatalism, many Americans have come to view the Apollo fire as a star-crossed sacrifice of pioneering on the hostile frontiers of space. The distinct parallels between the Apollo and the *Titanic* disasters (embarrassingly clear to some NASA spokesmen) might, perhaps, be masked by the great discrepancy in the number of casualties. This discrepancy is reduced, however, by the heroic stature of the astronauts and the Utopianism of the space age they symbolized.

■ Three separate boards of inquiry, investigating the sinking of the *Titanic*, uncovered little more than implausible, yet fatal, errors in human judgment. Long after the horrendous toll was registered, incredulous officials repeated the belief that this ship had been "unsinkable." Yet it was their very belief that had sunk the *Titanic*.

Three separate boards of inquiry (NASA's Apollo Review Board, the Senate Committee on Aeronautical and Space Sciences, and the House Subcommittee on NASA Oversight) investigated the Apollo fire. Their collective efforts uncovered "no point of culpability." NASA was charged with little more than self-confessed "overconfidence and complacency" in its failure to recognize that the fatal Apollo test had been hazardous. Yet it was this belief—that the plugs-out test was "nonhazardous"—that produced the "false sense of security" that culminated in the conflagration.

■ Because it was *believed* "unsinkable," the *Titanic* carried only enough lifeboats and life preservers for half its passengers. No adequate means of abandoning ship had been conceived.

Because the plugs-out test was *believed* "nonhazardous," Apollo officials provided their employees with improper gas masks and fire extinguishers. They had no fire-fighting plan for the support personnel, and no effective protection or exit for the astronauts.

■ Because the *Titanic* was *believed* "unsinkable," its officers ignored six urgent and timely ice warnings, which, if heeded, would have averted the fatal iceberg collision.

Because the plugs-out test was *believed* "nonhazardous," Apollo designers and NASA management ignored countless warnings about fire hazards in a 100-percent-oxygen environment. The lessons of no less than seven previous oxygen fires were ignored.

■ Because the *Titanic* was *believed* "unsinkable," a nearby ship, the *Californian,* broke off communications with it and stood idly by, even while the stricken giant sank. Distress rockets were mistaken for shipboard revelry.

Because the plugs-out test was *believed* "nonhazardous," bad communications were tolerated and unexplained odors and electrical anomalies were judged insignificant. While the cabin fire raged, some of the ground crew thought the danger was external to the spacecraft and that the astronauts would be safe as long as they remained inside. Others who knew that the fire was inside thought the astronauts could release the hatch any time they wished. Almost to a man, support personnel became aware of the fire only after having heard the cries of the trapped astronauts.

■ Because the *Titanic* was *believed* "unsinkable," its owners, unable to comprehend the scope of the disaster, advised newsmen and the public that their ship had been rescued—with only slight loss of life. Only as the severity of the tragedy became more apparent did the owners finally admit that the *Titanic* had gone down with the loss of over a thousand lives.

Because the plugs-out test was *believed* "nonhazardous," newsmen were caught napping. NASA information officers and management spokesmen, absolutely unprepared for such a disaster, attempted to diminish the number of casualties and the horror of the astronauts' last moments. Hours passed before NASA admitted that all three of the astronauts had perished. It was days before NASA admitted that their deaths had not been painless. They have yet to acknowledge that their deaths were avoidable and unnecessary.

■ Because the *Titanic* was *believed* "unsinkable," its class-conscious officials prevented third-class passengers, the "steerage" group segregated below decks, from reaching the upper deck until all life boats had been lowered and the ship was clearly lost. When escape routes were finally opened, it was too late for most to be saved.

Because the plugs-out test was *believed* "nonhazardous," NASA officials sealed the astronauts behind a "Rube Goldberg" hatch that could not be opened from the inside against the normally high cabin pressure, let alone in the event of fire. Only when the cabin ruptured, reducing the pressure, was escape possible. A safe exit would only have been possible if the support crew had been trained to respond more effectively and had been properly equipped.

■ The *Titanic* was thought to be "unsinkable" because of its watertight double bottom. Of the sixteen watertight bulkheads, any three or four of the forward five could have flooded without sinking the ship. The collision with the iceberg opened a gash that flooded all five of them.

The plugs-out test was thought to be "nonhazardous" because the Apollo contractors and designers believed that they had eliminated all electrical sources of ignition. They believed that they would never encounter a situation where the dangerous oxygen, combustible materials, and a source of ignition would exist together. They were, of course, wrong. Many possible sources of ignition were later found, and as many as 1,412 potential combustibles were found to have been placed in the high-oxygen spacecraft.

■ The comparison of the two disasters* ends with an anti-parallel. Legend says the captain, the first mate, and the builder of the *Titanic*, faced with the ignominy of the disaster, chose to go down with their ship.

NASA and its prime contractor, North American Aviation, shuffled some managers and executed broad reassignments of their factory workers to other projects. No one, however, was summarily dismissed. As Congressman Olin Teague, chairman of the House Subcommittee on NASA Oversight, said, before a nationwide television audience: "No point of culpability was

---

* Another parallel has been suggested to the authors by several newsmen who maintain that two men, scheduled to enter the Apollo spacecraft as observers, unwittingly spared themselves when they left the launch pad early. The two men (one an astronaut, and the other a NASA manager) allegedly left because of interminable delays resulting from the "fouled-up" communications between blockhouse and spacecraft. Similarly, one *Titanic* crewman escaped disaster by jumping ship before the *Titanic* had departed on its transatlantic voyage.

found." Except for Dr. Joseph F. Shea, the same men who were at the bridge of Project Apollo on January 27, 1967, were there a year later. And, while a handful of NASA executives have since resigned because of their personal disagreement with subsequent policy developments, most are still there today. To be sure, Grissom and White received posthumous awards from the space engineers' professional organization, the AIAA; and Bunker Air Force Base, in Grissom's native Indiana, was renamed Grissom Air Force Base. But then, too, several top NASA executives received prominent awards as well.

The loss of the Apollo 204 spacecraft and its prime crew—stripped of its frosting of lament and rhetoric, its aura of Homeric fate—ranks as a major national disgrace. The space program's national image, propelled on the winds of overconfidence and complacency, foundered on one of the great technological blunders in the history of American engineering. This fact was cautiously and reluctantly approached by the Senate Committee on Aeronautical and Space Sciences in its final report on the accident. A sense of genuine disbelief is readily apparent. The senators noted that hundreds of hours of successful testing with pure oxygen had apparently led to a false sense of confidence and complacency in NASA's ground operations. The Committee found no other explanation for "the failure of the hundreds of highly trained people on the Apollo program, including the astronauts," to evaluate properly the conditions under which the test was being conducted. In a note of apparent bewilderment, the report said simply:

> It appears that everyone associated with the design and test of the spacecraft simply failed to understand fully the danger and the cooperative effect of an ignition source, the combustible materials, and the pure oxygen atmosphere in the sealed spacecraft cabin.

The Apollo Review Board had revealed many examples of faulty, even "poor" design, workmanship, wiring, and test procedures that had contributed to the fire. NASA's selection of pure oxygen as the cabin atmosphere, however, turned out to be a key issue. It presented a most disturbing and all-encompassing moral dilemma. The "oxygen question" was explored, at great length and from many vantage points, throughout the Review Board investigation and the hearings held in both Houses of the Congress. The selection of pure oxygen was cited by NASA spokesmen as an example of the "overwhelming complexity" of Project Apollo—with the added implication that the choice of atmosphere was based on unimpeachably sound, scholarly judgment.

Because the oxygen issue seemed so complex—so terribly "scientific"—most congressmen apparently chose to regard it as something that could be fathomed only by a Ph.D. in biochemistry. The plethora of scientific and engineering problems centering around the "oxygen question" caused the legislators, members of the unsophisticated laity, to throw up their hands in frustration and despair. Chairman Anderson, of the Senate Committee, expressed this general sense of helplessness in a plaintive appeal to Dr. Floyd Thompson, chairman of the Apollo Review Board:

"I was wondering," Senator Anderson said. "If a decision is to be reached about oxygen as the sole atmospheric gas, where would a nonscientific member of the committee such as I am, find out what the judgments might be?" Anderson added, "it seems to me . . . that it is pretty complicated for a lay person to decide that."

"Well," Dr. Thompson replied, "I do not believe there is any subject that has been studied more than that particular thing."

Chairman Anderson's air of humble naiveté aside, there was very little sound scientific backing for the choice of pure oxygen. It is natural, therefore, for the supporters of the decision to defend their position by rationalization, obfuscatory verbiage, and just plain old-fashioned "mumbo-jumbo." Thus, ten months after Grissom, White, and Chaffee had died, the one person who had done the most to educate NASA about oxygen, reiterated, in as mild a manner as possible, his pre-fire misgivings about tacitly supporting NASA's choice of pure oxygen cabin atmospheres. Dr. Emanuel M. Roth of the Lovelace Foundation, author of many NASA reports, said: "The complexity and novelty of the . . . space crew environment makes it one of the weak links in the overall safety program. As is often the case in unforeseen failure of an otherwise well-planned and executed mission, it is the neglect of a minor, second-order factor which is often at fault . . . initiating a tragic chain of events."*

Roth implied that the space crew environment is a virtual Pandora's box of mysterious "second-order factors," "critical junctions," and possible "chains of events."

Could a "layman" dare to try to understand such weird and wondrous things? He not only can, but must. If informed confidence were the outcome of this fuller understanding, then a laymen need not fear that the astronauts were sacrified thoughtlessly and needlessly. He could confidently discredit the dark hints that persons in high places have been negligent in their eagerness to place Americans on the Moon by the end of 1969. Obviously, our efforts to understand are worth pursuing.

Discussion of oxygen fires in the U.S. space program is necessarily punctuated by the deaths of *five*, not three men. On January 31, 1967, just four days after the deaths of Grissom, White, and Chaffee at Cape Kennedy, Airman 3rd-Class Richard G. Harmon, age twenty-one, of Auburn, New York, and Airman 2nd-Class William F. Bartley, Jr., age twenty, of Indianapolis, Indiana, lost their lives in a pure-oxygen fire at Brooks Air Force Base, Texas.

The fire broke out in the same Brooks facility where two other nonfatal fires had already occurred. Rabbits were the test subjects. On the sixty-seventh day of this pure-oxygen test, airmen Bartley and Harmon were felled while attending the needs of their furry charges. The two men were trained for and experienced in the execution of their task—they had been in the chamber several times before. The Brooks Review Board found, however, that the airmen had not had proper fire-fighting instruction. "The most probable cause of the fire," according to the Brooks Board, "was an electrical arc in a work-lamp cord inside the chamber." While the cause of the small break in the cord's Teflon insulation remained undetermined, it was assumed that the electrical arc had jumped from the exposed wire to the aluminum floor of the chamber.

It seems likely that NASA might have adroitly side-stepped the widespread criticism subsequently encountered in the Congress,

* From a paper delivered before the fourth annual meeting of the American Institute of Aeronautics and Astronautics at Anaheim, California, October, 1967.

in the press, and indeed in NASA's own Review Board—*if* this Brooks incident had not occurred. Indeed, had it not been for this second accident, following hard on the Apollo fire, NASA might have succeeded in enshrining its initial "explanation" that the Apollo fire was a fluke—that, as the trade magazine *Technology Week* put it, the chances were "one in a million" that it would occur again.

There were only a handful of congressmen who dared make the inevitable observation. Senator Mondale was one of them. "We have yet to have a successful manned Apollo flight," he said. "We are already experiencing serious time delays. We have had overruns in the hundreds of millions of dollars. We have had five deaths."

The deaths of airmen Harmon and Bartley occurred on the very day the NASA astronauts were laid to rest, during memorial services that were marked by the highest official tribute of a grief-stricken nation and its President. The two Brooks airmen were buried with no such honors.*

Because of the untimely coincidence of the Air Force fire, American newsmen were prompted, many for the first time, to look into the story of fires in pure-oxygen or oxygen-enriched atmospheres. Their efforts, however, led to few significant disclosures. Some reporters, no doubt, listened to Colonel George E. Schafer, Vice Commander of the Medical Division of Brooks Air Force Base, who asserted there was "no correlation between this event and the Apollo fire." After all, the astronauts were in a highly sophisticated space cabin, in an oxygen atmosphere at 16.7 p.s.i., or pounds per square inch. (This is slightly more than atmospheric pressure at sea level—14.7 pounds per square inch.) The two Brooks airmen were merely servicing a few furry rabbits in an altitude chamber with roughly half normal sea level atmospheric pressure (about 7.2 pounds per square inch). Air Force spokesmen stated that the victims were wearing cotton clothing,

---

* The god-like attributes of space-age pioneers, as might be expected, are not confined by national boundaries. Yuri Gagarin, first man in space, died on March 27, 1968, in a routine aircraft accident. He was buried with highest Soviet honors. His ashes were placed in the Kremlin Wall, near the tomb of Lenin. (By the end of 1968, "routine" accidents had killed five U.S. astronauts: Elliot M. See, Jr., Major Charles A. Bassett II (USAF), Captain Theodore C. Freeman (USAF), and Major Clifton C. Williams, Jr. (USMC) all died in T-38 jet crashes. Major Edward G. Givens, Jr. (USAF) died in an automobile accident.)

rather than abestos or other flameproof clothing. Yet their superiors had had no reason to expect a fire, "and saw no need" for
unusual protection. The test, and the participation of the men,
was regarded as "routine."

The abrupt loss of five American servicemen in oxygen fires, in
both the "peaceful" and "military" (Brooks) space programs, has
been widely regarded as a blunder on the part of the science
community, foisted by "scientists" upon a too-trusting NASA
and Department of Defense. The former *New York World Journal
Tribune,* for example, carried, on February 1, 1967, the eye-catch-
ing headlines "Space Officials Baffled by Second Fatal Fire" and
"Science Gambled on Pure Oxygen—And Lost." The same day,
NASA Administrator Webb, in an address to the Washington
Club, a ladies' group in the capital, called attention to the "distinguished and able people in the government laboratories," and
to the "systems that have been developed through the use of
scientists and universities of this nation." He took care to note
that they "discharge the final responsibility that goes with governmental authority in the choice of the risks that must be taken and
the means through which we will meet those risks." Plainly,
Webb, too, wished to have the "scientists and universities" accept
a share in the responsibility for the Apollo fire. A review of the
history of oxygen as a cabin atmosphere, however, reveals the
relatively minor influence of unbiased "science" on America's current space program.

Even before the end of World War I, in January, 1918, a U.S.
military aeromedical laboratory was established in Texas. The
laboratory was concerned with the growing problems of high-
altitude flight—most of which are also encountered in space flight,
e.g., lack of oxygen, low temperature, and weightlessness. Eventually, this laboratory at Brooks Air Force Base became known as
the Air Force School of Aerospace Medicine. It was here, in 1967,
that the oxygen fire that killed airmen Harmon and Bartley
occurred. In 1949, a special division of the school was established,
the Department of Space Medicine. As early as 1951 and 1952,
experiments were conducted with mice and monkeys to help
determine whether humans would be able to survive weightlessness and the tremendous acceleration required to escape the
Earth's gravity.

In the late 1950's, with manned space flight about to emerge from the pages of *Astounding Science Fiction,* decisions on cabin atmosphere selection were urgently demanded. Years of research and testing with oxygen-enriched atmospheres, and pure oxygen as well, had yielded a mountain of data. A single-gas atmosphere (oxygen, of course), on principle, was simpler to regulate and easier to design into a spacecraft. One gas requires a minimum of containers, pumps, plumbing, and regulators. There was, therefore, a minimum of engineering hardware that could fail. Furthermore, one gas meant a minimum of weight penalties.

Launch vehicles used to place unmanned packages in orbit around the Earth, or, for that matter, around or on the Moon, require relatively modest rocket boosters. The decision to place men in space and on the Moon, however, created the urgent requirement of designing and constructing capsules with self-contained atmosphere, breathing apparatus (including carbon dioxide removal), water and food supply and containers, waste-removal systems, more sophisticated space suits, and a complex of plumbing, wires, and sensors to regulate performance. This requirement —the manned capability (man-rating)—presented special problems to designers, engineers, and technicians of the nation's space program.

Not only were big boosters, like the uprated Saturn 1B and the giant Saturn 5 required, but the cabin interior—the environmental control unit (ECU)—had to be kept as light and compact as possible. The Soviet rocketeers, already blessed with sufficiently oversized boosters, went directly to normal air for use in cabin interiors. The Russian cosmonaut simply took his everyday normal air supply into space with him; the added weight and engineering requirements were not considered as restraints.

The one-gas (100-percent-oxygen) system, on the other hand, was deemed the simplest and most reliable choice for NASA's initial manned venture—Project Mercury—at a time when the Saturn 5 rocket was still on the drawing board. The original plan, taking into consideration the fire hazard and certain medical complications associated with oxygen, called for pure oxygen at reduced pressure (about 3.5 pounds per square inch in the astronaut's space suit). It was hoped that this pressure, about the equivalent of nature's oxygen in the average gulp of air we breathe (called the "partial pressure"), would be adequate and safe. Any lower pressure was definitely out for space flights. The Mercury spacecraft cabin, however, (as opposed to the astronauts' space suits) was originally designed for a mixture. The procedure during the pre-launch activity was explained by Dr. Charles A. Berry,* chief medical officer at the Manned Spacecraft Center, Houston, in the opening session of the Senate Apollo 204 investigation: "On the pad," he explained, "air was present in the cabin. After launch, when the spacecraft passed 10,000 feet altitude, a flow of oxygen . . . was activated. This flow of oxygen enriched the cabin so that at 27,000 feet, the cabin composition was approximately 66 percent oxygen and 33 percent nitrogen." The concept sounded fine, but it did not work.

The first manned tests on life support systems for NASA projects were started in late April, 1960. A simulated space-cabin "chamber" was used. In the first test, Gilbert B. North, a test pilot and design executive at the McDonnell Aircraft Corporation, was "pre-breathed" in pure oxygen before entering the chamber. No purge of the chamber was conducted, since North was suited and had an independent oxygen supply. In the midst of this very first test, North fell unconscious. By the end of one hour of testing (the last forty minutes at 5 p.s.i.), enough nitrogen from the normal outside air had leaked into North's pressure suit, sharply reducing the supply of oxygen to his tissues and brain—a condition known as "hypoxia," or insufficient oxygen.

North's collapse was due to leaky lines leading into the test chamber and into his pressure-suit hose system; these leaks permitted normal air to "contaminate" the test pilot's pure-oxygen atmosphere. Later, nine additional tests were run—each failed as well. The problem that cropped up during this 1960 series of tests led John Yardley, spacecraft manager at McDonnell, to recommend that the Mercury cabin environment, during ground tests and launch phases, be changed from air to 100 percent oxygen at a pressure slightly greater than normal atmospheric pressure.

This normal pressure is 14.7 pounds per square inch at sea

---

* Berry will be remembered as the chief NASA physican who prescribed aspirin and decongestants for the Apollo 7 astronauts, anti-nausea and anti-diarrhea pills for the Apollo 8 astronauts.

level. It means that the envelope of air surrounding the Earth presses down upon each square inch of the surface with a weight of just under fifteen pounds. Human beings and other terrestrial creatures have evolved to withstand this amount of pressure on every square inch of their bodies. By conversion of the spacecraft atmosphere to pure oxygen, the dangerous nitrogen and other impurities were eliminated. Because the cabin pressure was greater than that of the outside air, the leakage was all one way—from the inside out. The Soviets must have been more careful on this particular problem, for as the editors of *Fortune* magazine observed, in 1962: "It has been up to [their] engineers to build [spacecraft] so that they do not leak."

The mixed-gas idea was dropped like a hot potato, and Yardley's recommendation, clearly the most expedient, was approved. It appeared to NASA and its contractors to be the only way to prevent the villainous nitrogen from seeping into a space suit.

But how, the medical people asked, would breathing pure oxygen at greater than atmospheric pressure affect the well-being of U.S. astronauts? Not all the long-term effects of breathing 100 percent oxygen were known at that time (and some are still not completely understood). However, there had been ample demonstration that men could survive for at least a few days breathing pure oxygen, without any serious physiological ill effects. Ordinary air—the stuff we breathe every day of our lives— consists of approximately 80 percent nitrogen and 20 percent oxygen, with tiny quantities of other gases, such as carbon dioxide and helium, thrown in. For human beings, oxygen is the essential substance in the air we breathe—that is, while we might survive if the nitrogen were suddenly removed from our atmosphere, we would definitely not survive if the oxygen were taken away. Just four minutes of oxygen starvation can cause permanent brain damage, and it is not much longer before death becomes a certainty.

But the fact remains that our lungs and the rest of our bodies have developed, through the long ages of evolution, to deal with ordinary, nitrogen-containing air. The nitrogen and the other gases play passive roles and are exhaled essentially unused. Nevertheless, exposure to a pure-oxygen, nitrogen-free atmosphere for long periods can be expected to disrupt the normal functioning of our bodies in any number of ways, some of which are well known and grouped under the general heading of "oxygen toxicity" (i.e., oxygen poisoning).

The effects of raising the *pressure* (measured in pounds per square inch, or p.s.i.) of the pure oxygen in a space cabin were also far from fully investigated at the time of Yardley's recommendation. However, it seemed, from earlier, short-duration experiments, that men's bodies suffered no lasting harm if the pressure of the oxygen varied over a wide range for just a few hours, e.g., from a low of two or three pounds per square inch up to and exceeding the pressure of ordinary air at sea level (14.7 p.s.i.). After about thirty days in high-pressure oxygen most test animals died. But the period of high pressure in the spacecraft situation only lasted during a pre-launch phase of a few hours.

Weighing all these facts, Yardley and NASA decided that a 100-percent-oxygen, pressurized cabin atmosphere seemed most suitable for the Mercury program. It is extremely significant, however, that the decision to use pure oxygen was not made because it was more desirable for the astronauts. Rather, space technology could provide neither a big enough booster to orbit a 10 percent heavier mixed-gas command module, nor leak-proof space suits, breathing hoses, and valves (suit loops) that could handle a second, diluent gas, such as nitrogen, to be mixed with oxygen.* Accordingly, Dr. Berry, the chief medical officer at Houston's Manned Spacecraft Center, told the Senate investigators, as he read from the official directive made at the time in 1960, the "requirement for purging the cabin with pure oxygen at approximately fifteen pounds per square inch [or a little over atmospheric pressure] during the pre-launch period of several hours has been continued for all manned spacecraft launched in this country. This same procedure has been used also on all manned spacecraft vacuum chamber tests in the Mercury, Gemini, and Apollo programs."

As it was explained, "state-of-the-art" procedures, consistent with all other aspects of the space program, dictated the selection of the Mercury atmosphere. It was a selection based "largely on

---

* A diluent gas, such as nitrogen, can be used in spacecraft simply to increase the total bulk of the atmosphere (e.g., to dilute the oxygen), reducing both oxygen toxicity and fire hazard.

the experience generated in the aeromedical support of military high performance jet aircraft and the man-high balloons."

There had been a general shift in these experiments during the 1950's, from oxygen-enriched air (i.e., air with more than its normal 20 percent oxygen) to pure oxygen. Systems had been designed for a cabin atmosphere at five pounds per square inch, with a breathing supply of pure oxygen. Dr. Berry added that the selection was basically a "trade-off" (i.e., the better of several evils) between factors of "oxygen toxicity, hypoxia, spacecraft leakage, and weight." In testimony before the Senate Committee he quoted excerpts from a Mercury report summarizing the discussion leading to the atmosphere selection. The selection of a pure-oxygen system, Dr. Berry testified, was made "primarily because of reliability requirements and also because of *critical delivery requirements.*" [Italics added.]

In other words, a pure-oxygen atmosphere was chosen because it was the only way NASA could continue its pell-mell rush into space and toward the Moon. All this had occurred before John F. Kennedy committed the space agency to a specific date.

The switch to pure oxygen in Mercury capsules was followed by an intensive period of *post facto* experimentation designed to demonstrate the validity of the decision. Preliminary results, however, were far from reassuring. Doctors at the Wright-Patterson Air Force Base, Ohio, and at the Air Force School of Aerospace Medicine, found a host of potential medical complications with pure oxygen. There were instances of dizziness, drying of nasal passages, reduced red blood cell count, and urinary problems, among other symptoms. Mice, rats, and monkeys exposed to pure oxygen for long periods frequently sickened and died. Thus, the problems of "oxygen poisoning" seemed definitely to limit the use of the pure-oxygen environment to space missions of short duration.

Naturally, the fire hazard of pure-oxygen or oxygen-enriched atmospheres was universally recognized, and numerous safety measures were suggested to reduce the danger. The simple facts are these: For something to burn, there must be oxygen. When something burns—say, a log of wood in a fireplace—the heat, light and flame result from a violent chemical reaction (oxidation) between molecules from the 20 percent gaseous oxygen in ordinary air and carbon molecules in the wood. If the amount or pressure of oxygen is increased, as in a spacecraft cabin, the reaction will occur proportionately more rapidly and intensely. Thus, as NASA reports indicated, the "fire hazard becomes a more important consideration as the concentration of oxygen increases." Low cabin pressure, therefore, was a priority consideration. Lower cabin pressure meant a lesser concentration of oxygen within the cabin, and thus a reduction of the fire hazard. For example, there is greater danger from fire in a pure-oxygen atmosphere at a pressure of 16.7 pounds per square inch than there is at five pounds per square inch, although the fire hazard in 100 percent oxygen, at *any* pressure, certainly remains very high.

What about fire extinguishers? Most conventional types available contained toxic substances or reacted unfavorably with pure oxygen, and appeared to present more problems than solutions.

There seemed to be just one satisfactory approach to the fire hazard—efforts would have to be made to eliminate all possible sources of ignition.

Members of the scientific community, however, grew more and more uneasy. As their experiments progressed, accounts of unexpected fires and other undesirable side effects became more frequent; safety measures seemed inadequate and the apprehension in university, government and industrial circles turned to firm opposition. The argument *against* pure oxygen, and *for* a mixed-gas atmosphere, grew more audible and noticeably more heated. Yet pure-oxygen Project Mercury was already well under way.

The medical risk of exposure to pure oxygen, based on abundant experience with military aircraft, was relatively slight—if used for short duration missions such as the Mercury flights of a few hours. However, the longer Apollo missions, fourteen days and up, were regarded as an entirely different matter. (At this stage, the Gemini program had not yet been initiated. Gemini was introduced in 1962 to explore, among other things, means of combating the medical ill-effects of space flight.) Thus, though the commitment had been made to an oxygen atmosphere for Mercury, researchers turned again to the problem of devising a mixed-gas cabin atmosphere (one that would work) for the nation's Apollo Moon missions, then thought to be some six or seven years away.

Dr. Berry described the original Apollo decision to the Senate Committee: "The original Apollo statement of work [August 2, 1961] specified a two-gas atmosphere composed of 50 percent oxygen and 50 percent nitrogen at a total pressure of seven pounds per square inch absolute." This composition, he explained, was based primarily on health considerations. Concern was focused primarily around the possibility of *pulmonary atelectasis*—collapse of lung tissues. He also noted that "the potential of bends problems associated with the atmosphere and space suit operations [common to deep-sea diving operations] at 3.7 pounds per square inch absolute was unknown at the time."

Thus, the experts originally wanted a mixed-gas atmosphere for the ambitious Apollo Moon project—on purely medical grounds. As a sort of bonus, the fire hazard was known to be less than in the pure-oxygen Mercury cabin atmosphere. NASA designers and engineers were faced with the more difficult task of building the machine around the man, as opposed to the original approach of forcing the man to fit their machines. The difficulty, NASA explained, was that "at the time of initial Apollo development, no multi-gas system suitable for space flight had even been demonstrated." (A lame excuse, since, by the same token, the vehicle that would carry the spacecraft and its atmosphere to the Moon had not even yet been selected. Furthermore, von Braun's Saturn 5, the rocket system ultimately chosen, was not even demonstrated to be flightworthy until 1968—one year after NASA had originally hoped to make the lunar landing.)

Thus, early in 1962, NASA was faced with the decision of whether or not to slow down the entire Apollo program to wait for some breakthrough in a workable multi-gas system and then redesign von Braun's launch vehicles to carry it. The prospect of such a delay was distinctly unpleasant to space officials—the rocket systems under consideration already had problems enough for the engineers. Besides, by this time, the President had taken NASA at its word and had announced to the world that the space agency would conduct the Apollo program with a specific deadline in mind.

It was at this juncture that NASA found a scapegoat: the awesome and hoary specter of the deep-sea diver's "bends" loomed suddenly large in NASA's evaluation of space environment risks. NASA began to equate the risk of fire in a one-gas (oxygen) atmosphere with the risk of the bends in a mixed-gas atmosphere. Indeed, experiments had shown that various mixed-gas cabin atmospheres under study for the Apollo project inevitably produced the same results. As long as there was any nitrogen in the spacecraft, the nitrogen was stored in the body or leaked into the space suit, forming bubbles throughout body tissue and blood vessels. The countless, tiny bubbles caused mild to severe pain, aching joints, blackouts, and could result, in a severe case, in death.

The only remedy for the bends at the time was a prolonged period of decompression identical to that required for an incapacitated deep-sea diver. To prevent nitrogen bubbles from forming in their blood, Soviet cosmonauts have had to stay in their capsules for several hours after returning to earth. A prevention of bends, on the other hand, was found in 1962, by isolating U.S. astronauts in an oxygen chamber for several hours before flight—an operation they dubbed "pre-breathing." NASA management decided that the prospect of an unlikely—and manageable—spacecraft fire was preferable to exposing their astronauts to the "bends." NASA's approach to this decision was explained by Administrator Webb, on February 1, 1967—five days after the Apollo 204 fire—to the ladies of the Washington Club: "One of our problems has been to determine how best to avoid worst risks. And so we have chosen in all of these flights to use oxygen and have these men on pure oxygen for some time before the flight to make sure there is no nitrogen in the bloodstream. The danger of decompression and the bends is one danger associated with these flights which must be counter-balanced with use of what is, of course, a dangerous [pure-oxygen] atmosphere . . . Our purpose has been to minimize the danger, to reduce it to an acceptable risk, and to operate on a very simple assumption: that if anything can go wrong, it will. . . ."*

Webb's and NASA's approval of pure oxygen for the Apollo cabin actually can be traced back to July of 1962, when pre-

* Known, in bureaucratic circles, as "Murphy's Law."

liminary results of studies on the newly planned Gemini atmosphere were completed. Gemini flights were to run as long as a week—and laboratory exposure of animals, and then humans, indicated that few if any really serious medical problems occurred from week-long exposure to pure-oxygen environments. These experiments were the basis for the decision to continue using the Mercury-type pure-oxygen atmospheres in the Gemini flights. A positive obverse of Webb's "very simple assumption," known as the success formula, was emerging. To wit: "If anything works once, do it again."

Using this formula, it was only logical, perhaps, for NASA to ask: Why not use a single-gas (pure-oxygen) environment in Apollo? Apparently no "in-house" medical objections were raised —none, at any rate, that NASA heeded.* Consequently, in August, 1962, according to Dr. Berry, North American Aviation, the prime contractor for the Apollo spacecraft and the launch vehicle, was directed to change to the single-gas atmosphere "for the Apollo missions."

Many uncertainties remained for the scientists, who traditionally take a conservative stand on anything that is not tested, retested, and fully certified. And there was always the extremely hazardous fire potential. NASA engineers could not completely ignore this latter threat. They assured the skeptics that they would remove *every* last possible source of ignition, be it an electrostatic discharge, electrical wiring, spontaneous combustion —or *anything*. As Dr. Berry repeatedly said: "The possibility of fire in any atmosphere has been understood throughout the program . . . The approach to fire prevention** is to prevent the initiation of combustion by attempting to remove all possible sources of ignition."

Mere assurance by NASA managers and their contractors that

---

* Senator Mondale, "acting as devil's advocate," asked NASA managers at the Senate Apollo 204 hearings if a change that had been made to conform to "critical delivery requirements," and thereby "avoiding long lead-times that would pace the entire program," might not suggest that NASA had put schedules before astronaut safety. The NASA managers said they just didn't see how their testimony could be interpreted that way.

** As will be seen in the following chapter, this is not the *only* approach to fire prevention. It is, however, the one which NASA adhered to until the Apollo 204 tragedy.

everything was going to be all right did not, however, satisfy some of the more independent researchers in the aerospace medical labs. NASA had contracted several studies of the relative merits of mixed- versus single-gas atmospheres. Emphasis was always more on the medical problems, but particular attention was also directed to the fire hazard of each system under examination. Studies were conducted by the Lovelace Foundation, in Albuquerque, New Mexico; Wright-Patterson Air Force Base, in Ohio; Brooks Air Force Base, in Texas; Republic Aviation, Farmingdale, New York*; and a few universities. Their results, generally, were hardly encouraging.

Perhaps most notable of these investigations was that contracted to the Lovelace Foundation. The first of four thin, paperbound, blue-and-white volumes dealt exclusively with the health aspects of cabin atmosphere selection. Released in 1964, it is entitled "Space-Cabin Atmospheres, Part 1—Oxygen Toxicity."** It is a summary of the state-of-the-art in aerospace medicine, compiled by Dr. Emanuel M. Roth.

On page 42, Dr. Roth states:

It must be remembered that, at best, we are dealing with environments on the borderline of safety . . . more animal and human studies are required . . . studies of borderline oxygen toxicity in animals should be followed up . . . pertinent human studies should be repeated . . . The subjects should be followed intermittently for the rest of their lives. *This should be done for the basic scientific information to be obtained and from a humane concern for their future health.* [Italics added.]

Throughout the brief volume such warnings are repeated again and again. Problem after problem seems unresolved and worth more study before any solid conclusions can be advanced. The signposts continue: "Oxygen therapy of . . . lung-blast victims should be further studied. This is important for both the space and nuclear weapons problems. The mechanism is unclear . . . it would be worthwhile to reevaluate these findings . . . current

* The Republic Aviation study seems to have been unique in that excellent precautions were taken against fire.
** NASA SP–47.

studies should be extended . . . it would be worthwhile to confirm the preliminary studies."

This is the scientific and scholarly "technical language" that NASA and the Congress have said is too complex to understand—it is the same documentation that is allegedly the basis of sound medical judgment on the selection of oxygen as a cabin environment.

Dr. Roth's shaky confidence in the uncertain conclusions of his first volume—the medical basis for the oxygen selection—contrasts sharply with the assurances trotted out, again and again, by NASA officials testifying after the Apollo disaster—over a period of more than a year—at Congressional hearings. Clearly, the medical findings were less than conclusive. The fire studies were downright disturbing.

Administrator Webb, however, in his Washington Club address, February 1, 1967, had this to say about that decision-making period in Apollo development: "I would not like to have anyone believe that the decision for such a solution of a complex problem as a one-gas, pure-oxygen breathing system was undertaken without the utmost responsible examination of all alternatives."

Nevertheless, some of these studies, especially those of the Lovelace Foundation, on which NASA relied most, were not even begun until long after NASA had made its decision to redesign the Apollo spacecraft for oxygen. Typically, pressures from NASA and contractor management seem to have been brought to bear on these various studies, particularly on the Lovelace contract. The result was that these "independent" research efforts were assigned the ignoble task of documenting and *justifying* a decision passed down from higher up. Dr. Roth, chief of the Lovelace project, described this as "putting the cart before the horse." Dr. Lawrence E. Lamb, chief medical researcher for the Air Force Manned Orbiting Laboratory (MOL) project, which was also to benefit from these studies, said: "ours has been reaction research. We had to run a crash project to determine how well and for how long man could function under these conditions. Since the 100-percent-oxygen environment has been determined, man's ability to function in it must be fully documented."

Such protests fell on deaf ears. George M. Low, director of

NASA's Spacecraft and Flight Missions, Office of Manned Flight, had summed up the philosophy, pertaining to all systems, before a distinguished NASA-industry conference, in February, 1963. Low's words bear repeating:

> . . . Our time scales may just be too short to permit developmental changes in Gemini, or to permit major design changes in Apollo . . . the goals of Project Mercury have been achieved, the Gemini and Apollo projects are now well underway, and all significant procurement actions have been taken.

Now that pressure was really on to keep Gemini and Apollo moving full speed ahead and in proper coordination, NASA managers decided to discontinue some of the wasteful and redundant practices of the Mercury "learning process." For instance, on November 9, 1964, *Aviation Week* observed that Apollo manager Joseph F. Shea, successor to Brainerd Holmes, had stated that NASA would no longer make any changes in upcoming flight equipment that might be indicated on the basis of previous flight results. Instead, Shea and other NASA officials would save up everything learned in the last three years (since Apollo had officially begun) and would make all modifications in one big lump effort in the Block 2 spacecraft—the spacecraft design which would make the actual Moon landing. Block 1 spacecraft, (e.g., the disastrous Apollo 012) would perform the preliminary Earth-orbital Apollo missions.

In this context, there is little wonder that Grissom was not always pleased with the training and apparatus available to Apollo astronauts. Nor is it surprising that he thought of the Block 1 spacecraft test simulator as a "lemon," and termed his ship, the Apollo spacecraft, a "bucket of bolts." One brush with death is enough for any man. After all, he had nearly drowned when his first capsule, Mercury's Liberty Bell 7, sank at sea.

The Block 1 Apollo spacecraft, by the end of 1966, had become such a patchwork of compromises that any resemblance with the new generation, the Block 2 spacecraft, was quite surprising. The strategy, adopted by Shea, his boss, Dr. Mueller, and their industrial program managers at North American, was fondly referred to as the "Block concept of manufacturing." This meant that unless any serious malfunctions occurred (such as the Apollo tragedy), major design changes would wait until it was time to use the actual spacecraft designed to make the perilous journey to the Moon and back. Until then, astronauts and their colleagues would have to put their faith in Apollo's equivalent of the Edsel, Block 1.

Regrettably, too many changes had been put aside for Block 2 because Apollo 012, the very first manned Block 1 spacecraft, was gutted in a conflagration of bad communications, lost wrench sockets, bad wiring, short circuits, flaming fabrics, and toxic gases—while still being preened for its maiden voyage with human cargo.

It is a sad commentary on America's space program that for so long so many persons in responsible positions seemed to think they were doing everything exactly right. The Apollo fire was still some way off when, in 1966, the *Gemini Midprogram Conference* report was going to press. Within its pages, Dr. Berry had jibed the fuddy-duddy critics in this fashion: "It is difficult to realize that just two years ago, only an uncertain answer could be given to the question, 'Can man's physiology sustain his performance of useful work in space?'" He noted that many apprehensions had been overly pessimistic, even contradictory, and with the exception of problems in sleeping, defecation, and orthostatic hypotension (low blood pressure in the lower extremeties), they had all been overrated. Thus, he observed, space medicine had reached the "great day . . . when man has equaled the machine."

Almost a year after the Apollo fire, Dr. Emanuel Roth, a colleague of Dr. Berry, could not bring himself to such euphoric heights. On the contrary, he noted: "In the final analysis, one hopes to be able to treat the human element with the same degree of certainty as one treats the propulsion or aerodynamic systems in the face of unknowns in the physical environment of space."

Before the Apollo fire, NASA might have pointed with pride to the fact that the ghastly "bends," particularly on the long Gemini flights that included "space walks," had been overcome by denitrogenating the crew with "pre-breathing." The follow-up operation, the oxygen purge (which was under way during the fatal plugs-out test), might have also been cited as a triumph of "space medicine." In this procedure the cabin air was slowly replaced by 100 percent oxygen until internal pressure exceeded normal atmospheric pressure outside the spacecraft. This was necessary to prevent air from leaking into the cabin from outside; the higher pressure inside the cabin acted as a barrier to air seepage, since any leaking was to the outside. Thus, during the plugs-out test the cabin pressure was slightly greater (16.7 p.s.i.) than the pressure outside the cabin (which was normal atmospheric pressure, or about 14.7 pounds per square inch). Similarly, the three astronauts' suits, fed by a common oxygen supply, were pressurized to a slightly higher level than the cabin pressure. The pressure inside the suits needed to be just a little higher simply to keep the suits from collapsing around the astronauts. Throughout the entire Mercury program, and in the Gemini program that in ten flights lofted twenty men, this pre-launch purge worked apparently without incident.*

Dr. Berry and his NASA colleagues had further cause for self-satisfaction in their recommendation of a 100-percent-oxygen atmosphere. Other NASA scientists were able to provide information that indicated that at least one potential cause of a fire in space seemed to have been exaggerated.

Space scientists have long been aware that, far from being empty, the space between the Earth and the Moon is surprisingly well populated. It is occupied by a very, very thin extension of our atmosphere, gaseous plasma, charged particles (the solar "wind") from the Sun, and a large and seemingly unpredictable number of tiny satellites. These small particles of cosmic dust whirl through space in their own orbits at extremely high velocity. Should they collide with a spacecraft, or with an astronaut's pressure suit during a "space walk," they could hit with explosive force—like tiny bullets. It had been feared that a swarm of cosmic dust and other space debris could penetrate a spacecraft or space suit—with dire results. Explosive penetration of a spacecraft filled with pure oxygen could conceivably start a fire. If the astronaut were outside his cabin, his suit would depressurize

---

* After launch the cabin pressure was gradually reduced, until it reached 5 p.s.i. when the spacecraft was in orbit. Suit pressure remained always just a bit higher than cabin pressure. An uninflated suit would collapse around the astronaut, while a fully inflated suit, like a balloon, would be so rigid as to render him immobile.

instantly, and he would (if at all) barely have time to return to the safety of his spacecraft.*

However, during the months marked by the conclusion of the Gemini spectacles, other (unmanned) U.S. scientific satellites began to paint a far less formidable picture of the micrometeoroid hazard. The pro-oxygen faction was absolved—its champions had not only solved the "bends problem" by the use of pure oxygen, but also were the beneficiaries of recent research that indicated the risk of fire in space was less than predicted. So delighted were NASA program managers and their medical experts with the performance of the astronauts in their 100-percent-oxygen machines, that they forgot about lesser, "mundane" things, such as fire hazard on the ground.

The fire hazard always existed—and NASA, North American, and everybody else connected with the Apollo 204 test should have known it—because inside the command module were all three factors that could start, and feed, a raging fire: a source of ignition, such as frayed, worn, or improperly insulated electrical wiring; combustibles (materials that would burn); and finally, a pressurized 100-percent-oxygen atmosphere, in which materials that might not catch fire and burn in ordinary air would burn vigorously. Truly, it was an oxygen bomb.

The wisdom of the oxygen decision was challenged—just a little—in the Congressional hearings that followed the Apollo disaster.

Colonel Borman, for example, was questioned by the Senate about this point. It was a very sensitive question, since (as he himself said) he spoke both as a member of the astronaut team and as a representative of the investigating management. Borman could only say: "None of us were fully aware of the hazard that existed when you combine a pure-oxygen atmosphere with the extensive distribution of combustibles and the likely source of ignition . . . and so this test . . . was not classified as hazardous."

By this time, even the Senate Committee's chairman, Senator

* If the spacecraft atmosphere were *mixed*, with nitrogen, for example, he would be exposed to the possibility of the "bends," just as he had been on the ground. However, as laymen may learn from the motion picture *Space Odyssey—2001*, mammals, such as monkeys, have been able to survive exposure to the near-vacuum of space for two to four minutes—with no ill effects.

Clinton P. Anderson of New Mexico, had acquired a healthy respect for pure oxygen. He testified that one of his science advisers had confided to him: "If you light a match in pure oxygen, it will burn your arm off!"*

Senator Margaret Chase Smith of Maine then asked Colonel Borman if he had been aware of the electrical deficiencies in the Apollo systems before having been appointed to the Review Board. He answered with a forthright, "Yes, Ma'am." Asked later by Senator Carl T. Curtis, of Nebraska, if he would have entered the spacecraft willingly, before the fire, he replied, "Yes, sir." Asked the obvious, by Senator Charles H. Percy, of Illinois, if he would have refused to enter it knowing what he now knew as a result of the investigation, he replied, "Yes, sir."

Out of this kind of testimony finally emerged an observation familiar, no doubt, to every general science student—pure oxygen is a very dangerous substance to play with. Yes, Colonel Borman knew that there were electrical deficiencies, and, unless he had exclusive informants, we must assume that a great many other people, including NASA management, also knew it.** Borman and NASA officials have outlined the three requirements of a cabin fire: oxygen, a source of ignition, and combustible materials. By NASA's own admission, two of these were known to have existed together—pure oxygen and bad wiring, which could have provided many potential sources of ignition. The last ingredient, combustible material, was also present—and in great profusion.***

Within the cloistered chambers of the Senate Committee on Aeronautical and Space Sciences, flickering memories of previous oxygen fires cast momentary doubt on the validity of NASA's

---

* A paperback book available in most college bookstores, *Space Biology*, by James S. Hanrahan and David Bushnell, Science Editions, 1961, explained this phenomenon as follows: "The Aerospace Medical Association and John P. Marbarger [early workers in space medicine] . . . had shown that even in reduced cabin pressure with oxygen, in jetcraft, "lipstick, chapstick, and the fats and oils of the human body will act as flammable materials."

** Baron had failed to get through to NASA management with his complaints on this subject. See Chapter 6.

*** Paul Haney, public information officer at Houston, was asked, just hours after the fire, if there had been any combustibles in the Apollo 012 spacecraft. His answer had been "no." Since Webb, Seamans, Mueller, Thompson, and Berry repeatedly said that safety of the astronauts was an ever-present consideration, they too must have *thought* that there were no combustibles in the spacecraft.

historic decision. NASA Associate Administrator Dr. Mueller boldly met the tide of tongue-clucking disapproval in joust after joust:

> DR. MUELLER: Well, I think, of course, in retrospect, it is always easy to say that one should have done something different.
> SENATOR DODD: I know that.
> DR. MUELLER: In fact, however, we do carefully evaluate each such incident . . . *It was not through overlooking the problem, that we arrived at the 204 accident.* [Italics added.]

If NASA was not "overlooking the problem," then how in the name of logic did the Apollo 204 fire occur? It is a simple matter of record that neither NASA, its contractors, its Congressional watchdogs, nor the three "independent" investigating bodies were able to propose even a glimmer of an intelligent answer. Having defended the oxygen decision before all combatants for many weeks, Administrator Webb finally threw NASA's failings at the mercy of the Congress. Webb declared, in July, 1967, before the budget hearings: "I think there is no doubt that the classification of this test should have been hazardous. It was not so classified, and from that failure to classify it as extremely hazardous, flowed a number of events which appeared to be and were foolish and stupid under the conditions that existed, but which would have been avoided if the classification had been correct."

This admission of human frailty might have gotten everyone— NASA, the congressmen, and the Apollo contractors—off the hook, *if* it had been uttered openly, immediately after the disaster occurred. In the summer of 1967 it had become superfluous. Both James Webb and his lieutenants, particularly Dr. Mueller, had already gone on record, insisting for seven long and windy months, that *no one* in NASA had ever done anything, or made any decision, that could in any way have endangered the astronauts.

Yet James Webb and the NASA organization still sought to show the Congress and the nation that, in spite of the Apollo fire, they were "an able-bodied team." They sought to do this by pointing to the successes of previous months. They sought to do this by inundating the investigating committees with tons of technical and mostly irrelevant data. They described the choice of oxygen as a cabin atmosphere as a medical and engineering necessity. They described the fire as a regrettable setback, but one which should be understood and seen in a more favorable perspective.

During the opening session of the House Subcommittee on NASA Oversight, dealing with the Apollo 204 disaster, Representative Joseph E. Karth of Minnesota participated in the following exchange with North American Aviation research and engineering executive, Dr. John McCarthy:

> MR. KARTH: I realize that hindsight is always 20/20, which is considerably better than foresight. Yesterday, however, Colonel Borman suggested strongly to this committee that while they (the astronauts) are in flight they are ever conscious of the fire hazard. I think documentation will prove that the hazard in flight is substantially less than the fire hazard on the ground. But yet, they were never conscious of the fire hazard that accompanied the spacecraft on the ground. Do I understand that this was also the opinion of North American Aviation?
>
> DR. MCCARTHY: In our *initial* design we did not anticipate all three elements being present at the same time: namely oxygen, an ignition source, and the combustibles. We did not design for a fire on the ground. [Italics added.]

Dr. McCarthy seems, unwittingly perhaps, to have hit the nail on the head.

Obviously, the choice of pure oxygen was based on knowledge and hardware that was available in the beginning of the decade. Its choice was a matter of expediency. It stemmed from engineering rather than physiological considerations. According to testimony by Dr. Berry before the Senate Committee, the race to beat the Russians would not have influenced the selection of oxygen "at that time." Yet it is undeniable that if the space race had not been the major factor, knowledge and hardware developed *after* the initial decision would have effected a dramatic change. This then was the failure of NASA: by freezing designs, failing to adapt to new information and new needs, NASA witlessly pursued the "tried-and-true"—and Grissom, White, Chaffee, Bartley, and Harmon died.

Implausible as it may seem, the Apollo disaster comes down to exactly that. By "overlooking the problems" associated with pure-oxygen atmospheres, America's space program suffered five avoidable deaths and the waste of hundreds of millions of dollars. The nation's honeymoon with space travel came to a bitter halt.

The Apollo Review Board made no reference to this simple fact. How could it have? Most of the Board's membership consisted of the very people who had spent the previous seven years "overlooking the problem."

■ *I do think it would be well for all of us to place
this accident in its proper perspective. One way
this can be done is to remember that prior to
this one accident, NASA's space flight record has
been most impressive from the standpoint of . . .
safety covering a period of almost six years.*
SENATOR MARGARET C. SMITH,
Ranking Minority Member (who
supplied italics), Apollo 204 hearings,
Senate Committee on Aeronautical
and Space Sciences, February 7, 1967

■ *In all . . . [previous] . . . fires, inadequate safety
precautions had been taken to either prevent or
extinguish the fire or to protect the occupants.*
Report of Apollo 204 Review Board—
introduction to "Summaries of Other
Oxygen Fires"

Chapter 8 ■ Fire Prevention: "A Bucket of Sand, a Bucket of Water"

First a light bulb burned out. One of the four men climbed up
to the ceiling fixture, and, while replacing the bulb, heard a
sound "like the arcing of a short circuit." Suddenly, a half-inch
flame flashed from the fixture. On asking for water to extinguish
the flame, the man was advised to "snuff it out with a towel."
While he was trying this, the towel caught fire and burned so
vigorously that the fire spread to his clothes. Someone grabbed an
"asbestos fire blanket" to snuff out the clothing fire, but the
"fireproof" blanket also burst into flames. Meanwhile, some melted
insulation had dripped onto a bunk, setting it afire. Another man
tried to slap out the bunk fire with his hands—and "his skin
caught on fire." Vainly, he beat his hands against his chest to
smother the flames—and then his chest was on fire as well. The
frantic efforts of the other men to help, succeeded only in spreading the flames to themselves. Within seconds, the clothes of all
four men were ablaze.

This macabre sequence of events is a factual recreation of the experiences of four men who participated in a NASA experiment using a 100-percent-oxygen atmosphere on November 17, 1962.

The test was conducted at the Navy's Aircrew Equipment Laboratory, in Philadelphia, Pennsylvania, for the Manned Spacecraft Center, Houston, Texas. Its purpose was "to obtain data concerning the physical effects on subjects using a proposed 100-percent-oxygen, 5 p.s.i. atmosphere, while being exposed to . . . launch and reentry [conditions] . . . associated with project Gemini." Six Navy and Marine pilots participated in the simulated flight, which began on November 1, 1962. Four of them were in the chamber when fire broke out on the seventeenth day of the test. The men escaped within about forty seconds after the first report of fire. Nevertheless, all four men sustained first-degree and second-degree burns over 15 to 20 percent of their bodies—one required hospitalization for eleven or twelve days due to the "severe" burns on his hands. The "asbestos fire blanket," coated with an organic filler, flamed because it had been "soaking" in the pure-oxygen atmosphere for seventeen days.*

There was no flash fire. No "unusual chemical extinguishers were used on the flames—in fact, "there were no fire extinguishers in the chamber." Since the chamber atmosphere was continuously vented, it was not tested for poisonous vapors. The composition of the ground wire insulation that yielded the initial tiny flame was unknown, and it remained unknown to other investigators for more than two years. A Board of Investigation was convened, but neither its proceedings nor a formal report of the accident was published. Nevertheless, of all the fires NASA has experienced, this was the only one in which the specific source of ignition, a short in the ground wire of a lighting fixture, was actually identified.

Discussion of this dramatic accident occupies but two separated pairs of lines in a detailed forty-five page report published by NASA in January, 1965. The first of these reads: "Fire occurred in the [chamber], requiring removal of the remaining subjects and

* Dr. Mueller, asked by the Senate about the report of this incident, said that there was very little connection between a material's flammability and the time it had been exposed to an oxygen-rich atmosphere: "Since the time of that report, we have actually made tests on materials with different times of exposure to pure oxygen atmosphere. *There is a very weak coupling* [connection] *in this case*" [italics added].

early termination of the experiment." By contrast, Appendix D-1 of the same report, "Nutritional Aspects of a Diet Used in a Study of a Simulated Space Environment," runs for ten full pages. This Appendix discusses experimental menus for the men.

There have been many other fires in pure-oxygen or in oxygen-enriched atmospheres. The Apollo 204 Review Board Report's "Summary of Other Oxygen Fires" states it includes a discussion of five fires—actually seven are described (including the fatal Brooks fire). Dr. Emanuel M. Roth, of the Lovelace Foundation for Medical Research and Education, Albuquerque, New Mexico, cited still another fire, one that occurred before all the others noted by the Review Board. With the fatal Apollo 204 fire, then, NASA has a grand total of *nine* fires to defend. Yet Senator Smith, ranking minority leader of the Senate Committee on Aeronautical and Space Sciences, implored her fellow committeemen not to let the *one* Apollo 204 fire throw things out of perspective.

True, the fires overlooked by Senator Smith may have been less spectacular, but were by no means less significant. No specific source of ignition was found for any of them except the 1962 Navy Aircrew fire mentioned above. The Review Board report of each, like the Report of Apollo 204 Review Board, reads to the effect that *"the exact cause of this fire will likely never be known."**

Why—and how—could the clear warnings given by these many earlier fires be ignored by NASA? There are simply no satisfactory answers to these questions. The impression emerges, however, that they were ignored because of a traditional preoccupation with "hardware" rather than with basic principles.

The first of the oxygen fires took place early in the manned flight program, at the USAF School of Aerospace Medicine, Brooks Air Force Base, Texas. A two-man crew was taking part in a space-cabin experiment conducted at a simulated altitude of 33,000 feet, in pure oxygen. When a power tube in the TV cabin monitor overheated, the "resin" base ignited, dripping onto coolant lines located below the chassis of the TV monitor. "Fumes from the hot resin alerted the cabin crew." Their mission was halted "without further injury to cabin or crew." The fact that

* See Appendix G for description of other fires.

neither the power-tube resin nor the insulation on the coolant plumbing broke into violent flame, in pure oxygen, "gave the investigators more confidence in the safety of this potentially hazardous environment than they had prior to the experience." Thus, an official account says, "instead of focusing attention on the hazards of fire, *the accident gave a 'false sense of security'* [italics added]."

A second fire occurred at Brooks Air Force Base, on September 9, 1962, in the same facility as the fire just described. The two-man space-cabin simulator was in the fourteenth day of a test using pure oxygen at a nominal pressure of 5 p.s.i. The two men were fully clothed in pressure suits with their helmet visors closed. One of the men was asleep when the fire broke out, and, in fact, *"the fire was not detected by the sight or smell of smoke* [italics added]." The sleeping crewman awoke with the fire alarm and for some unexplained reason opened his helmet visor. The noxious fumes from the blazing panel entered his suit and the breathing hose connecting him to the other crewman. Both men passed out.* The one who had opened his visor suffered "respiratory tract damage." Neither victim was burned. The damage to instruments, due to the fire, "probably obscured any subtle defect that may have been responsible" for the blaze. "It is not known how sophisticated a fire safety analysis was performed on the materials which were used in the cabin."

NASA's documentation of the previous fires is, in itself, a damning indictment of NASA's negligence. The accounts speak most articulately for themselves. They show a remarkable resemblance to many remarks made following the Apollo 204 fire. They spotlight the complacency and the tragic absent-mindedness of the many professionals who planned, supervised, participated in, and reported on these experiments which, like so many others, ended with a fire. It was one mistake avoided by the Russians. The Soviet designer, Korolev, was sufficiently impressed by *one* bad electrical fire in a space simulator to reject pure oxygen.

These fires, harbingers of the Apollo 204 disaster, could have

---

* A surge in the oxygen flow of Grissom's suit loop led investigators to speculate that he might have opened his visor in the Apollo 204 fire. The theory was ruled out. But, since one of the crew's space suits was burned through—all three astronauts were, in this case, as in 1962, exposed to the poisonous fumes.

averted the deaths of Grissom, White, and Chaffee. They clearly show that helmeted astronauts cannot see or smell a spacecraft fire until it has reached major proportions or burned through their space suit loops. Furthermore, opening the helmet visor, as with the burned-through Apollo space suits, only exposed the rest of the crew to the poisonous vapors. Unconsciousness, without immediate rescue, is certain death. Finally, that a rather *mild* cabin fire should give a *"false sense of security"* brings to mind NASA's explanation that the Apollo 204 fire resulted from "complacency and overconfidence." Representative Olin Teague, NASA Oversight Subcommittee chairman, went even further, suggesting, ". . . instead of the word 'careless,' or instead of the word 'overconfidence' . . . I would say that we had been . . lulled into *a rather false sense of security*, that *we just kind of forgot* that we were dealing with a very hazardous and a very dangerous situation [italics added]."

Statements of this kind act as a sort of smoke-screen for deeply rooted ills within NASA, the Congressional space committees, and the aerospace industry as a whole. The basic defect is one of inferior management and communications. The proof, as we will see, is that all of the fires preceding the Apollo tragedy could have been averted. Most damaging of all has been NASA's claim that they were adequately prepared for a fire in space—but had somehow missed the likelihood such an incident might occur on the ground. Note: Every one of the nine accidental fires in the nation's space program to date have all occurred on the ground. Not one has occurred in space. The problem was not simply overlooked, it was side-stepped.

The "just kind of forgot" excuse does not sit well with one familiar with the four thin volumes known as the "Roth Report." Dr. Charles A. Berry officially introduced this report to the Senate in the opening session of its Apollo fire hearings, appropriately directing attention to "Space-Cabin Atmospheres, Part II—Fire and Blast Hazards." He told the Senate Committee that "probably one of the most authoritative compilations of this research [on spacecraft atmospheres] is contained in a four-part series on 'The Selection of Space-Cabin Atmospheres,' prepared for NASA by Dr. E. Roth of the Lovelace Foundation for Medical Education and Research."

Roth's report is indeed a laudable survey and summary of all the literature available for study at the time. (Part I—"Oxygen Toxicity," has been mentioned in the previous chapter.) Furthermore, at the time of the Apollo fire, the second of the two volumes then published was the *only* reference on spacecraft fire hazards that was included in the space agency's mammoth annual cumulative index of literature.

The problem of fire hazard in pure-oxygen or oxygen-enriched environments was not new information. Nor was it new to space or aircraft projects. It is a problem common to hospital operating rooms around the world. Astronauts, just like nurses and doctors, wear special nonconductive clothing and specially soled shoes to prevent the build-up of static electricity on their clothing, which might cause the release of tiny but potentially explosive electrostatic sparks. It is clear, then, that pure oxygen is exceptionally hazardous.

Roth prefaces Part II of the space-cabin atmosphere studies with: "The confusion and controversy arising from attempts to evaluate the space-cabin fire problem appear to stem from past failure to compile the scattered data and to expose it to critical review and selection." Roth was chosen to set the record straight. Implicit in his task was to put the state-of-the-art research of the entire field in one volume.

Roth reports that pure oxygen causes combustible things, natural or synthetic fabrics, to burn violently and almost completely. So complete is the combustion that often no smoke is even produced. Even "flameproof" material, such as a special rayon with an aluminum coating,* burns completely. It is obvious, Dr. Roth warns, that flameproof materials need to be retested in high-oxygen environments. Roth's warnings, published in 1964, were not heeded. Three years later, in January 1967, astronauts Grissom, White, and Chaffee died while clothed in "flame-resistant" *Nomex*** pressure suits that burned. Pure-oxygen

---

* Scotch-Shield Type 82.

** *Nomex*, manufactured by DuPont, may soon be available for upholstering in jet aircraft. It is also highly prized as a fire-fighting suit material. DuPont advertisements boast that the wearer will not receive first-degree burns for better than three seconds; second-degree burns for as much as seventeen seconds—in heat of 2500°F. of a flash fire.

fires may burn so hotly and violently that rather bizarre effects are seen with electrical wiring. In one case, Roth reports, "the wire melted so fast that the insulation was not ignited, and gases from the overheated Teflon, in another case, *tore the insulation off the wire* [italics added]." Nor is alarm over the potential gaseous products of combustion, poisonous to astronauts, overplayed by Roth. He writes quite simply: "*In a sealed cabin, the products of combustion of most materials present hazards which might conceivably match those of the fire itself* [italics added]." Unfortunately, he adds, "Products of burning in 100-percent-oxygen environments were not found in the literature."

One is reminded of the autopsy findings of the three dead astronauts: "Cause of death—Asphyxia due to inhalation of toxic gases due to fire." Studies of this sort were apparently made, but NASA had just not shown enough interest to benefit from the results. For, as Dr. Roth says:

The Boeing Co. has studied the toxicology of various burning electrical insulations by exposing mice in bell jars to the vapors from overheated wires . . . No reports have been obtained from Boeing or the Air Force Systems Command.

These specific remarks are just a few examples of the great amount of general and detailed material compiled in the Roth Report.

The report is a mother lode rich with neglected nuggets. For a reader reluctant to venture deep into the "unknowns" of space, into (so he might think) an abyss of complexity and claimed expertise, the introduction to Roth's Chapter 6 of Part II, "Fire and Blast Hazards," might serve as a trustworthy guide. It readily becomes apparent that the study of oxygen fires is neither so complex nor esoteric—it is a matter of common sense.

The introduction begins:

The problems of prevention and extinguishment of fires in space cabins are, except for a few specific situations, not much different from those at sea level or in aircraft situations. The unusual atmospheric environment and limitations of space and fire-fighting equipment [only] compound the general problem.

Roth's Chapter 6 of Part II, "Problems of Fire Prevention and Extinguishment in Space-Cabins," sorts out most of the possible ways in which a cabin fire can start. It then proceeds to recommend measures for prevention and extinguishment. Again, NASA apparently paid very little attention to Roth's recommendations. The report was published three years after spacecraft designs had been frozen.

Roth begins with a general and self-explanatory rule:

The selection of optimum material with the lowest potential as an ignition source, the highest ignition temperature, slowest rate of combustion, lowest explosion potential, and lowest potential as a source of toxic combustion products is of paramount importance.

He then presents a list of gear,* noting the danger each item presents in a space cabin. He goes on to amend this list, suggesting that, among others, "Plumbing for oxygen and water, etc." should be "upgraded" from "Improbable Fire Sources" to the category of "Other Potential Fire Sources." Roth's judgment was uncannily accurate—for as the Apollo Review Board learned, one of the major contributors to the Apollo 204 inferno was leaky plumbing for the coolant, water-glycol. While not necessarily an "initial source of ignition," it definitely helped to feed the fire. The leaking fluid not only corroded its own plumbing, but was itself highly combustible, and figures as one of the three most abundant combustibles in the Apollo capsule.**

In keeping with the design trend of space vehicles and aircraft prevailing in 1964, Roth indicates that attempts should be made to limit the amount of combustible materials in a spacecraft. The minimum is defined as the basic amount required for pilot comfort and capsule operation. He gives examples of many types of flammable materials that should be "minimized or possibly eliminated" because of their combustibility.

Clothing, maps, books, and papers required for normal mission tasks and relaxation are termed "unavoidable risks." Foam rubber and plastics in the astronauts' seats are, similarly, judged neces-

---

* From Ciccotti, J. M., *An Analysis of Fire and Explosion Hazards in Space Flight.* WADD TR 60–87, 1960 (ASTIA No. AD–252762).
** See Appendix E, Finding No. 10.

sary evils. Roth states emphatically, however, that the necessary presence of these dangerous fabrics demand special "fire-testing" precautions:

> Although these materials have relatively high spontaneous-ignition temperature, they are often placed near potential "hot spots." This should be avoided. *Fireproofing of fabrics should be accomplished.* No material which supports combustion after the ignition source is removed should be used . . . *tests should be performed at the maximum temperature expected at the potential locations* within the cabin. Textiles and papers* should all be made flame-resistant to this [maximum temperature] degree . . . If the potential fire and explosion hazards due to hot-gas ignition are to be evaluated for flammables for which the ignition temperatures under high-oxygen conditions are not known, *the ignition temperatures should be established by testing.* [Italics added.]

NASA violated Roth's timely and authoritative recommendations over and over again. For instance, the fire in the Apollo 012 command module began very near and below the combustible foam couch of Command Pilot Grissom. This was also where the coolant leakage occurred. Neither books, papers, nor space suits were flameproofed. In fact, a very large number of other combustibles (over a thousand) were also found to have been included in the spacecraft. Most importantly, no mock-up fire tests had ever been attempted until *after* the fatal fire.

Roth also makes some startling statements about electrical sources of ignition. Indeed, Roth's survey of current research led to this sweeping, totally unambiguous conclusion: "Only low-energy electric or electronic equipment *which has been demonstrated* not to be an ignition source *for all flammables concerned, under any possible oxygen environment* and *under any failure condition,* should be considered safe [italics added]."

All electric and electronic equipment, otherwise screened and protected, he goes on to say, should also be "explosion-proofed"

---

* George Low, of the Houston office, Joseph Shea's successor, in a predictable rebirth of post-fire zeal, early in 1968 announced sternly that NASA would settle for nothing less than the best that modern technology could provide. In future Apollo flights, books, maps, and other reading materials also would be composed of a new fireproof "paper."

by means of three techniques: flameproofing casings, hermetically sealing the casings, and "potting" [coating] with materials that will not ignite and burn when overheated or exposed to electrical failures.* In any event, "explosion-proof testing should be . . . performed at *ground level* (16 p.s.i.) and at *altitude* (5 p.s.i.), with a mixture ratio and pressure which is *most* conducive to flame propagation and ignition [italics added]." After all, Roth implies, a system can only be certified as reliable and safe when it has been tested exhaustively, and under the worst conditions imaginable. Fire testing under any and all conditions was not, however, deemed adequate. Both fire detection and fire extinguishing equipment were considered absolute "musts." Furthermore, says Roth, "The wall connectors for fire detection and extinguishing systems should operate properly under the most severe conditions of fire, vibration, and duration of exposure likely to occur at their location."

Roth had come to have a healthy respect for oxygen. He was wary of leaving any stone unturned. While aware that no satisfactory extinguishing system had yet been made available, he had no doubt that NASA's technical ingenuity and prowess could be applied to create one. It was all a matter of the will and the cash to do the job. He had a similar view of the state-of-the-art of fire sensors: "The development of an automatic fire and explosion protection system is technologically feasible; whether it is economically justifiable will have to be evaluated."

NASA apparently evaluated the cost of an extensive "automatic fire and explosion protection system" and decided against it. Chemical extinguishers then available would expose the astronauts to poisonous vapors. Water would only complicate an electrical fire. There really seemed to be no ready solution. Thus it was that neither Mercury nor Gemini flights ever included any kind of fire extinguisher. The thought had been considered, but was finally rejected.

---

* Standard "potting" materials used in the Apollo spacecraft were highly combustible uralane and polyurethane foam plastics. "Sqawk sheets," complaining of this discrepancy, were issued shortly before the fatal fire. Corrective actions were postponed until after the plugs-out test. Following the Review Board investigations, NASA officials announced that "potting" would be "hermetically sealed"—apparently, however, the "potting" material was not replaced.

The "can do" attitude paid off for all those early years without a hitch. As NASA Associate Administrator Mueller said: "The fire in the Apollo spacecraft cabin occurred under conditions and using procedures which had been verified by seven years of manned spacecraft operational experience. Standards of design, manufacture, test, and operations . . . had demonstrated that the possibility of a fire in the spacecraft cabin was remote." Yet he added: "The fire proves the approach we had been using of preventing fires by preventing their ignition is inadequate."

NASA is not the only party guilty of ignoring the warnings of one of its employees. In 1964, Frank J. Hendel, a researcher at North American Aviation, the Apollo spacecraft contractor, published a paper in the AIAA journal, *Spacecraft and Rockets*. He unmistakably branded the high-pressure, pure-oxygen, pre-launch period of space tests and space flight as "extremely hazardous" from the point of view of fire potential. North American succeeded in ignoring Hendel—just as NASA ignored Roth.

Neither Dr. Roth nor his scientific colleagues implied for a moment that a "policy" of preventing ignition sources would actually prevent fires. To have thought so would have meant the denial of a history of accidental fires. Rather, Roth tried to draw attention to the numerous steps that could easily be taken by NASA to reduce the frequency and severity of future fires. He writes: "These accidents illustrate in concrete fashion the potential danger of 100-percent-oxygen atmosphere. It can be argued that the lack of professional fire-safety engineering may have been a major factor in these accidents." Human error was a factor in some of the previous fires, but not in the majority of cases.

Roth was no "Monday-morning quarterback." But, with the obvious advantage of what might be labeled by some as "enlightened hindsight," he stated what seems to amount to a soft-pedaled criticism:

In two situations, either safety design or fire discipline might have prevented entirely these accidental fires.*

---

* As noted earlier, the Apollo 204 pad crew had no fire-fighting training—nor is there any record of the astronauts themselves ever having been drilled on fire fighting on the ground or in space flight.

Dr. Roth made it quite clear that fire prevention is not enough —safety engineering is required in the design of a spacecraft.* (Administrator Webb: "If anything can go wrong, it will.") Fire drill and discipline—for the astronauts and their support crew alike—are mandatory. Roth's admonitions were an exercise in futility. Apparently this volume (Part II)—available over two years before the Apollo fire to all interested aerospace executives, engineers, and newsmen—gathered considerable dust until the deaths of the astronauts brought it to their attention.

Roth did his assigned job well. He detailed exactly what would have to be done if 100 percent oxygen were to be used in future space flights. Leading off a rebuttal to the elimination of 100 percent oxygen, he announces that "the argument against this step could be mustered as follows":

1. The data presented were "of an idealized nature."
2. The probability of an explosively uniform, contaminated but well-mixed cabin atmosphere was extremely low.
3. All hazardous equipment (as outlined) can be eliminated from the cabin. Most pieces could go out altogether or to isolated storage compartments.
4. All combustibles, other than electrical insulation, clothing, mattresses, paper, and fuels, could be eliminated.
5. Necessary combustibles could be fireproofed, sealed, or separated with pre-tested fire-breaks.
6. Adequate fire discipline would reduce the hazard of even those few combustibles.
7. Meteoroid penetration, once a great fear, had been found to be over-rated. Studies showed a spacecraft was not likely to encounter a particle except once every 2.3 years.
8. Automatic fire prevention and detection systems could be included.

* This, however, was about as far as Roth was apparently willing to go. After all, NASA officials had hired him to document the restrictions (if any) to the use of pure oxygen *after* the decision to use it was already in effect. He was hired, among other things, to justify the oxygen selection for Apollo four years after it had become operational. His prime responsibility was to point the way for longer, more perilous projects of the future. It was perfectly all right to make recommendations for the *future* of manned flight, but criticizing past and present practices was apparently quite another matter.

9. Adequate venting and location of combustibles would further enhance reduction of the fire hazard in flight.
10. Since potential (and frequently "overlooked") "hot spots" could be pre-determined by testing, the hazard they represent could be eliminated by good safety design.
11. Weightlessness, resulting perhaps in a lack of convection currents, in space (while most often a source of "a false sense of security") could be a factor (if "not relied on too heavily") in reducing the fire risk.

On the basis of such a list, Roth must have felt that NASA, and even its critics, would be suitably impressed and reassured. He asks rhetorically: "After considering all the above arguments, is not the concern about fire and blast risk resulting from the 100-percent-oxygen environments *only academic?* [italics added]."

But Dr. Roth, a scientist by training, was practical and, of necessity, placed little trust in the human element. He felt compelled to add:

At first sight the arguments presented do seemingly reduce the concern. [*But*] It is easy to say that sophisticated safety design will eliminate ignition sources and fuels and that training will eliminate human errors. It is also easy to rely on the dumping of cabin pressure, zero-gravity fire attenuation, and detector-extinguisher systems as a backup for potential design failures. *It is difficult, however, to assign to many of these factors a probability of success or failure.* [Italics added.]

Fortunately for NASA, Roth had found a way to get around the human element. A research team out in Columbus, Ohio, with the Batelle Memorial Institute, had figured a possible technique leading to a quantitative approach to fire risk. Since the fire risk is only one component of the "overall mission hazard," it can be expressed as one variable factor, in the layman's bugaboo—a FORMULA! Batelle's equation, reducing human as well as mechanical factors to an orderly series of numbers, is of interest because of its vacuous irrelevance to the Apollo fire—or any of its predecessors. Thus, purely for the experience of visualizing the handiwork of latter-day witch-doctors, here is a representation of what must be termed contemporary "mumbo-jumbo": *

$$P_H = 1 - (1 - P_1) \times (1 - P_2) \cdots (1 - P_f) \cdots (1 - P_i) **$$

Naturally, probability of fire (P_f) is but one element in a series that runs to infinity. How significant then, can the fire factor really be? Surprisingly, Roth did not trust the formula any more than a layman might. He suggested instead a more generalized but compact HAZARD INDEX!*** It looks like this:

$$H = \frac{h_c}{M\overline{C}_p}$$

This neat little formula says everything in a nutshell. It epitomizes the failure of NASA and the aerospace community to pay to their human payload a fraction of the attention lavished on more challenging tasks—rocket propulsion systems. Yet "mission success" could hardly be achieved at the expense of astronauts' lives.

Roth goes on to a more traditional approach to fire risk evaluation. "How helpful is the historical approach?" he asks. "Will the experience of the aircraft industry be of any use?" His answer is "No . . .

"Experience with aircraft fires is . . . limited to only one possible parameter in the space-cabin atmosphere . . . In aircraft cabins, the design of the cabin and the atmospheric constituents are basically fixed. An analysis is needed only to determine *if* a . . . fire protection system is needed. Whereas, in the space cabin, . . . *an analysis is required for the actual cabin design and choice*

---

* This is a common and increasing problem of our technological age. John W. Finney, *New York Times* editor, in a review of Lapp's *New Priesthood*, described modern scientists as "heirs of the medicine man" and priests who, in earlier generations, had used *their* mumbo-jumbo to over-awe their flocks.

** Wherein P (Probability) and subscript H (Hazard) stand for the sum total of all predictable hazards. P_f stands for probability of fire hazards, and P_i, for an algebraic description for the last in a series (of hazards) extending to infinity.

*** An explanation of terms in the Hazard Index, for those who are interested in the more abstract things in the space age, follows:

H = hazard index
h_c = maximum total heat-energy release from all possible combustion reactions within the compartment
$\overline{C}$ = average heat capacity of all materials within the compartment
M = total mass of all materials within the compartment

of the atmosphere. This actually puts the cart before the horse and thereby complicates the whole picture [italics added]."

After helping the space agency to justify and adjust to its selection of oxygen as a space-cabin atmosphere (a decision endorsed by Dr. Roth's employer—the Lovelace Foundation) Roth found that NASA was doing everything backwards. He might have thought: Before you can design your spacecraft, NASA, and before you select a cabin atmosphere, you must decide what kind of fire protection your state-of-the-art can provide. Once you have selected your fire-prevention strategy, then you may proceed with the other matters. Obviously, this was out, since it appeared NASA would then have to abandon the Moon to Russia, apologize to the President, to the Congress, to the nation, and go back to the conference drawing-board and start all over again.

Concluding his report on "Fire and Blast Hazards," Dr. Roth decides to punt. He does not give a recommendation. Instead, in what is a truly remarkable admission, he offers the following cryptic appraisal:

It appears that the ultimate decision relative to the weighting of the fire hazard in the total selection of a space-cabin atmosphere will be made on a *semi-quantitative level* with *intuition* playing a major role. The *time* needed for more quantitative appraisal of the fire problem appears to run well beyond the maximum time available for engineering decisions regarding single- versus multi-gas systems. [Italics added.]

Roth thus spelled it out for all the world to see. Given NASA's devotion to deadlines and the lunar landing, the decision to use pure oxygen was going to proceed *on approximations and guesswork*. This statement belies, once and for all, the repetitious claims of NASA's top management to the effect that neither schedules, the race with the Russians, nor lack of study had in any way preempted the safety of the astronauts.

Roth very clearly outlined the numerous hazards that attended the oxygen atmosphere. He carefully outlined the precautions necessary to ensure even a slight margin of safety. His tentative conclusions were all based on the assumption that NASA would not ignore his recommendations and would implement changes with all due haste. Yet, even at that, he was not sure enough of the safety of pure oxygen to give it an endorsement.

NASA officials ignored Roth's warnings. No significant changes were made in the Apollo systems. Then, practically before the ink had dried on Parts I and II of Roth's report, NASA had another oxygen fire on its hands. In fact, there were three more fires between 1964 and the Apollo fire. Two of them were in the very life support system that killed the Apollo astronauts.*

On or about July 1, 1964, an explosion occurred in an unmanned test facility at one of NASA's key contractors. The test involved the Apollo environmental control system (ECS) (which includes the astronauts' life support system) at the Airesearch Corporation, a division of the Garrett Corporation. No connection with the hazard of oxygen was made.

Seven months later, on February 16, 1965, another fire broke out—the second recorded at a Navy facility. It occurred in the decompression chamber of the Navy Experimental Diving Unit at Washington, D.C. Surely the most remarkable feature of this fire is the concluding remark of the Apollo Review Board's account of it, which reads as follows: *"Fire extinguishing equipment consisted of a bucket of sand and a bucket of water, neither of which was used* [italics added]." Apparently, all Emanuel Roth's many months of scrupulous research had gone to waste: "A bucket of sand and a bucket of water." Every military installation in the world has regulations about that sort of primitive fire-fighting gear. Four pieces of equipment were found to have failed: a fan, a sensor, a valve, and a transducer. No reflections seem to have been made concerning the hazard *oxygen* presented to the astronauts who would one day inhabit the ECS.

Fourteen months later, the familiar alarms pierced the air once again at Airesearch. It was another unmanned qualification test of the same Apollo ECS. The test, conducted in 100 percent oxygen at 5 p.s.i. (flight conditions) was aborted on April 28, 1966. The fire occurred after 2,479.5 hours of testing.

An investigation noted that "16 components had malfunctioned prior to and during the test, and 18 had failed due to damage by the fire . . . Also, test equipment and procedures were improper for the environment, there was no fire detection or extinguishing

---

* See Appendix G for Review Board history of previous oxygen fires.

equipment, and there were no emergency procedures." The review revealed that Airesearch procedures and documentation were "inadequate," that quality-control personnel were given "inadequate direction," and that a NASA Test Readiness Review "might have precluded the accident." The board recommended that "short and arc" potentialities be checked in the Apollo spacecraft. It recommended that wire bundles and circuit breakers be checked for adequacy, and that all nonmetallics in contact with wire bundles be eliminated. The board further recommended that it was about time specifications requirements for nonmetallic components be imposed on all contractors and that NASA improve its materials selection and application program.

No reflections seem to have been made about the wisdom of using pure oxygen.

Nine months later, on January 27, 1967, the same unit was shaken by explosion and flames for the last time—only this time three astronauts were involved in the test. Many of the April, 1966 recommendations had been taken care of, or were at least on the roster for attention. But, as the Apollo 204 Review Board learned, these earlier findings were incomplete and superficial symptoms of a "hornet's nest" of wiring and specification problems. Neither NASA, North American Aviation—the spacecraft contractor whose men took part in the reviews of these fires— nor Airesearch, nor even the astronauts themselves seem to have seen the handwriting on the wall. The three Apollo ECS fires at Airesearch were merely dress rehearsals for the tragedy that was later to unfold on launch pad 34, followed four days later by the fatal oxygen fire at Brooks Air Force Base, a facility which had previously experienced two other fires.

The very week of the Brooks and Apollo 204 fires, the National Research Council, a branch of the traditionally elite National Academy of Sciences, was scheduled to release a multivolume study concerning the broad medical aspects of respiration in space cabins. The study, as prepared by the Academy for NASA, was not particularly concerned with the problem of fire.

However, one contributor, Dr. Wallace O. Fenn of Cornell University, *was* concerned with the problem of fire. He did not mind saying so. His contribution (Chapter 14; "Inert Gases"*) pointed out that only *if* and *when* NASA finally added an inert gas to the cabin atmosphere (to dilute the oxygen**), would the risk of fire at last be reduced. Even then, he noted, "it seems impossible to rule out completely the danger of fire in a space capsule." He reminded his readers that previous investigators (Dr. Emanuel Roth in particular) had shown the dangers of pure oxygen in relation to high temperatures. Reemphasizing the point, Fenn suggested that an oxygen fire could even melt hardware made of stainless steel. His report took a dim view of the fact that no fire-prevention and fire-fighting techniques had yet been adopted in American spacecraft.

And so, as all eyes turned to the upcoming Apollo flights, Dr. Fenn feared for the safety of the astronauts. He made a noble effort to focus attention on the real seriousness of the fire hazard in the space cabin. He pointed to the studies of Emanuel Roth, among others, adding that (as we have seen) several other fires had occurred since 1964, the time of the first two sections of the Roth Report. Fenn concluded, naturally enough, that "the danger of fire might now be given even more weight than the author [Roth] gave at the time [1964]." Dr. Fenn and his colleagues "strongly recommended" that a fire-extinguishing system be installed and that the astronauts be provided emergency oxygen masks as a safety precaution in the event of suit failure or cabin venting in space.

When the Apollo 204 fire occurred, the National Academy of Sciences, holding Fenn's report in hand, found itself in an exceedingly awkward position. To release Fenn's report in the emotion-charged days immediately following the fire would have seemed, at least, a case of extraordinarily bad timing, or worse, a slap in the face to NASA. Accordingly, the Academy withheld distribu-

* Dr. Fenn treats nitrogen as the principal "inert gas," although it does not belong to this chemical family, whose members are comparatively rare elements in our atmosphere. They are: helium, neon, argon, krypton, xenon, and radon. They are nonreactive gases, some of which are under consideration (along with nitrogen) for use in spacecraft primarily to dilute the oxygen necessary to sustain life.

** Nitrogen and helium have long been the preferred diluents. But nitrogen can have narcotic effects, while helium causes a "Donald Duck" voice distortion. Recent investigations also show that helium may be damaging to the body at some as yet unknown biochemical level. Consequently, neon is getting a second look.

tion of Fenn's report with the explanation, to those few curious news reporters, that Fenn's recommendations had been made in connection with "post-Apollo flights." Fenn himself was available for brief comment only.

The Academy had been asked to do the study by NASA management, and found itself, like so many predecessors, cooperating with NASA when conditions seemed less than inviting to blunt truths. No one, not even the lofty National Academy of Sciences wished to brave the inevitable challenge of "enlightened hindsight."

The facts, as have been seen, are that NASA did not eliminate combustibles; they did not compartmentalize electrical components; they did not provide either fire-detection, fire-prevention or fire-extinguishing equipment; they did not fireproof the necessary combustibles that remained in the spacecraft; they did not supervise and restrain the location of all wires and combustibles; they did not use fireproof "potting"; they did not compensate for the fact that the fully suited astronauts would be unable to see or smell a fire until it was too late; they did not take steps to protect the astronauts from poisonous vapors that are *always* produced by fire; and finally, when called to account for these failures, they did not tell the truth. NASA officials claimed, "it was not through overlooking the problem that we arrived at the Apollo 204 accident." They repeated, defensively, that the use of oxygen as a cabin atmosphere (even at 16 p.s.i. during pre-launch preparations) was based on seven years (twenty flights and twenty men) of successful operation that had demonstrated that the possibility of fire was "remote." Indeed, the possibility of a fire on the ground seemed so remote that the state-of-the-art had advanced little beyond the unused "bucket of sand and bucket of water."

■ *Scientists and technicians are fallible; and the unexpected can always happen.*

FORBES:
"The Case for Space," July 1, 1968

■ *We found that we lacked in NASA anyone really familiar with the details of fire and investigation of fire.*

DR. ROBERT C. SEAMANS,
Deputy Administrator, NASA,
April 13, 1967

Chapter 9 ■ The Apollo Tragedy: Who Is at Fault

Shortly before his death, Virgil Grissom prepared a manuscript that was published posthumously in April, 1968. The book, entitled *Gemini,** included an epilogue in which his editors took the liberty of stating that death had come "as Gus Grissom would have wanted it to come, aboard his own spacecraft, still probing for more answers to the mysteries of space." They noted that Grissom, "even in death," had moved America closer to the Moon "with spacecraft improvements designed to prevent a repetition of the tragedy that took his life."

While such a eulogy from a saddened publisher is certainly understandable (and has been echoed and reechoed by several other recent books), its implications have little basis in fact. Naturally, no one knows for certain what Grissom would have wanted. It is, however, virtually certain that he would not have entered command module 012 if he had known just how many potential trouble spots there were. And we do know that he was less than elated with the shameful sequence of events leading to and continuing into the ground test that took his life. Grissom was well aware that he was in a risky business, but, like any good test pilot, he did not care to expose himself to unnecessary risks. We also know that the "spacecraft improvements" referred to in the *Gemini* Epilogue had been called for, unmistakably

* World Book Encyclopedia Science Service, in association with The Macmillan Company (New York, 1968).

and uncompromisingly, nearly four years earlier by scientists such as Roth, Hendel, and Lamb.

Even after the fatal fires, the reports of Roth, *et al.*, were dismissed by most of the NASA public relations men and their "civilian" friends among the news media. These "obscure documents," buried, until then, somewhere in the deep recesses of a dusty library file, were thought to contain merely esoteric or largely irrelevant information. Even if this had been so—and it definitely was not so—at least one chronicler of aerospace news, read faithfully by members of the Washington staffs of NASA, the Congressional space committees, and industry lobbyists, had not considered the earlier warnings too obscure for a timely repetition.

Space Business Daily, a newsletter available by subscription to members of the trade, is published in Washington by a former staff writer for *Aviation Week,* Norman Baker. On March 14, 1965, he made his own concerned bid to the powers that be with the following, now familiar recommendations: "The careful choice of materials will minimize, but cannot eliminate, the hazard from this source [i.e., combustible material] . . ." *Space Daily* reemphasized that "many materials which do not support combustion ('fireproof') in the normal atmosphere burn vigorously in 100 percent oxygen at 5 p.s.i. [altitude]."*

Only after five men had been killed in one week—three of them astronaut heroes—did NASA officials begin, very reluctantly, to see the two factors that were common to all the accidents—oxygen and sloppy procedures.

But to have seen this earlier, as Roth did, was to be ignored. To have said as *Space Business Daily* did, in the aftermath of the tragedy, "I told you so," was to be guilty of "enlightened hindsight." NASA, with Congressional assistance, endeavored to turn the two most recent and fatal fires into sources of "new knowledge." Once again the space agency attempted to milk a "success" from a monumental failure.

* *Space Business Daily,* critical of Webb's handling of the Apollo 204 Congressional hearings, reprinted this article in April of 1967. The desired effect, to show that not all the aerospace industry had been asleep at the switch, backfired. *Space Daily's* statement was used, as one of many other quotes, to lay the foundation for cutting back NASA's budget—as a penalty for its mismanagement. The editor then joined the ranks of those who resented the fact that Webb's loss of prestige was exposing NASA to budget cuts.

After all, what greater proof of managerial ability could the Congress and the public ask than that NASA glean "new knowledge" from the ashes of the Apollo accident? What better tribute to the dead astronauts than applying that "new knowledge" in a safer and improved Apollo spacecraft?

Here, then, we must turn our attention to what followed in the aftermath of the Apollo disaster. Having gained in the two preceding chapters a familiarity with the pre-fire "old knowledge," it will be relatively easy to recognize the "new knowledge." *The truth is that very little knowledge that was really new emerged from the fire investigations, for in many respects the Roth studies were more complete and specific. Furthermore, little if anything was done for astronaut safety after the fire that could not have been done before the Apollo 204 fire.*

The story of how the "new knowledge" ruse was managed is particularly revealing.* It suggests that, while NASA used new antics and trick plays in its scrimmages with the Congress, and while the players may have donned new suits or new face masks, the rules of the NASA-Congress game remained unchanged. It also suggests that NASA overlooked or mishandled many potential (and truly new) changes that might well have been "discovered" both before and in the wake of the tragedy. Thus were NASA's few critics seized once again with the familiar sense of futility and waste.

In late January, 1967, in the same week as the Apollo fire, there appeared the *Report to the Congress from the President of the United States, U.S. Aeronautics and Space Activities, 1966.* Its preparation, executed for the Office of the President, is one of the prime responsibilities of the National Aeronautics and Space Council, headed by the Vice-President. The annual Report was not, of course, written by Council members Hubert H. Humphrey, James E. Webb, or Glenn T. Seaborg. Rather, it was done under the supervision of the Executive Secretary to the National Aeronautics and Space Council, Edward C. Welsh.

One of the final and thinnest chapters of the Report deals with advances made in 1966 that fell in the common domain of NASA and the Federal Aviation Agency (FAA). The FAA is

* One example has already been mentioned in Chapter 6. See pp. 119-20.

charged with ensuring "safe and efficient utilization of the Nation's airspace, by military as well as civilian users." Since this is also at least part of NASA's purview, one would expect that the FAA and NASA would work together on matters of safety and efficiency. After a survey of the year's efforts at "determination of flammability, smoke, and toxicity characteristics of cabin-interior materials," a list of specific advances was presented under the heading: OTHER RESEARCH AND DEVELOPMENT. Fourth on this list, on page 131 of the Report, was the following entry:

development of a promising device to save aircraft passengers' lives in postcrash flame and smoke environments—a *flameproof bag with 8-minute air supply to be fastened over the head.* [Italics added.]

A fuller description of the device was later published in April of 1967, by the FAA's Office of Aviation Medicine. The document, designated AM 67–4, provided the rationale behind the design of this "promising device." If aircraft passengers could be protected from the "immobilizing and incapacitating effects of inhalation of smoke, toxic gases, and flame" for just a few minutes after a crash landing, then the number of survivors could be expected to increase considerably. Consequently, a flameproof, aluminum-coated plastic hood, of a material known as "polyimide film,"* had been fabricated. It was tested with human volunteers under realistic conditions—with very favorable results. The men were able to don the hoods after their airplane fuselage was filled with smoke, stay in the smoke for two to three minutes, find their way to the exit, and then endure a prolonged and direct flame of natural gas in the face. While it has no melting point, the plastic film was known to resist charring up to 1,472°F. in normal air.

* The polyimide film is very nearly of the same composition as the debris net used in the Apollo 012 cabin. It is only speculative that the astronauts could have used the smoke hood successfully while the polyamide debris net provided a path of propagation for the fire. Had the net been absent, however, it might very well have worked. If it passed mock-up tests, it could be used successfully today. Early in 1968, NASA finally recognized the potential value of this new material. *Kapton,* its commercial name, was then considered for use as a cabin and wire insulator. There is no indication, however, that a smoke hood will be used by future astronauts.

The FAA report concluded that usefulness of the hood could be expected to be improved with further modifications, among which could be a self-contained supply of fresh air for ventilation. On January 10, 1969, the FAA finally made public its recommendation that commercial airliners carry the newly developed *Kapton* smoke hood. Needless to say, astronauts Grissom, White, and Chaffee were not provided with any such device as this flameproof bag—or a model suitable for use in pure-oxygen atmospheres. Yet, the FAA version may soon be as familiar to civil air travelers as the airsickness bag is today. NASA's failure to utilize either the device or its principle, both before and for more than a year after the fatal fire, is a glaring example of bad communications. It also points to an evident violation of NASA's charter, which specifically charges NASA to maintain proper liaison with the FAA.

If NASA officials had recognized and dealt intelligently with the known fire hazard in pure oxygen some such device would have been neatly tucked in the breast or shoulder pocket of each astronaut. All he would have had to do was to remove or open his space helmet and don his smoke hood. If, as was the case, support personnel failed to detect the fire first, the astronauts would have had time during the fifteen to thirty seconds after their suit loop was breached and they could smell the fumes (but before they were rendered unconscious) to don the smoke hood. The time required for this operation could easily have been bridged simply by the astronauts' holding their breaths for a minute or two.*

Far more incriminating, however, is the fact that sample specimen hoods were not rushed to all aeromedical installations

---

* This sounds too simple. And yet, the original seven Mercury astronauts wrote a book for World Book Science Service in which they claimed that they had been able to hold their breaths for as long as *three* minutes in a physical fitness test in astronaut selection trials, explaining that all anyone needed to match the feat were self-confidence and proper motivation. There is ample precedent for this crude but effective method of survival in such emergencies. Jacques Cousteau, the noted French oceanographer and skin diver, has related how he saved his life on one occasion—just from having held his breath. When he first began diving he used pure oxygen, as had others before. The first attempt ended in a broken breathing tube and reduced pressure that would have produced the bends—had not Cousteau intuitively held his breath. A similar accident occurred the next day and Cousteau's diving partner successfully used the same simple technique.

using pure oxygen after the astronauts had died. There is no excuse for not having provided the Brooks airmen with this protection by NASA-FAA liaison.

In the wake of the two most recent and horrendous of many oxygen fires, the urgings of NASA and the Congress for the public to remember that 100 percent oxygen had been successfully used in more than 914 hours of testing at 16 p.s.i. were hardly reassuring. Neither NASA, the Apollo Review Board, nor the investigating congressmen felt compelled to add up the totals in the other column of their highly subjective balance sheet. They handily omitted any reference to a far more meaningful statistic: the grand total in the debit column shows approximately 1,037 hours of testing, at various pressure levels—and with various concentrations of oxygen—that ended in destruction, injury, or death.

Thus, it should be eminently clear that the fatal plugs-out test, while not classified as "hazardous," should have been so classified, and that there is no excuse that it was not. According to NASA, hazards associated with fire in flight are far fewer than those on the ground. But then how, if the risk of fire in space was considered *less* than that on the ground, could the plugs-out test have been classified "nonhazardous," especially since all previous fires (seven before Apollo 204) had been ground fires as well? Truly, there is no satisfactory answer, except that perhaps almost everyone from the top down seems to have assumed that Roth's recommendations had been acted upon.

And what if the Apollo fire had not occurred on the ground? What if it had happened in flight—far out in space? NASA and its Review Board have repeated the assurance that risks (such as a fire in flight) were not only recognized, but that every reasonable precaution had been taken. In other words, one might presume that no "new knowledge" was necessary to deal with a fire in space. Astronaut Borman, as a member of the Apollo 204 Review Board, was singled out on several occasions to reaffirm both NASA's and the contractor's preparation for this known hazard. It is fair, then, to ask: What would in fact have happened had a fire broken out during a manned Apollo flight?

According to NASA, the hazard associated with fire in flight is far less than on the ground because of three factors: first, the cabin pressure in orbit is only one-third the pressure on the ground; second, weightlessness during space flight reduces convection currents and other circulation from spreading the fire and its poisonous by-products; and third, the reduced cabin pressure is easily "dumped" (vented to the vacuum of space). The complete removal of all cabin oxygen snuffs out the fire. Thus, the fully suited astronauts would merely sit it out while the fire was extinguished and the cabin was then replenished with a fresh, clean oxygen supply.

In the first instance, we know that oxygen at lower pressure *is* less dangerous than oxygen at higher pressure (although pure oxygen at *any* pressure carries a high fire risk). If the risk of fire in space were based only upon the difference in oxygen pressure, NASA's assertions about the low fire hazard in space could be accepted. But this is not the case. In 1964, Dr. Roth, as part of his study for NASA, clearly warned that weightlessness was a common source of a "false sense of security." He urged, as has been noted, that actual fire tests be conducted to determine where "hot spots" might be located during an actual space flight (points 10 and 11 in Roth's arguments against eliminating pure oxygen, cited in Chapter 8). His reason was simple: If weightlessness prevents convection currents, then it necessarily creates a localized build-up of both heat and toxic fumes. Therefore, "hot spots" should be isolated, compartmentalized and fireproofed. No such provisions had been made for an actual space flight. Furthermore, the spacecraft was provided with a fan to keep the cabin "air" moving. Emergency procedures, as noted by the Apollo Review Board, called for switching off the fan last, rather than first, in the case of a fire.

Finally, and perhaps most deceptive of all, is the in-flight solution of "dumping" the cabin atmosphere to outer space—the technique of simply "opening the spacecraft windows" and letting the fire rush out into the vacuum of space. Since NASA had not provided their astronauts with fireproof space suits, a cabin fire could logically have been expected to burn the suits of the astronauts—which is, of course, exactly what happened in the Apollo 204 ground fire. Why should NASA have assumed that the astronauts' suits would be so less vulnerable in space? Once the suits of the Apollo 204 crew had been burned through, Grissom,

White, and Chaffee no longer had independent and uncon-
taminated oxygen supplies. They were all exposed, at once, to
the poisonous vapors produced by the holocaust.*

The situation in space would have been little different. Lower
cabin pressure, at altitude, would probably have allowed the
venting action to have the desired effect. However, the venting
would not have been instantaneous. A complete "dump" of cabin
pressure (from 5 p.s.i. to vacuum within the cabin) would have
required approximately one minute and forty seconds. (On the
ground, of course, venting would have proved to be useless.)
During this time, the astronauts' suits might well have been
burned through and the astronauts might have died from lack
of oxygen. However, assuming they were still alive and un-
harmed by flames once the cabin was evacuated of all oxygen, the
three weightless astronauts would have found themselves with
breached suits, and therefore with neither primary nor backup
oxygen supplies. In such a hypothetical situation, they would have
been no safer in space than they were on the ground—especially
since restoring the oxygen supply to the cabin required about an
hour.

Furthermore, even if their suits were not breached, their spacecraft would have suffered extensive electrical damage due to
the fire. A spacecraft with a defective navigation and guidance
system is nothing more than an orbiting coffin. Thus, in space, the
astronauts would have died a slow and in some ways even more
horrible death. Ignoring these possibilities amounted to little
more than a calculated gamble.

The Congressional investigations, however, did not raise this
point, permitting the impression to persist that only on the
ground—in the most implausible and bizarre of circumstances—
were the astronauts in danger of death from a cabin fire.

Another flaw in the in-flight fire-fighting concept was completely overlooked by the Apollo Review Board and both Congressional inquiries. Hendel and Roth, the critics of 1964, both
warned that the danger of a cabin fire, during launch and reentry

---

* Since the Apollo fire, "new knowledge" culled from Roth and Fenn has provided Apollo astronauts with (a) independent breathing systems via an automatic valve, and (b) emergency oxygen masks—in the command module, but
not in the Lunar Landing Module (the LM).

periods, was as great, if not greater, than during the high-pressure pre-launch period. The reasons are very simple: During launch and reentry the capsule undergoes extensive gravitational acceleration (G-forces) and resulting vibrations. The shaking could well unloosen a faulty wire, or rupture a vital fuel line. Secondly, during both launch and reentry, the strapped-in astronauts are subjected to the same G-forces. The thrust effectively pushes them into their couches during the six or seven minutes from blast-off to "insertion" into Earth orbit, and a similar period during reentry. If a fire were to occur at either of these times, they would be completely immobilized and helpless to do anything in the way of fire fighting or self-preservation.

At long last the pieces of the Apollo 204 puzzle begin to fit together. Responsible persons on all levels, from the NASA administrator, his deputy and associate administrators, program managers, and their industry counterparts—even to the astronauts themselves—thought that the possibility of a spacecraft fire had been eliminated. Why else would the astronauts so meekly have placed themselves in a position of such enormous and senseless danger?

Some of the Apollo team thought that oxygen could be "lived with," because ignition sources and combustibles had been or would be eliminated. Others thought that ignition sources could be "lived with" because the other two ingredients had been or would be eliminated. Some people, no doubt, even assumed that no fire could occur—simply because they thought that none had occurred before. And, as Dr. John McCarthy of North American Aviation had said, it was in the "initial design"—dating back to 1961 and 1962—that the error was first made. As we have seen, scheduling and costs had frozen these designs early in the Apollo program. Thus, knowledge gained from the studies of Roth, Hendel, Lamb, and Fenn, were never permitted to alter the "initial design."

Senator Carl T. Curtis of Nebraska raised this specific question before Dr. Floyd Thompson, the Apollo Review Board chairman. He asked: "Was the error or shortcoming, if there were such, in the field of scientific decision, of our space scientists, or was it in the area of executing what our space scientists said should be done?" Dr. Thompson replied: "I don't think that there was anything wrong in that sense. It was simply the execution, detailed execution that resulted in this event."

The way that such an oversight had occurred was probably best explained by Mr. George White, member of the Apollo 204 Review Board. He testified that "design reviews have been devoted primarily to the more broad questions of design of subsystems, and capability of subsystems to do their jobs. And, in this sense perhaps the design review did miss some of these fine details which turned out to be very important."

The simple fact of the matter seems to be that the various parties concerned never got together and compared notes. *Each responsible person in NASA and contractor management seems to have been preoccupied with more important things and thought that someone else was handling the job.* As an inevitable consequence, no one handled it at all.

James Webb had a less harsh analysis when speaking before the ladies of the Washington Club on February 1, 1967, five days after the fire. Urging the ill-informed not to be too hasty, but rather to wait for the final and expert judgment of the Apollo 204 Review Board investigation, he said: ". . . I think that when that process [the investigation] is through, people will find that while this instance was a tragic one, . . . the systems that have been developed and have proven out are good. They may require some modification. *This remains to be proven* [however,] because many, many very careful tests have been run in which these young men, all of them who have to fly these spacecraft, have participated [italics added]."*

However, Webb's ultimate confession that the circumstances leading to the Apollo fire were "in retrospect, . . . foolish and stupid" implied that the cause of the tragedy was a kind of typographical error—"a failure to classify it [the plugs-out test] as extremely hazardous."

All along, NASA spokesmen had insisted on the basic competence and integrity of their agency. On one occasion during the opening session of the Senate fire hearings, Dr. George E. Mueller, Webb's associate administrator, who was responsible, ultimately, for the performance at the Manned Spaceflight facili-

---

* Such extensive changes were required that it would be about twenty-two months before Apollo astronauts would fly again.

ties at Houston and at the contractors' facilities, had expressed particular impatience with his questioners on the subject of competence. "As we have testified, in years past," he retorted, "the Apollo program is probably the longest R. and D. [research and development] program we have undertaken in this nation."

To illustrate this point, and the care with which the responsibility had been executed, NASA compared the relative testing and check-out periods of Mercury (one-man), Gemini (two-man), and Apollo (three-man) systems on the ground. The following information was submitted for the Congressional record to illustrate that Apollo had had more than its share of attention:

On the Mercury, we spent about 7.8 weeks in factory tests; in Gemini, we spent about 16.3 weeks. Our experience on Apollo has been that we have spent about 20 weeks in factory tests and checkout.

In the case of KSC [Kennedy Space Center] modification and hangar testing, we spent about 14.5 weeks on Mercury, about 9 weeks on Gemini, and then because of the problem with environmental control system, which accounted for about 11 additional weeks, we actually spent about 21 weeks on Apollo spacecraft 012.

On pad test and checkout, we had about 4 weeks on Mercury, about 4.5 weeks on Gemini, and a total of about 6 weeks on the Apollo. I only bring these out to illustrate the fact that we were not pressing too hard on the test and checkout of the vehicle.

These figures did not impress everyone.* By the closing of the first session of the Senate Committee hearings, on February 7, 1967, Dr. Seamans was urged to come up with an answer to the sensational charge, by newsmen, that "the Apollo capsule was plagued by troubles . . . 20,000 changes over the past five years." Dr. Seamans stated, uncompromisingly, that 20,000 specific

---

* Rocket expert and author Erik Bergaust, in his critical book *Murder on Pad 34*, cites these same figures to indict NASA and its contractors for bad workmanship on the Apollo project. Apparently, Bergaust feels that the check and recheck process on Apollo should have taken no longer than the time spent on Mercury and Gemini. Given the greatly increased complexity of the Apollo systems, and the fact that the "11 additional weeks" on the Apollo environmental unit were due to a *fire* on April 28, 1966 (see Chapter 8, p. 166), Bergaust's logic is curious.

defects, for a piece of machinery as complex as the Apollo system, with its one and a half million components, compared to 236,000 components for Gemini, was not an unreasonable proportion. Besides, added Seamans, this figure represented failures *discovered*, a clear example of good inspection.

The Apollo spacecraft, designed to escape Earth's gravity and go to the Moon and back safely, is a Rolls-Royce, compared to the Earth-orbiting Gemini Model A's and the Mercury Model T's that never left "near space." Thus, Dr. Seamans used both the "twenty thousand changes" and the extra weeks of testing to demonstrate the extra-careful precautions taken by NASA with Apollo.

Unfortunately, an understanding Congress did not call NASA on such glaring contradictions. Why, if Apollo were many, many times more complex than Mercury and Gemini, was something less than twice the time spent in inspection and testing?

It became evident in the Senate hearings on the Apollo tragedy, that NASA managers at Washington headquarters, Houston, Cape Kennedy, and on the contractor levels, had responded to the warnings of Roth and his colleagues in a most haphazard fashion. What had happened was revealed in a particularly embarrassing encounter between Drs. Mueller and Berry and their Senatorial questioners. The discussion concerned the validity of "flame tests" on materials included in the Apollo 012 command module.

Senator Holland began by noting that all of the tests involving the burning rates of combustibles mentioned by Dr. Mueller seemed to have been conducted *after* the Apollo disaster. The Senator then put this question directly to Mueller: "Did you perform tests of this nature prior to the disaster?"

Dr. Mueller replied forthrightly, "Yes. There were a number of tests . . . prior to the disaster." These earlier tests had been "particularly germane," because the Apollo Review Board had been "interested in how one might have gone about extinguishing the fires." Mueller added: "I think that, in general . . . we do not know a satisfactory way of extinguishing flames."

The Senate Committee, for once, was not put off. Rather, the senators kept the pressure on, closing in with increasingly specific and discomforting questions. Mr. James J. Gehrig, staff counsel for the Committee, wanted to know precisely why NASA had permitted all the little Velcro pads and the nylon "debris net" to get into the spacecraft. Dr. Berry, for instance, had stated that NASA's flame tests had resulted in very "stringent" rules for such materials. No materials that burned more than half an inch per second were allowed. Yet, right after the fire, the Review Board had demonstrated that both Velcro and nylon burned at a rate of *two* and a half inches per second. Reminded of these findings, Dr. Mueller replied: "I would like to hasten to clarify the fact that the rate of propagation varies depending on a lot of factors . . . the [burning rate] is one of the less precise kinds of measurements." Then he said: "Relatively, it burns fast, is the statement I would like to make."

Gehrig pressed on. "How did these materials get into the spacecraft if they had higher rates of burning?"

Mueller answered, "Those tests and our specifications at that time related to 5 p.s.i. of oxygen [the normal reduced cabin pressure of flight]. In this particular case we are talking about the burning rate in 16 p.s.i. of oxygen [the approximate cabin pressure at which the Apollo 204 fire occurred]."

Gehrig tried again. "But in the 16 p.s.i. pure-oxygen atmosphere, [the materials] do burn at two and a half inches per second. Was this known prior to the accident?"

Mueller could only reply lamely: "Not at 16. Almost all the material tests we made were at 5 p.s.i."

Senator Cannon, who had unsuccessfully tried the same line of questioning earlier, could not contain his disappoinment. "Mr. Chairman," he interjected, "I asked the doctor a question a moment ago, specifically to bring that out. Dr. Mueller, you said that you did perform tests of that nature prior to the accident."

Mueller answered blankly, "Yes, sir."

Senator Cannon, having patiently heard out Gehrig's questioning of Dr. Mueller, pressed home: "Now, did you or did you not perform tests of the proposed materials under 16 p.s.i., prior to the accident?"

Mueller responded: "We did perform some tests at 16 p.s.i. In particular, we did not perform tests at 16 p.s.i. with either the nylon net or the nylon Velcro. We did perform tests on those materials at 5 p.s.i."

In 1964, Emanuel Roth, NASA's hand-picked authority on the

documentation of fire prevention, had insisted that *all components* "regardless of how well they are protected," remain potential sources of ignition. He had recommended, most urgently, that all components, after careful screening, should also be "explosion-proofed," and then tested *both* at altitude (5 p.s.i.) and at ground level (16 p.s.i.). Three years later, Dr. Fenn had advised the fire hazard might be considerably greater than Roth had indicated. Yet after two fatal fires that claimed five victims, apparently all NASA could tell congressmen was that it had tested the *wrong* materials at ground level pressure, and the relevant materials at the *wrong* pressure.

During the opening session of the Senate hearings, NASA witnesses had managed, temporarily, to steer clear of this self-incrimination. An attempt was made to establish the idea that increasing cabin pressure from 5 p.s.i. to 16 p.s.i. had little or no effect on burning rates (i.e., "a weak coupling"). Mr. Gehrig, on behalf of the Senate Committee, had asked for a graph or some similar visual aid to show this relationship. Laymen, it seemed, would need something more concrete—something that would show, exactly and pictorially, the relationship between the percent of oxygen, its pressure, and the probability of ignition. Drs. Seamans and Mueller produced a crude freehand graph. The trouble with it was that the vertical and horizontal scales did not match, and there were no intersecting coordinates on the background. (See Fig. 5.)

According to NASA this Figure "shows that there is not a significant increase in flame propagation rates for these materials (Nomex, Neoprene-coated nylon, and Velcro hook) in a pure-oxygen atmosphere as we increase the pressure from 5 p.s.i.a. to 15 p.s.i.a. (one atmosphere)." Actually, the graph shows burning-rate increases of roughly 10 to 15 percent

But perhaps this is really just splitting hairs. Roth, in 1964, had flatly stated: "Increasing the oxygen generally effects all the combustion parameters in the direction of increasing the hazard." Oxygen pressure was described as very critical. Why then the evasiveness demonstrated by this specious graph? The actual tests performed by the Apollo Review Board, as already noted, demonstrated that the increase for the most critical items, velcro and the nylon netting, had been from a half inch to two and a half

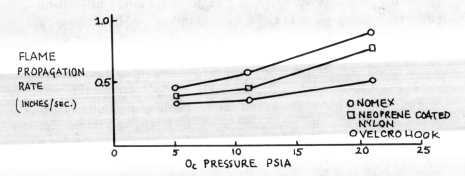

Fig. 5: NASA Rendering of "Flame propagation rate as a function of pressure."

inches per second—a fivefold increase. The graph simply failed to prove anything.

However, the incomplete flame tests did serve to introduce some safety restraints. It had been determined that if, by some unhappy but sufficiently remote oversight, all ignition sources were not eliminated, the capsule should be free of any materials that would burn at temperatures of less than 400°F. in a 5 p.s.i. pure-oxygen atmosphere. The 400°F. cut-off point was selected, somewhat arbitrarily, because it represented the "general" temperature at which most materials (such as Velcro, Nomex, and Teflon) were expected to burn or decompose. It was also "about" the same temperature at which the soldered joints in much of the capsule's plumbing would "melt."* Thus, NASA's reasoning went, if nothing supporting combustion below 400°F. was in the spacecraft, there would be no fire of catastrophic proportion. As James E. Webb said: "So in essence, while we had not tested these particular materials in a fire, we had gone through very careful tests to make sure that it would take 400° or so to start them burning. And *our whole plan was based on the prevention of the attainment of that much heat in the capsule* [italics added]." These precautions did not keep unprotected foam rubber couches and hatch cushions, which burned at about 250°F., from being included.

Unfortunately, the fire occurred at a much lower temperature and it spread at a lightning speed. The cabin pressure was more than three times (16.7 p.s.i. vs. 5 p.s.i.) that which had been the basis for the 400°F. restraint. It had happened exactly as Roth had suggested it might—increase the pressure and you decrease the "kindling" temperature and also increase the rate of burning.**

There was yet another flaw in NASA's fire-prevention policies. Many electronic components, necessary for mid-flight and lunar

---

* In the Apollo 204 fire, the solder joints did melt, and spilled forth combustible coolant (water-glycol) that added an abundant amount of fuel to what had already become a raging fire.

** Meanwhile, NASA officials managed, somewhat belatedly, to head at least one more of Roth's recommendations. In the late spring of 1968, tests were run to see if either the mixed gas of ground conditions or the pure oxygen of space reacted chemically with new materials in the spacecraft to produce poisonous vapors.

landing navigation, had been designed in such a way that a cabin temperature in excess of about 125°F. would throw them out of calibration. One might therefore survive a minor ground or in-flight fire, only to be lost in space without a "compass."

The manner in which NASA attempted to retrieve its lost prestige was singularly pretentious. It was done by means of a supposedly routine report a year after the fire, to the Congress and the people, entitled *Status of Actions Taken on Recommendation of the Apollo 204 Accident Review Board,* in two volumes. This report, purportedly packed with "new knowledge," was distributed to the press at Cape Kennedy before committee members actually received it. It was sent by Dr. Mueller, on December 29, 1967, to Olin Teague, chairman of the House Subcommittee on NASA Oversight. The report stated NASA's "new" approach to fire prevention:

> The amount of combustible materials in the command module has been greatly reduced. *There were 1412 non-metallic materials identified in the CSM. Seventy-nine percent, or 1113 have been deleted, replaced, redesigned, or determined to be acceptable. The remaining non-metallic materials are currently being evaluated and work on this effort is scheduled for completion early in 1968.* This effort includes flammability tests to be conducted early next year at MSC on a full-scale command module boiler-plate (BP–1224). [Italics added.]

The House Subcommittee on NASA Oversight was so delighted with this forthright and unambiguous statement that it printed the two volumes under one new cover on January 27, 1968 (the anniversary of the fire)—publishing, therefore, the same report twice within a month at government cost. (They had done precisely the same thing with the original fifteen-volume Apollo Review Board Report.) Three days later, NASA's other and more prestigious watchdogs, of the Senate Committee on Aeronautical and Space Sciences, indicated that they, too, were pleased with NASA's progress and went on record, in their final Apollo 204 Report, with this expression of their lofty trust:

> . . . no manned flights have been or will be attempted in the Apollo program until the astronauts, *in the light of their newly acquired technical information* are completely satisfied . . .

Some of the more important procedure and hardware changes that have been initiated by NASA follow:

1. All tests taking place in 100 percent pure-oxygen environments are now defined as hazardous. . . .

2. A significant change has been instituted in the approach to the selection and placement of materials inside the command module. *This change . . . is more significant than any other improvement resulting from the accident.* [Italics added.]

Both NASA and the Congressional space patrons must have assumed that their "mock trial" would dissuade those with too critical an eye. All efforts were made to suppress the fact that every "new" recommendation had been made *before* the Apollo fire, but had not been pursued.

Only once, on November 8, 1967, did the brutal truth come out in the open. More than six months after the Congressional Apollo 204 hearings had been concluded, Mr. Webb told the Senate Committee on Aeronautical and Space Sciences: ". . . we have incorporated many changes which relate to developed new knowledge following the fire *or new knowledge that was available at the time of the fire but which we could not incorporate without major change in the whole schedule* [italics added]."

In other words, changes recommended by Roth and others had not yet been incorporated because they would have upset NASA's timetable: This, more than any other one cause, is why Grissom, White, Chaffee, Bartley and Harmon died.

The reader will naturally be interested in the final outcome of the oxygen saga.

After all the previous months' defense of the pure-oxygen decision, and solemn testimony made in behalf of the astronauts' safety, Webb's associate administrator, Dr. Mueller, found himself telling the world that "since the fire hazard [on the ground] was clearly more dangerous than the bends [in space]," a change in atmosphere during the high-pressure periods of launch and reentry would have to be made. While this change had been resisted for years because of threatened schedule, weight, design, and monetary restrictions, the actual change—when it took place in March, 1968—did not alter the 5 p.s.i. in-flight atmosphere and thus required "no changes to the existing spacecraft environmental control system." Postponement of the changeover, however, took an awful toll in lives, time, money, and prestige.

Pressed as NASA finally was, it began to come around to the inevitable. In a news article, March 6, 1968, entitled "NASA Acts to Cut Apollo Fires," Thomas O'Toole, in *The Washington Post,* quoted an unnamed Apollo official as saying, "We've decided that there will be no more Apollo fires—not even little ones that can be put out." O'Toole noted, however, that "when the command cabin was put through 29 of 31 scheduled tests in pure oxygen at 16 p.s.i., 15 separate fires started." Emergency oxygen masks and water-gel "squirt guns"* were also to be provided the Apollo astronauts. When the fire mock-up tests (a "newly discovered" product of the Apollo 204 investigations), conducted under the direction of project manager George Low, at Houston, failed to eliminate all instances of fire during the pre-launch period of 16 p.s.i., the changeover to a mixed gas, on the ground, was so simple, so smooth, and executed in such an offhand manner, that it went almost unnoticed. While most major newspapers made note of the changeover in their back pages, the major television networks, with the exception of CBS, considered the subject too technical and unimportant for the layman. CBS noted the change, but not the significance.

Pure oxygen was retained for the reduced-pressure in-flight environment.

The reader may remember the account (Chapter 7) of the very first atmosphere test in 1960 in a simulated spacecraft during the early stages of the Mercury program. This test, conducted for the purposes of finding a livable cabin atmosphere, involved a mixed gas (nearly normal air) during pre-launch phases. This was the test that felled Gilbert North of McDonnell. He blacked out when his suit loop leaked and let nitrogen into his bloodstream. His suit pressure was considerably lower than that of the pressurized cabin, which was at about 15 p.s.i. NASA and McDonnell's John Yardley arrived at the expedient solution of

---

* The squirt gun is a slender, long-nosed water pistol designed to be inserted into strategically located access holes in the paneling that now covers wire bundles and electrical components. Since ordinary water is a hazard in electrical fires and would run down over otherwise unaffected areas, a gelatinous form of water, a relatively new development, is used. The gel smothers the fire and stays in place.

going all the way in the other direction—to pure oxygen during pre-launch as well as during space flights. More importantly, they also increased the astronaut's suit pressure so that it was slightly above the cabin pressure at all times.

Eight years later, after the tragic Apollo fire, NASA's designers found themselves right back where they had begun: mixed gas on the ground, during launch, and reentry; pure oxygen during space flight. Only they had managed somehow to reduce leakage in the suit and spacecraft (as would have been expected).

They also found themselves confronting two new volumes, Parts III and IV, of a study by NASA's consultant, Dr. Emanuel Roth of the Lovelace Foundation. By some unhappy coincidence these final two volumes of Roth's study had not been published at the time of the two fatal oxygen fires. They appeared in 1967—after the Apollo 204 investigations were already under way, and they made pure-oxygen space-cabin atmospheres look worse than ever before. Part IV, "Engineering Trade-offs of One- Versus Two-Gas Systems," managed, at long last, to settle the oxygen question once and for all.

In one of several tables,* the fire hazards of pure oxygen are compared with the various other atmospheres that had been under consideration. In this table ("Fire and Blast Hazards") pure oxygen makes a very poor showing, indeed. It is the least desirable (most dangerous) atmosphere in six out of eight categories. It is second to last in the only remaining two. It seems safe to say that by the time these studies were completed, just months before the fatal fires, there was precious little "new knowledge" to be marshaled in favor of oxygen as a cabin atmosphere.

In another table ("Engineering Factors for 30-Day, 2-Man Orbiting Mission"), pure oxygen is preferred from the point of view of hardware reliability, weight penalty, and leakage rates, for instance. But, as the title of the table indicates, these are all engineering considerations. In still a third table ("Physiological Factors"), oxygen is preferred over mixed-gas systems in only one of seventeen categories, that of problems associated with the bends.

Other factors involved in the original oxygen decision are no more reassuring. The weight penalty paid in changing over from

* See Appendix H.

a pure-oxygen to a mixed-gas atmosphere, for example, has been estimated at about fifty-two pounds—an increase of less than 10 percent. Furthermore, reliable nitrogen sensors, which are necessary to monitor mixed-gas atmospheres—and which seemed so far in the future during Gilbert North's ordeal in 1960—became available in late 1966, through a separate NASA project, the Biosatellite program. Since added weight and a lack of good nitrogen sensors were considered severe limitations to the change-over to mixed gas for Apollo, one cannot help but balk at an entry in a Congressional report prepared in 1965—the Apollo Pace and Progress volume. The entry is a simple table weighing the relative complexity of changes that will be required of NASA's systems when switching from Project Apollo to the Apollo Applications (AAP) in 1970. The switch from a pure-oxygen to a mixed-gas atmosphere (throughout the entire mission, including launch and reentry) is distinctly labeled, "minor change."

And what about the bends, the chief reason for having changed from a mixed gas to pure oxygen in the first place? On February 1, 1968, the Associated Press reported that research physicians at Cal Tech had observed that the bends (dysbarism) is accompanied by an abrupt loss of three to four quarts of plasma from the blood. It was found that a remedy of sorts—symptomatic, life-giving relief—may consist of simply injecting new plasma into the blood vessels of the victim.

Unreported in the newspapers were the far more meaningful and promising results of Dr. Chryssanthos Chryssanthou, research director of Beth Israel Medical Center in New York.

Dr. Chryssanthou and his colleagues, whose efforts over nearly five years have been supported by the Navy and the Air Force School of Aerospace Medicine—but not by NASA, who seems to have been unimpressed or uninterested—may have found a way, ultimately, to prevent the bends altogether.

The most painful, sometimes fatal, result of the bends is a condition known as hypolemic shock, a condition in which the protein and accompanying fluids of blood plasma leave the vessels and invade the surrounding body tissue. The Chryssanthou research group has experimented with one drug that reduces the effects of hypolemic shock and increases the survival of decompressed mice from 15 percent to nearly 80 percent. This technique means that the subject of an experiment may be injected *before* exposure to the bends and thus carry the means of defense in his own bloodstream.

Lack of funds, facilities, and time have prevented the projection of these experiments to humans as yet, but the Navy and the Aerospace School of Medicine see the hope of ultimate protection for deep-sea divers, tunnel workers, and even millions of civilian scuba divers. NASA's astronauts also may benefit one day soon, but not because NASA funded and otherwise supported the research.

What, then, did NASA really learn from the Apollo 204 fire? Very little, indeed, as was demonstrated by Houston's attempt to remove the on-board TV monitor during the first of upcoming Apollo flights because the monitor represented an undesirable weight penalty.* NASA had apparently already forgotten that the deaths of astronauts Grissom, White, and Chaffee resulted, at least in part, from the fact that the TV monitors had not been properly installed or manned. The helmeted astronauts, whose mobility and vision were severely restricted, actually saw the fire before their support crew. This was possible in spite of the fact that Roth, four years earlier, had stressed time and again that helmeted astronauts could not be relied upon to detect fire and smoke by sight or smell. The Brooks Air Force facility, after its fatal fire, guaranteed that TV monitors would be installed and manned during all future oxygen tests. NASA headquarters, intervened and vetoed Houston's decision. The reasoning, however, may have been based simply upon the public relations value of the on-board camera.

Reneging on the camera would surely have created a furor. Unprecedented interest had developed among the reporters and camera men of the major TV networks for the live coverage of the astronauts' in-flight activities, including changing of clothing. As noted in *TV Guide*, the astronauts would focus the black-and-white camera on themselves and their cabin, and out the spacecraft windows for views of Earth as well as space. "Live commentary by the Apollo team will accompany the TV feeds . . .

* It was indicated at that time that the twenty-million-dollar camera would only be used, briefly, on the third manned orbital flight and while the astronauts walked on the moon. It saw extensive use, however, beginning with the first manned Apollo flight, Apollo 7.

all three networks will air the impromptu space 'shows.'" It may be worth noting that NBC is an RCA subsidiary; RCA built many of the systems (rendezvous and landing radar in particular) that will be used for these flights. The decision to retain the on-board camera obviously had nothing to do with the safety value of constant surveillance of the Apollo crew—the lack of which was a major factor in the Apollo 204 tragedy. The feud between the astronauts and NASA officials was ended during the Apollo 7, October 11-21, 1968, flight, Commander Schirra complaining that television transmission, as scheduled, would "foul up" the timing of a critical rendezvous maneuver. Refusing to perform, as it were, he cancelled more than one day's space "show," telling ground controllers that he wanted to end talk about the television "without further discussion." NASA, of course, could only use the television when Schirra turned it on.

The fatal fires cannot be excused by repentance or promises, for they are symptomatic of the inefficiency of the whole NASA organization. An organization as large as NASA (450,000 employees at the time of the fire) has countless built-in bureaucratic checks and balances. There are consultants and experts at all levels—from within, from industrial contractors, and from universities. Nevertheless, NASA and North American Aviation violated a host of safety recommendations in their preliminary preparations for the flight to the Moon. Improvements were resisted successfully up to and even after the fire investigations.

NASA had said that "the exact cause of the fire will likely never be known." Dr. Thompson, Apollo Review Board chairman, had suggested that the blame lay on the "design and layout" level—a clear-cut case of top-level administrators passing the buck to nameless underlings. Others have simply pointed to NASA's overzealous attempt to beat the Russians to the Moon.

The real reasons for the tragedy were far less palatable. They were: a lack of perspective and flexibility within NASA management at all key levels; inept, competing, or nonexistent channels of communication throughout the organization's many facilities; lazy, sloppy, and unduly profit-motivated contractor performance; myopic Congressional indulgence (often referred to as "moon-doggling"); irresponsible public relations—to the point where NASA actually believed its own inflated propaganda;

and finally, a remarkable aloofness from and disdain for the legitimate interests of the taxpaying American public. Any one of these would suggest that NASA was poorly equipped to administer the multibillion-dollar Moon project—each is the antithesis of good management. And after all, the Moon stunt is nothing but a gigantic experiment in the management and coordination of modern technology.

Against such a background NASA has described itself as "a model, with no ingredients left out," for all future national large-scale, top-priority technological endeavors.

The military space program, for those who have forgotten that there is another "national space program," was never allowed to take such risks as those taken by NASA. As Webb himself has said: "NASA . . . unlike the Air Force, does not depend on non-government minds for its extraordinarily complex decision-making processes." The showpiece of the Pentagon, the Air Force Manned Orbital Laboratory (MOL) project, had from its very beginning, opted for a mixed-gas atmosphere. For MOL, and for long-duration post-Apollo projects, a new generation of two-gas regulators had been under development all these hectic years. The two-gas selection for MOL was not made, however, for any of the reasons that have thus far been cited. On the contrary, even Dr. Roth, in 1964, saw no point in dodging the necessity of *absolute* fire prevention in a military space program. "For orbiting laboratories, military operations, and other missions where the probability of fire and blast accidents looms large, addition of inert diluents to the [pure-oxygen] atmosphere appears to be the prudent choice."* After all, how safe would an Air Force MOL technician** be in a potentially explosive oxygen atmosphere while engaged in potentially hostile military space activities?

---

* Dr. Roth, at one point in Part III of his atmosphere selection studies, indicated that the complexity of fire hazards in space vehicles "preclude definitive conclusions." He felt in 1967 that in "Gemini and Apollo missions, where crew activity is restricted and optimum fire prevention and control can be attained, 100% oxygen at 5 p.s.i. is not precluded as a choice . . ."

** Quite possibly to avoid the hero-making process that made the deaths of Grissom, White, and Chaffee so great a national shock, the Air Force officially avoids calling its space pilots "astronauts," but instead refers to them as the "MOL crew members."

■ *An arms race in space will not contribute to our security. I can think of no greater stimulus for a Soviet thermonuclear arms effort than a United States commitment to such a program. This we will not do.*

ROSWELL GILPATRIC,
*Deputy Secretary of Defense
(September, 1962), as quoted in*
The Rise and Fall of the Space Age,
Doubleday, 1964

■ *I have thought all the while that great military value could result from orbital operations, that out of space technology could come a weapon that transcended anything that we already had. For a long time this has not been publicly discussed, but now we are beginning to get news of this kind.*

SENATOR JOHN STENNIS,
*Committee on Aeronautical and Space
Sciences, November 8, 1967*

Chapter 10 ■ NASA and the Military: An Umbrella of Death

The statement must be made unequivocally, at the outset of this chapter, that it has been the Department of Defense, not NASA, that has called the shots in America's space program. This is true despite the fact that NASA's astronauts have dominated the public's image of space projects. Not only is NASA's "open" program defense oriented, but there has always been, concealed from public view, a vigorous Defense Department space program.

Because this is so, the exhilarating hope of John Kennedy and others that space exploration might prove an alternative to military competition is seriously challenged. Also in doubt is the hope of Kennedy's Space Task Force (1960), headed by Jerome B. Wiesner, that "very ambitious and long-range space projects . . . could be carried out in an atmosphere of cooperation as projects of all mankind instead of in the present atmosphere of national competition." The space arena, it was hoped, could be another neutral theater, such as Antarctica, set aside for cooperative, international exploration and study.

Such high hopes fade slowly. As late as September, 1966, then Vice-President Hubert H. Humphrey, in a speech at San Fernando Valley State College, could reassert, with evident sincerity, the theme of peace in space: "Space activities—even competition in space—can be a substitute for aggression, a bridge for mutual understanding and the identification of common interests with other nations, and a major tool of arms control and disarmament."

Vice-President Humphrey seemed to have been as confused as the rest of the American public about what was really going on in space. It is little wonder. The reflexive attempts of NASA, DOD, and other military-oriented agencies to convince the world that such peaceful hopes, on the one hand, are still strong—or, of more "realistic" spokesmen, on the other hand, to claim that such peaceful "options" never were available, even from the beginning—imply abject ignorance. Or is it a crass and cynical manipulation of the American people, who remain starry-eyed about NASA and its exhilarating "peaceful" motives, while the space agency actually devotes much of its resources to the attainment of military objectives?

How, especially since NASA's charter specifically defines its role as "civilian" and "peaceful" in nature, could this be so? Unfortunately, it is true simply because, as Richard S. Lewis said in November, 1967, in the *Bulletin of the Atomic Scientists,* "The motivations of the spacefaring powers remain the same as in 1957. They are primarily military and political; secondarily scientific and economic."

Because the prime motive behind space activities is an extension of the military power struggle born on land, and nurtured on the seas,* even the most "peaceful" of NASA's space ventures

---

* As General Bernard A. Schriever has said, "history has shown that every medium which affords military possibilities has been exploited for military purposes. This has been the case for land, sea, and the atmosphere; and . . . there is little reason to believe that space will be an exception." (From: "Does the Military Have a Role in Space?" by General Schriever, an essay included in *Space: Its Impact on Man And Society,* ed. Lillian Levy (New York: W. W. Norton, 1965), p. 59.

very often have a military tie. When they are not purely aggressive (as in the case of the "doomsday" machine envisioned by Senator Stennis in the quotation at the head of this chapter) they are "defensive" or "psychological." And all too often, NASA has openly violated its charter in direct support of the military. It has done so in the Vietnam war.

This tainted association, so contradictory to the "open" space program heralded by congressmen and NASA alike, has laid the foundation for a far more ominous atmosphere of international *non*-cooperation with NASA as its most vocal proponent. In the aftermath of the Apollo 204 disaster, NASA's James Webb rattled the saber, the missile, and the orbiting bomb before the Congress. It was NASA that claimed "secret" information which indicated that the Soviets were on the threshold of lambasting America in space.

Webb's scare talk—seemingly intended to recast NASA as a major factor in the nation's defense—was not met by unanimous approval in Washington. Even the Pentagon denied the existence of the "private" information NASA spokesmen were dispensing, for example, about Soviet development of a rocket twice as powerful as the 7.5-million-pound-thrust Saturn 5. In a way (if only temporarily), Webb was bucking the tide by stressing the military significance of America's space efforts. In mid-1968, President Johnson had actually begun to carry through on some of the "peace-in-space" aspirations of Eisenhower and Kennedy. In July the U.S.S.R. and the U.S. agreed to begin preliminary discussion about disarming and destroying nuclear stockpiles. A tentative effort was finally being made to reverse the trend of the arms race—the trend that had always spelled out "more weapons." These developments could only mean trouble to the defense establishment and the more militant of NASA's supporters, who seemed still to be traumatized by the military significance of Sputnik 1. In August, 1968, however, these same hawks had reason to feel their position had been bolstered by the U.S. decision to proceed with flight tests of the MIRV (Multiple Independently Targeted Re-entry Vehicle), a super-weapon capable of carrying from three to ten hydrogen bombs and depositing them, with great accuracy, upon widely separated targets.

Within a week after the Apollo fire, the Review Board received notice that two congressmen—both members of the House Armed Services Committee, chaired by Lucius Mendel Rivers of South Carolina, would pay a visit to Cape Kennedy. On February 2, Colonel Strang, loaned by the Air Force to help set up Apollo investigation procedures, announced to his fellow Board members that the visitors would arrive Friday afternoon (February 3, 1967) at Patrick Air Force Base. The congressmen were then expected to proceed to the launch complex, "where they would like to talk to the authorities in reference to the investigation and conduct of what's going on." They would then conduct a "little investigation" of their own at Brooks Air Force Base, before returning to Washington.

The leanings of Chairman L. Mendel Rivers of the House Armed Services Committee are no secret in the capital: Rivers is a full-blooded super space hawk. Described in *Science* as "clearly a romantic of the horse cavalry school," the South Carolina Democrat was quoted shortly after North Korea's capture of the *Pueblo* as declaring: "I would have gone to war yesterday." He exhibits unflinching respect for "military judgment" and utter disdain for "civilian strategists," who, he claims (among other sins) "tied Westmoreland's hands in Vietnam with the manacles of slow escalation." Representative Rivers believes generals are great, likes admirals, and did not like former Secretary of Defense Robert McNamara (the feeling was apparently mutual). His views were shared by a majority of the forty Committee members (twenty-three Democrats and seventeen Republicans of the Ninetieth Congress), who, with Rivers, had often been known to increase, gratuitously, the budget requests of the armed services. Rivers' Committee played an important role—beginning as early as 1966—in getting money appropriated toward the operational anti-ballistic "Chinese" missile system (ABM) so reluctantly approved two years later, under the name "Sentinel," by Secretary McNamara.

The question naturally arises: What were two of Rivers' men doing on a tour of the Southland's space facilities?

As with so many other elements of the Apollo tragedy, the deaths of the three astronauts, as well as those of the two airmen at Brooks Air Force Base, laid open—if only for a short moment in history—the inner workings of both the "open" civilian and the "closed" military camps of America's space program.

Rivers' colleagues came because they were worried—worried generally about the exposure of some of the military's more secretive space ventures. They were also worried, more specifically, about how the two notorious fires might affect the image and the schedule of something very close to their hearts—the U.S. Air Force's Manned Orbiting Laboratory (MOL), then being put together and tested at Brooks Air Force Base, Texas, the death place of the two Air Force technicians.*

What was bothering Rivers' two delegates was simply this: Would the Apollo 204 fire mean, also, a delay in the launching of their pet Air Force project?

Essentially, MOL would provide the U.S. military with its first manned, undisguised, orbiting space station. According to the *Report to the Congress from the President of the United States, U.S. Aeronautics and Space Activities, 1968,* MOL crews would remain in orbit for approximately thirty days conducting "defense-oriented experiments" involving very complex equipment. The MOL would be launched into orbit by the Titan 3M launch vehicle, a bigger, modified version of the Air Force rockets that had launched the Geminis.

From its very conception, the MOL has been full of both promise and frustration for those Americans who believe that only the United States can be entrusted with preeminence and control of space. In the late fifties and early sixties, there was some jabbing, bruising in-fighting as to who would "get" MOL. The CIA wanted it in the worst way, to succeed the badly discredited U-2's; so did the Air Force, as a successor to its unmanned Samos reconnaissance satellite. Indeed, the very future of the U.S. Air Force seemed to some extent to depend upon their obtaining MOL. Yet Defense Secretary McNamara delayed, apparently unsure what role the military should play in space. A compromise, suggesting, "let NASA have it," was eventually hooted down by a strange coalition of space hawks and space

* A MOL mission control center, costing approximately $6 million, was authorized at the Air Force Satellite Test Center, Sunnyvale, California. When complete, the MOL craft will be launched from Vandenberg Air Force Base, California (for polar orbits) or from Cape Kennedy (for equatorial orbits).

doves.* The hawks thought the military should get a foothold in space, while the doves still clung to the idea that NASA was in the business of exploring the peaceful use of space. Finally, on August 25, 1965, President Johnson announced that the Air Force had been authorized to proceed with the development of the Manned Orbiting Laboratory and to determine the strategic usefulness of man in space, already in the process of being demonstrated by the Gemini series.

MOL champions included, of course, the aerospace industry, which saw huge military space contracts coming up. President Lyndon B. Johnson's decision to permit development of a manned orbiting space laboratory by the military was hailed by aerospace spokesmen as a milestone in the advancement of manned space flight. Johnson's decision followed close on the heels of Cooper and Conrad's record-breaking endurance flight of Gemini 5, the flight that lasted almost eight days (190 hours, 56 minutes) and seemed to prove man's place in space.

So impressed were they with the Gemini missions that the Air Force MOL project managers decided by late summer 1965 to use the Gemini spacecraft (eventually the modified Gemini B) as the space shuttle to its permanent (MOL) spy base. Pentagon strategists planned on frequent trips of thirty-day duration, during which the crew would use a host of sensors to catalogue the military value or threat of targets exhibited on the Earth below. (It was felt that one man could "seek out and locate at least one thousand targets per orbit" and that their classification would be equally "time-consuming" for the second crewman.) MOL would be serviced and sustained by using manned docking procedures developed during the Gemini program. Energy-producing fuel cells could be replenished and the crews exchanged.

The fact that the United States was finally and openly improving its capability to defend "itself and the rest of the world" by means of manned space vehicles was viewed as reassurance to

---

* Similar rivalry for a stake in space has existed from the dawn of the space age. The Wiesner Task Force report (1960), for example, noted: "Each of the military services has begun to create its own independent space program. This presents the problem of overlapping programs and duplication of the work of NASA." Time, evidently, does not mellow a government agency's acquisitive instincts.

our allies and as a source of dismay for our enemies. In the aerospace community, the MOL program was seen as one of the most important efforts this nation had ever made to improve its defenses in the nuclear age. And, as *Aviation Week* asserted, "it is technically feasible and nationally necessary."

The President's agreement to proceed with MOL meant the end of a ten-year struggle by the Air Force to gain a role in manned space flight.

It was also a reversal of policy, on this very point, maintained by two previous Presidents.

As *Aviation Week*, September 6, 1965, said: *"For too long, the military role was blocked by the 'peaceful uses of outer space' motto so hastily and ill-advisedly concocted by the Eisenhower Administration, which also interpreted 'peace' to mean 'non-military'* [italics added]."

Such elegant distinctions, that "peaceful" did not necessarily mean "non-military," went a long way toward comforting the consciences of those who had once dreamed of the "peaceful uses of outer space." Besides, there was a feeling of futility about the whole subject: unmanned "spies in the sky"—Russian ones as well as the U.S. Air Force's Samos, Midas, Ferret, and Vela series—were already whirling overhead anyway, filming and televising objects as small as a foot in diameter. Did putting a human spy in the sky really make much difference? For others, however, the question nagged: Is a spy any less a spy if he carries, not a gun, but a microfilm camera to record secret documents? (Many a spy has been imprisoned or sentenced to death for a bit of "peaceful" stealing of secret information.) Moreover, in addition to MOL's camera and telescopes, vague hints have linked MOL to the potentiality of disarming enemy orbital bombs—a job that a man, so it seems, could do better than a machine. And if MOL crew members could disarm hostile satellites, is it not also feasible that they would service and arm the United States' own satellites—replacing, for example, obsolescent warheads with newer and better ones?

This may sound somewhat sinister, but can one really expect the military to sit quietly with hands folded—to simply hold "maneuvers" in space? It's much too inviting, and there are possibilities—just now beginning to emerge from secrecy, to the delight of men such as Senator Stennis—for the development of advanced space weapons systems that could make our present-day ICBM's look like World War I Spads. Weapons systems, after all, are the business of the Pentagon strategists.

On the other hand, those who favor the precedent for the military use of space set by the spying satellites believe that they are, in fact, more "peaceful"-minded than those who oppose such satellites. In an article in *U.S. News & World Report* (September 9, 1968), later condensed by the American family-centered *Reader's Digest* (December, 1968), this rationale was given:

> U.S. spy satellites are a factor for peace in the U.S. [Air Force?] view. They are vital to any further progress in U.S.-Soviet talks on mutual disarmament.
>
> If satellites can be improved to the point where on-site inspection by Americans is not required, one major problem now obstructing a far-reaching agreement will be removed.*
>
> The Russians are starting now to understand that one of their centuries-old weapons against the rest of the world—their secrecy—is rapidly being removed.

President Johnson on occasion seemed anxious to reassure the nation that MOL's purpose was similarly benign. His *Report to Congress from the President of the United States, U.S. Aeronautics and Space Activities, 1965* contained the following observation:

> MOL is to be neither a weapon nor a weapon's carrier and in no way contradicts America's peaceful purposes in space. Rather *it aims* to increase knowledge of man's usefulness in space and *to relate this ability to free world defense.* [Italics added.]

More recently, the President's *Report* of January, 1968, reaffirmed that MOL had no missions as a weapons system. Perhaps, however, this must be read to mean "at this time." For, as Richard J. Barnet declares in his review of Ralph Lapp's *The Weapons Culture*, published in *Science*, April, 1968, "The accusation that

---

* This is debatable. See page 224.

the 'military mind' lacks imagination is absurd, as readers of *Air Force/Space Digest* and its Army and Navy counterparts can testify." Barnet then proceeds to describe the contents of such periodicals: "The threats that leap up from the pages of these journals are equaled in inspiration only by the reassuring panoply of instruments they recommend to burn, shock, bore, disintegrate, poison, or blow apart those who dare to pose such threats."

The United States Information Agency (USIA), therefore, had a critical mission in regard to MOL, for, according to the President's Report: USIA's mission was to follow out the President's directive to make the whole MOL business look as "peaceful as possible."

One development that made USIA's assignment particularly difficult was the fact that NASA had already planned "peaceful," long-duration missions in its Apollo Applications Program (AAP) —a series of shots designed to make use of leftover Apollo hardware after the Moon landing had been accomplished. The President's Report described AAP's mission this way:

> . . . to conduct long-duration space flights of men and systems; to perform scientific investigations in Earth orbit; to conduct Earth-orbital missions, such as meteorology, communications, and Earth resources surveys; and to conduct extended lunar exploration. . . .

The "Orbital Workshop" was the grandest of the two "major experiments" planned for AAP. It would consist of the empty upper stage of a Saturn launch vehicle transformed into a living space (the "Saturn Workshop") for long-duration missions. Astronauts could enter and leave their "Workshop" through an airlock, during rendezvous or docking by means of an Apollo spacecraft.

Both MOL and the AAP had highly vocal backers. The trouble was that, to a few people who had something of an overview of the space program, both missions looked pretty much the same. To Representative Wydler of New York, in fact, they looked identical. In late June, 1967, he commented in the *Congressional Record*:

> It [AAP] is the same program doing essentially the same things for which the American taxpayer is going to have to pay twice.

In March, 1968, Congressman William Ryan of New York spelled it out again with dollars and cents that meant something to the taxpayer. He branded the two projects as "parallel program objectives, parallel mission plans and parallel space systems. The Air Force Program," he said, "is budgeted at over a half billion dollars for fiscal year 1969 alone. Reportedly, about three billion dollars is already invested."

That same month, in a radio interview with Congressman Ryan on March 25, 1968, DOD-NASA critic Ralph Lapp fairly exploded with indignation over the AAP-MOL duplication: "I wouldn't reduce [Apollo Applications], I'd cut it out! . . . Apollo Applications, of course, is simply use of the big boosters . . . which can hurl a hundred and twenty tons into orbit . . . a hundred and twenty tons of what? It has to have man in it to justify such weight. We're going to send a hundred and twenty tons of microminiaturized equipment up there . . . The MOL Program and the Saturn Workshop are almost identical . . . That's duplication! That's wasted money!"

To these challenges could be added many more, particularly the strong denunciations of AAP-MOL duplication by Representative James G. Fulton of Pennsylvania. Their collective effect has been minimal—primarily because the challenge came much too late.

In February, 1967, in a pamphlet entitled "The National Space Program—Its Values and Benefits," a staff study for the House Subcommittee on NASA Oversight, MOL received the blessing of both President Johnson and Vice-President Humphrey. That study declared, more boldly than ever before, the close cooperation between NASA and DOD. This "cooperation," at a second glance, is almost entirely one-way. NASA cooperates with the Defense Department; DOD does pretty much as it pleases, under the conventional cover of classified and secret activities.

As proclaimed by the House staff study, in *all* U.S. manned space flight programs—Mercury, Gemini, and Apollo—"the actual experiments flown on the various flights were selected jointly by NASA and DOD, and in fact all of the original seven NASA astronauts were military trained personnel."

Reading on in the House Subcommittee pamphlet, one finds: "Some people have suggested that the MOL program of the

Department of Defense and NASA's Apollo Applications Program should be merged, alleging that these programs are inherently overlapping and duplicative. This proposition was presented to Vice-President Hubert H. Humphrey, chairman of the National Aeronautics and Space Council. He countered it by saying:

> There already exists a high degree of cooperation between the Air Force and NASA on the MOL program, and I expect it will continue. However, I have no reason to predict an actual merger of the MOL research and development effort with any of NASA's manned projects. . . .

Additional rationale for keeping the two very similar programs went back to a speech in October, 1966, by Air Force Under-secretary Norman S. Paul at the National Space Club. Paul explained "that because space is not ours alone, we must also have a defense space program . . . In other words," Paul concluded, "although the U.S. space program is dedicated to using space for the benefit of the whole world, we cannot, at the same time, compromise the vital security of the United States."

Later, on April 19, 1967, at the 1968 NASA Authorization Hearings before the Senate Aeronautical and Space Sciences Committee, NASA's Dr. Mueller attempted to affirm the Johnson-Humphrey "no-duplication" thesis. The NASA associate administrator explained the relationship between Apollo Applications and MOL this way: "The programs are not directly related." But even more important, said Dr. Mueller in reply to Senator Percy, NASA's work was helping the Department of Defense do its job (MOL) better. Mueller elaborated as follows: ". . . there is not any direct output from our program into their program in the sense that we are providing equipment for them other than the fact that we have already provided the Gemini capsule and many of the subsystems that they are using for their program to come out of both the Apollo and the Gemini programs."

In return for Gemini and Apollo systems and hardware, the Air Force MOL was expected to test out a single NASA experiment, using a carbon dioxide sensor.

Mueller's testimony mostly confirms the *Report to the Congress from the President of the United States, U.S. Aeronautics and*

Space Activities, 1968, which states that NASA is actively supporting the MOL program, while (according to testimony in the 1967 NASA Authorization Hearings before the Senate Committee) "there is no payload weight available for NASA experiments on the currently approved series of manned MOL launches."

Here, again, the NASA-MOL links raised disquieting questions. Besides the United Nations "no-bombs-in-orbit" resolution sponsored in 1963 by the eighteen-nation Committee on Disarmament, there were treaties in the making* that would keep space open "for the benefit of all mankind." How then could an exclusively military space station be justified in the eyes of the anticipated signatories? The space hawks echoed, predictably, the words of Air Force Undersecretary Paul that treaties should never be permitted to jeopardize "vital security." Besides, MOL represented a *support* military activity (surveillance and reconnaissance), not a *direct* one (e.g., bomb in orbit), a distinction that space hawks are terribly fond of making.

The fuss derives both from the fact of the obvious duplication and the fact that weapons and warfare are not the business of NASA and were never intended to be. Furthermore, the duplication, in some quarters, may have seemed necessary simply to assure that work in space will not be preempted exclusively by either the military or the civilian factor.

President Richard M. Nixon's views in this critical area are quite clear. The Republican platform "deplored the lack of emphasis on the military use of space for America's defense." While Nixon wishes the United States to be "first in space," he has been known to talk of judicious cuts in the civilian space program, especially for NASA's immediate, uncertain future. Given the fact that the scientists to whom he is closest have, as a group,

---

* The *Report to the Congress from the President of the United States, U.S. Aeronautics and Space Activities, 1968,* states: "In furtherance of the desire of the United States and other nations for peace, the Treaty on Outer Space was approved without dissent by the Senate on April 25 and went into formal effect on October 10, when ceremonies were conducted in Washington, London, and Moscow. Also, the United Nations General Assembly unanimously passed an agreement on December 19, providing for assistance in the rescue and return of astronauts as well as of their space equipment." On October 8, 1968, the U.S. Senate ratified 66 to 0, the treaty among over seventy nations providing for search, rescue and return of astronauts and space vehicles downed on foreign soil or on the high seas.

a rather hawkish cast,* given further his stated preference for clear-cut U.S. weapons superiority over "the peculiar, unprecedented doctrine called 'parity,'" and given finally his contention that a "research gap" perils American military superiority, it is obvious that MOL appeals to him more than AAP. It is doubtful that he will move quickly to put NASA more openly at the service of the military, or propose the still bolder step of merging the civilian and military space programs. Yet if he chose to do either, he could probably count on some solid support in Congress. The chairmen of the key defense-oriented committees— Senator Richard B. Russell of Georgia (Armed Services Committee), Senator John C. Stennis of Mississippi (Select Standards and Conduct Committee), and Representative L. Mendel Rivers of South Carolina (House Armed Services Committee)—are all Democrats, but they would probably side with Nixon in a showdown between MOL and AAP. So would a majority of the Ninety-First Congress, if it followed the lead of the preceeding Congress. In a session marked by drastic cuts in research and development support, the Ninetieth Congress gave the Air Force roughly $500 million of the $600 million it had requested for MOL, while slashing the AAP's $440 million request by two-thirds to $140 million. It is also likely that under the Nixon Administration some additional links will be forged between NASA and the military space effort.

There is ample evidence that NASA will not prove an altogether bashful bride in these circumstances. As Richard D. Lyons of *The New York Times* wrote in late October, 1968:

> NASA, which was once reluctant about associating itself with the military uses of space, now appears more relaxed. In order to sell the space agency to Congress and the taxpayers, NASA

---

* During the 1968 Presidential campaign, Hubert Humphrey said that Nixon's science advisers were drawn "largely from the ranks of persons identified with the nuclear arms race and military applications of science." Nixon's early appointment of Dr. Lee Alvin DuBridge, president of the California Institute of Technology, as his Science Advisor did not entirely conflict with Humphrey's observation. During World War II, DuBridge had headed a government radar-development laboratory at MIT. Among Nixon's earlier supporters, besides General Schriever, were Admiral Lewis L. Strauss, head of the Atomic Energy Commission in the 1950's, Dr. Edward Teller, "father of the hydrogen bomb," and Nobel prize-winner Willard F. Libby, chemistry professor at UCLA and a former member of the Atomic Energy Commission.

officials now adopt the line that military objectives are among the beneficial "spinoffs" from the $43-billion [spent through 1968] national space program.

Nevertheless, as noted in Chapter 4, the NASA charter makes a very specific distinction between the activities of NASA, a civilian agency, and "the development of weapons systems, military operations, or the defense of the United States (including the research and development necessary to make effective provision for the defense of the United States, [which] shall be the responsibility of, and shall be directed by, the Department of Defense)."*

These questions must be asked:

■ How can the Congress and the taxpayer causally accept the fact that "NASA assists the military in meeting their [sic] requirements [and] the military in like manner supports NASA's requirements"?

■ Why did NASA find it necessary to state in the 1968 Authorization Hearings: "DOD technology requirements and research activities are taken into account in the formulation of *practically all* of NASA's research and technology programs [italics added]"? Such programs include ballistic and lifting entry vehicle performance, thermal coatings for temperature control, and advanced launch vehicle technology—to name just three of a dozen general areas where NASA does its best to dovetail with DOD's wishes. Such is the type of information that is, as James Webb told Senator Brooke in the fiscal 1968 Senate Authorization Hearings, "fed to the Defense Department. Many of their problems are fed toward us. We work in close and intimate association."

■ Why does NASA lend its personnel and facilities to DOD —free just for the asking? Why has NASA proudly boasted that it spent 5,611 man-hours testing a Titan rocket model for the Air Force; 2,900 man-hours conducting wind-tunnel test on a

---

* Foreseeing a possible argument as to which agency got what, this section concludes with: "Determination as to which such agency has responsibility for and direction of any such activity shall be made by the President . . ." For example, only the President could take MOL away from the USAF and assign it to NASA or elsewhere.

Titan 3, again for the USAF; and 15,000 more man-hours testing a one-fifth-size scale model of the Titan 3, once again for the USAF?

■ Why does the space agency make it known that "in summary, it is estimated that approximately 75 percent of NASA's Space Vehicle Division effort, while aimed at NASA objectives, is 'of direct benefit' [, not to 'all mankind,' but] to DOD and contributes to their *specific military requirements* [italics added]." Examples of the kind of project where NASA lends a helping hand are the GAP Missile, the Polaris, the Titan 3, the Teton Missile, and again, MOL, to name only a few of the "classified and unclassified projects" in which NASA is engaged for the sole benefit of the Department of Defense.

■ How could it be that a *Washington Post* staff writer, Thomas O'Toole, could write on December 4, 1967, of "the growing role of the civilian space agency in the Vietnam War . . . that NASA's Office of Advanced Research and Technology is spending between $4 million and $5 million a year directing the efforts of 100 scientists and engineers to tasks vital to the Vietnam War"? Rumor? Newspaper sensationalism? No—the facts were formalized by a report, three months later, in *Aviation Week*, March 11, 1968. The notice read:

> National Aeronautics and Space Administration is planning to establish a special projects branch within its Office of Advanced Research and Technology to aid in identifying and utilizing aerospace technology concepts *applicable to limited warfare problems.* [Italics added.]

As O'Toole pointed out, NASA's defense of its military work is based upon a clause in the 1958 National Aeronautics and Space Act (amended 1962), which directs NASA to make "available to agencies directly concerned with national defense discoveries that have military value or significance." Envisioned by the Act, however, is a two-way street, in which the military agencies hand over "to the civilian agency [i.e., NASA] . . . information as to discoveries which have value or significance to that agency."*

* One of more recent examples is a full-scale ground investigation of the proposed "VTOL fighter model aircraft"—a study conducted by Northrup Corpo-

Clearly, the framers of the Space Act did not intend NASA to run a poor second to DOD in the bureaucratic pecking order. Moreover, as noted earlier, the same Act precludes NASA from "space activities . . . peculiar to, or primarily associated with, the development of weapons systems, military operations, or the defense of the United States."

Nevertheless, one of NASA's "limited warfare" teams was reportedly working on a super-quiet aircraft engine that would permit an airplane to drop its bombs and fire its guns before the enemy was aware of the plane's approach. (It is perhaps too much to hope that the principles behind this "silent airplane" will be applied by the Federal Aviation Agency to the problem of "noise pollution" around airports.)* Another "limited warfare" team has developed an "acoustic detector" that can pinpoint the location of enemy mortars by measuring slight ground vibrations. O'Toole quotes a NASA official as saying, "I don't think anybody is so naive that he might feel an agency spending four billion dollars a year on technology shouldn't spend some of it trying to win a war we're fighting."

■ Out of NASA's new and zealous devotion to "limited warfare" problems came a bright idea for completely revolutionizing guerrilla warfare. The House Subcommittee on NASA Oversight boasted that NASA could loft a synchronous satellite over the Vietnam jungles—a satellite equipped with a huge mirror designed to reflect the sun's rays twenty-four hours a day. The satellite could be used to illuminate the darkened battle area, putting the enemy at a distinct and obvious disadvantage. Only the loud protests of civilian astronomers, concerned that their celestial observations would be hampered, seem to have quelled that unique idea.

One must ask, of course, had such a reflector been launched, were the North Vietnamese and their Soviet allies expected to leave it intact? Would we really have been surprised if Russia knocked it out of orbit, thus enacting the first hostile counter-maneuver in space?

ration for the Ames Research Center, NASA. The report, NASA CR–1098, was published in June, 1968 by NASA.

* *American Aviation* (August 19, 1968) reported that NASA was expected to select a contractor in 1969 to develop a "quiet jet engine."

■ How can it happen that NASA's wind tunnels and tracking stations "are operated for the Department of Defense" as military space observation posts—*without reimbursement to NASA?* Furthermore, it was arranged in 1967 that DOD would "support and eventually . . . operate the NASA satellite tracking facilities on Grand Bahama Island" (which is *British* territory). Must not our allies eventually begin to think that, with the arrival of NASA, the U.S. Department of Defense cannot be far behind? And why cannot NASA and DOD realize that by using such sleight of hand they will eventually outsmart themselves in the "image" and "posture" games they so frequently play?

■ On May 17, 1968, there was an attempted launching of a NASA "Nimbus-B" experimental weather satellite from the Western Test Range in California by a Thorad Agena-D rocket assembly. Something went wrong,* however, and the launchers had to blow it up forty-five miles from the launch pad, sending a rain of debris down through the California skies. The event had been heralded in a nine-page NASA release, explaining that Nimbus-B, in addition to gathering meteorological data, would be the first "oceanographic" satellite to pick up electronic signals relayed from buoys in both the Atlantic and Pacific Oceans. Not until page 5 of this release, however, did one learn what was really special about this third Nimbus: Nimbus B carried a "piggyback" DOD payload, designed to be injected into its own separate circular orbit. The DOD payload was the tenth in the U.S. Army's "SECOR" series. SECOR stands for "Sequential Collation of Range." For "Range" one should read "ballistic missile range." In other words, NASA was boosting into orbit a military payload that would help improve the accuracy of U.S. ballistic missiles. The NASA release blithely explained that NASA was doing this "as part of an interagency program to use available booster power for maximum space research *cost effectiveness* [italics added]," the now long-familiar McNamara phrase.

The Nimbus-B affairs raises, once again, the question posed by Sputnik: What is a military, as opposed to a peaceful, satellite? Fortunately for space hawks, there can be no clear-cut distinction,

---

* The "something" was that somebody had installed a piece of equipment called a "yaw rate gyro" in a position 90 degrees wrong.

as indicated by the following statement by the House Subcommittee on NASA Oversight:

It was recognized also that basic principles or building blocks necessary to operate in this new medium of space are applicable to both civilian and military needs. For example, it is now possible . . . for orbiting satellites carrying remote sensing equipment to pick out various food crops on the ground, and even to tell if those crops are healthy or diseased. *If it is possible to do this, it does not take much imagination to realize that it is equally possible to detect missile sites.* [Italics added.]

These represent only a small sampling of the mazelike intertwining between NASA and DOD. No doubt many more examples could be cited if the relationship between NASA and DOD were truly "open."

No better proof of the shrouded, if not closed, nature of the NASA-DOD relationship can be found than in the following exchange between James J. Gehrig, staff director for the Senate Committee on Aeronautical and Space Sciences, and Dr. John S. Foster, Director of DOD's Defense Research and Engineering office. The discussion occurred during the 1967 NASA Authorization Hearings:

MR. GEHRIG Dr. Foster, your discussion on nuclear test monitoring in the prepared statement was very interesting. [Deleted.]
DR. FOSTER [Deleted.]
MR. GEHRIG [Deleted.]
DR. FOSTER [Deleted.]
MR. GEHRIG [Deleted.]
DR. FOSTER [Deleted.]
MR. GEHRIG [Deleted.]
DR. FOSTER [Deleted.]
MR. GEHRIG [Deleted.]
DR. FOSTER [Deleted.]
MR. GEHRIG [Deleted.]
DR. FOSTER [Deleted.]
MR. GEHRIG Mr. Chairman, that is all the questioning I have . . .

Thus does the American taxpayer learn of the activities of his "peaceful" and "open" space program. Even a congressman finds the going tough when he attempts to learn about the dealings between NASA and the military, as the following remark by Representative Wydler to Olin Teague, chairman of the House Subcommittee on NASA Oversight, indicates:

I think, Mr. Chairman, you will remember when the Air Force appeared before our committee last year we tried to find out what they were planning to do with the MOL program. Practically every answer to every question was that it was classified. We couldn't find out anything. And I just wondered how you managed to do it. It seemed impossible for the committee to find out.

The relationships between NASA and the Department of Defense and the various military branches have always been very close. They have had to be. The bases from which satellites were launched belonged to the Air Force; many of the satellite-launching rockets had been developed for the Air Force, some for the Army; the ships that picked up astronauts after splashdown were U.S. Navy ships. Across the board, NASA has had to "borrow" facilities and support from the military.

As Eisenhower's Science Advisory Committee (PSAC), headed by James R. Killian, Jr., stated in 1958 in a paper called "Introduction to Outer Space": "The development of military rockets has provided the technological base for space exploration. It will probably continue to do so, because of the commanding military importance of the ballistic missile." (Despite the apparently "all NASA" Saturn series of rockets, this statement has continued to hold true over the last decade. The timing of "peaceful" launches did then—and still does—have to be cleared with DOD. In May, 1962, U.S. Air Force General Bernard Schriever spelled out NASA's dependence upon the military before the National Meeting on Manned Space Flight in St. Louis, Missouri: "Space boosters are modified versions of military rockets, and they are launched from military facilities." The John F. Kennedy Space Center, on Merritt Island, is NASA-owned, but Cape Kennedy, site of most NASA launch complexes, is a military facility. "The Air Force," General Schriever reported, "is assigned responsibility for range management, and in addition 102 Air Force research and development officers are now assigned to duty with NASA."

General Schriever has described in detail just how much the early Mercury launches depended upon DOD:

One indication of the magnitude of military assistance to NASA is the fact that the Air Force, Army and Navy together provided 24 ships, 126 aircraft, and 18,000 people in direct support of the first Mercury manned orbital flight. For Major L. Gordon Cooper's successful 22-orbit flight in May, 1963, this support was increased to 29 ships, 171 aircraft, and more than 18,000 people. In addition, nearly 200 military officers are assigned to duty with NASA, and military facilities throughout the country provided extensive support to many phases of the nation's space program.

Despite the nigh overwhelming support the military had given to NASA, even a cursory reading of the National Aeronautics and Space Act reveals that its framers clearly did not intend NASA to become a kind of puppet government under the Department of Defense—a trend now inexorably gathering momentum. Over and over again, in the opening paragraphs of the Act, appear the words "civilian" and "peaceful"; the language, too, is resplendent with such phrases as "peaceful and scientific purposes . . . peaceful activities . . . peaceful application of the results." Further on, the Act *requires* that NASA's administrator and deputy administrator "shall be appointed from *civilian* life* by the President . . . [italics added]."

The charter framers, however, were not so idealistic as to suppose that NASA and the military could completely ignore one another. It made economic sense for NASA to utilize the vast array of support equipment and facilities offered by the military services. It also made sense for NASA "to cooperate with other public and private agencies and instrumentalities in the use of services, equipment, and facilities" and for "each department and agency of the Federal Government to cooperate fully with

---

* Prior to the death of the late Senator Robert F. Kennedy, his supporters indicated that Colonel John Glenn, former astronaut and the first American to orbit earth, was the senator's choice of a replacement for outgoing NASA Administrator James Webb. An interesting controversy over Glenn's military career might have ensued had Kennedy lived and won his campaign for the Presidency.

the Administration of NASA in making its services, equipment, personnel, and facilities available to the Administration, without reimbursement, aeronautical and space vehicles, and supplies and equipment . . ."* NASA, after all, *was* the whole nation's space agency, and its developments quite naturally should be made available to the entire federal government, as representative of the American people.

So far, so good; and even when one's eye pauses (in reading the charter) at the subheading "Civilian-Military Liaison Committee," there seems to be no cause for undue alarm. The language under the subheading seems to define a kind of "separate but equal" status between NASA and the Department of Defense— a separation, as it were, of Church and State. The Liaison Committee consists of a chairman (who, the Act suggested, should be a retired military officer), appointed by the President, and "one or more representatives from each of the Departments of the Army, Navy, and Air Force, to be assigned by the Secretary of Defense"; this military contingent is balanced by the same number of "civilian" representatives, appointed by the NASA administrator. It is the Liaison Committee's job to hear out both NASA and DOD "on all matters within their respective jurisdictions relating to aeronautical and space activities and [see to it that each keeps] each other fully and currently informed with respect to such activities."

The spirit of equal brotherhood between NASA and DOD envisioned by the NASA Act has not, however, survived the harsh realities of matching a stronger and far richer agency (DOD) against a weaker one (NASA). One reason why DOD has come to dominate NASA is the notable "old soldiers and sailors" clause in the NASA Act, authorizing (but not requiring) the administrator "to employ retired commissioned officers of the armed forces of the United States and compensate them at the rate established for the positions occupied by them within the Ad-

* Among the departments and agencies with which NASA cooperates, besides its biggest and best friend, DOD, are: the Atomic Energy Commission, the Department of Transportation, the Department of Commerce (ESSA-Environmental Science Services Administration), the Department of Agriculture, the Department of the Interior, and the Smithsonian Institution, the last of which works out together with NASA the "custody and display of NASA historical artifacts."

ministration." This broad hint to hire old soldiers has resulted in NASA's becoming topheavy with admirals and generals.

The next clause allows NASA, if it so desires, to fill out the lower echelons with "borrowed" military personnel, i.e., "with the approval of the President, to enter into cooperative agreements under which members of the Army, Navy, Air Force, and Marine Corps may be detailed by the appropriate Secretary for services in the performance of functions under this Act to the same extent as that to which they might be lawfully assigned in the Department of Defense." At the end of 1967, there were 323 military personnel "on detail" to NASA. These included 189 from the Air Force, 99 from the Army, 32 from the Navy and three from the Marine Corps.*

One might expect, with so much intermingling with NASA, that the Pentagon would require only a small-scale space program of its own—if any. But no—such is not the case. For the military space program is far more extensive than just the Air Force MOL project.** In every year since 1959 DOD has launched more satellites and more space probes than NASA. (See Table 1.) True, these have not been manned missions, but MOL and its successors may be expected to reduce that discrepancy.***

Nevertheless, the general impression has lingered that the American space program is primarily civilian and peaceful—and that military objectives are decidedly secondary. Thus, as early as 1965, in a short biography of Edward C. Welsh, Executive Secretary of the National Aeronautics and Space Council (the group that advises the White House on space matters), a kindly observer of America's space program, Shirley Thomas, pointed

---

* Perhaps to show that NASA was not being overrun by the armed forces, the President's National Aeronautics and Space Council noted in its January, 1968 *Report to the Congress from the President* that "13 NASA employees had been assigned to DOD organizations."

** In a booklet, *Space: Progress and Posterity*, issued in 1964 by the House Committee on Science and Astronautics, it was noted: "The Department of Defense . . . is developing . . . technical competences and applying them to such fields as navigation, communications, *observation, detection, interception, command and control techniques,* and manned and unmanned space flight."

*** In an NBC-TV space special, *The World of Tomorrow*, Frank McGee noted that in the 1970's, following NASA's Apollo lunar landings, the military space activities, manned and unmanned, are expected to far outnumber the civilian-NASA missions.

TABLE 1:   Comparison (approximate) of U.S. and Soviet space launchings primarily civil-oriented versus presumptively military-oriented.*

Year	Primarily or ostensibly civil				Presumptively specialized military	
	NASA	DoD	U.S. total	USSR	DoD	USSR
1957	0	0	0	2	0	0
1958	0	5	5	1	0	0
1959	5	0	5	3	5	0
1960	5	1	6	3	10	0
1961	10	0	10	6	19	0
1962	18	1	19	15	33	5
1963	10	2	12	10	26	7
1964	22	2	24	17	33	13
1965	23	9	32	24	31	24
1966	30	9	39	20	34	24
1967	25	6	31	29	26	37
1968	19	4	23	32	22	42
Totals	167	39	206	162	239	152

* Table updated through December 31, 1968, by Dr. Charles S. Sheldon, II, Acting Chief, Science Policy Research Division, Library of Congress, from "Review of the Soviet Space Program," Report of the Committee on Science and Astronautics, prepared in 1967 by the Science Policy Research Division, Legislative Reference Service, Library of Congress.

out that the Executive Branch of government, during the 1964 political campaign, was accused of "downgrading" the military potentials in space. She noted how this had dismayed Welsh, who said, ". . . such misuse of the facts tends to undermine our whole space effort. In refutation, it is not necessary to express opinion, as a recitation of fact is thoroughly convincing. During the four-year period of 1957 through 1960, space expenditures for the DOD totaled $1 billion. On the other hand, during the last four years, that is 1961 through 1964, the DOD spent about $4.6 billion on its space responsibility."*

In the late 1960's, this trend has accelerated. Both the Congress and the Executive Branch, for the most part, have favored spending money on anti-poverty programs or "hard" defense goals,** yet

* Thomas, op. cit., p. 259.
** The Atomic Energy Commission Budget for fiscal 1969 is a good example The AEC asked for $2.9 billion—$277 million more than it received in fiscal

it remains imperative to have NASA keep its status as the decorous front parlor of the space age in order to reap public support for *all* space projects and give Defense Department space efforts an effective "cover." (Also, NASA's promises of humanitarian and economic by-products for the man in the street suggests a sort of substitute for anti-poverty programs.) DOD, and often, too, the Atomic Energy Commission (AEC), meanwhile do their business in the war-gaming rooms behind the front parlor.

The Gemini program, in many ways, characterized NASA's place as second in the space-age pecking order below DOD. If Gemini had not been so successful, or had run into bad trouble with Congressional budget-cutters, it is certain that the MOL program would not be so far advanced as it is today.* In such a way, NASA often serves as a proving ground for DOD plans. DOD's attitude can be roughly summed up as: "If it works, we'll take it; if it doesn't, we'll either discard it or give it back to NASA for further refinement." Everybody in Washington who has anything to do with the U.S. space program tacitly admits to these facts.

A clear case in point occurred in the fall of 1967, when James Webb was telling the Senate Committee on Aeronautical and Space Sciences how he would like to put up a large (260-inch-diameter) solid-fueled rocket for industry bids. The solid rocket, Webb explained, could be used as the lift-off launch vehicle for a nuclear-powered rocket. Committee Chairman Clinton P. Anderson of New Mexico, was not sympathetic. He asked Webb:

> I wonder how you stop this project? *The Department of Defense abandoned it. They assigned it over to NASA.* [Italics added.]

To a lesser man than James Webb, this kind of insinuation—that NASA was, really, a second-class agency—might have been

---

1968. The Joint Committee on Atomic Energy recommended a cut of $302 million, thus making the AEC budget $25 million lower than that of 1968. Significantly, all AEC military proposals survived without cuts—one military activity was actually increased. The total military portion of the AEC's budget now exceeds $1 billion.

* It would not be unfair to list at least one half of the Gemini program as military—a prelude to MOL—despite the fact that NASA footed most of the Gemini bill.

a blow to bureaucratic ego, grounds for angry self-defense. But Webb was very good at reading the handwriting on the wall. His response to such remarks had been, consistently, to show how closely NASA's aims dovetailed with those of the Department of Defense. In little ways—such as slipping in some "cost-effective" talk here, adopting a DOD management system named PERT (Program Evaluation Review Techniques) there, or by reviewing the "grave risks" the communists have taken in the Cold War (and might again)—he showed senator and representative alike that NASA might not be as big as DOD, but their hearts beat as one.

Webb was capable, too, of grand gestures. One such was his personal interpretation of the NASA charter, on the occasion (December 29, 1967) of the retirement of one of NASA's old sailors, Admiral W. F. Boone, USN (Retired), from five years of service as NASA assistant administrator for defense affairs.* In expressing his appreciation for the admiral's services, Webb succeeded in making NASA sound like a junior Pentagon:

> One of the most important responsibilities placed on the National Aeronautics and Space Administration and the Department of Defense by the National Aeronautics and Space Act of 1958 is the establishment of effective cooperation and common effort to develop and put to use the knowledge required to insure success in our national aeronautical and space programs, *whether civilian or military. This must constantly look toward the prompt and effective utilization by the military services of capabilities which grow out of our national programs.* [Italics added.]

There is little doubt that Webb viewed space as the area where, as he was fond of saying, "the big decisions as to the future" were to be made.** It is evident, too, that Webb wanted the United States to have those "big decisions" go the American way

---

* Admiral Boone's office, renamed the Office of Department of Defense and Interagency Affairs, was filled by General Jacob E. Smart, USAF (Retired).

** Another example, from Webb's essay "Education for Space," in *Space: Its Impact on Man and Society,* ed. Lillian Levy (New York: W. W. Norton, 1965), p. 11: "It took the burst of Soviet Sputnik I to compel us to re-examine our attitude toward science, to assess the capability of our engineers to design and build the space systems which were clearly required *if we were not to lose our place at the table where international decisions are made* [italics added]."

—whether by peaceful competition or by conflict, threatened or actual. Webb's patriotism, though subdued in the early sixties, ran red-blooded and deep. As *Fortune* pointed out in August, 1967, he wished to make "NASA a central force in U.S. defense."

The tragedy, for James Webb, was that his "civilian" space agency was being slowly whittled away beneath him, while other men—the space clique in the Defense Department—were getting the funds that were being taken away from NASA. As Fig. 6 clearly shows, DOD's space spending has risen every year since 1966, while NASA's budget has steadily fallen. There is little evidence that this trend will reverse itself. As John Noble Wilford of *The New York Times* wrote in mid-April, 1968: "After a heady decade of uninterrupted hiring, building and dreaming great dreams of far-reaching exploration, the American [civilian] space program is gearing down to a slower pace and a less certain future." Wilford goes on to quote former NASA Deputy Administrator Seamans as saying: "There's no question but that things will be bleak in the early seventies." What Wilford does not emphasize in his article are the clear signals from the Pentagon and the aerospace industry and press that *Defense* space spending will most probably soar in the seventies. The loser, the only loser, will be NASA—and with it those who dreamed great dreams for the peaceful exploration of space.

The outlook, we believe, is ominous. One need only read the views of the militant space hawks to understand just how ominous. Two examples will suffice, the first from a booklet prepared by the House Committee on Science and Astronautics, *The Posture of the National Space Program, 1963:*

> . . . the DOD policy on military space missions, even if not clearly defined, appears to be one of passive containment. According to the old maxim: *"The best defense is a good offense."* [Italics added.]

The second example is from a 1965 essay by USAF General Bernard A. Schriever, who directed the development of the U.S. ICBM system and was, as commander of the U.S. Air Force Systems Command, responsible for the research, development, and production of a complete, operational "defense" aerospace system. The logic of the following passage, with which General

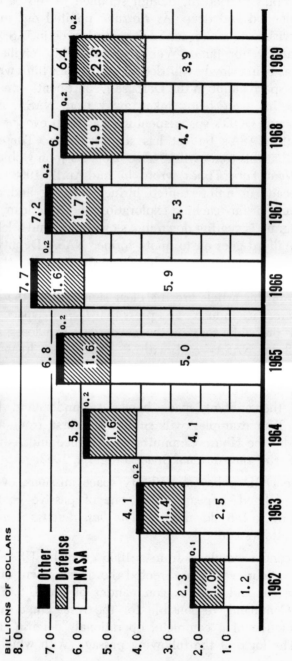

Fig. 6: U.S. Space Budget, 1962–1969

Schriever's essay concludes, should be followed with the most rigorous attention, for it prophesies the darkest of Orwellian nightmares: "The advance of space technology in itself will not automatically produce a better world. But spacepower can form the protective umbrella under which we work for better ways to solve the problems of mankind."

Quoting President Kennedy, Schriever elaborates: "Space science, like nuclear science and all technology, has no conscience of its own. Whether it will become a force for good or ill depends on man, and only if the United States occupies a position of preeminence can we help decide whether this new ocean will be a sea of peace or a new terrifying theatre of war."

He then goes on in his own words:

United States military capabilities in space must insure that no nation achieves a position in space which threatens the security of the United States. It provides an essential guarantee that space research will be carried on in an atmosphere of freedom and that the scientific knowledge which results can be used to benefit all mankind. This is the promise and challenge posed to the military by the Space Age.

Under the guise of benefiting "all mankind," General Schriever is urging that the Defense Department of the United States of America achieve military preeminence in space, so that one agency of one nation may hold a club ("protective umbrella") over the head of all mankind. Is "club" too harsh an interpretation? We think not, for as Schriever says, close cooperation between the Air Force and NASA, far from being inconsistent with the national policy that space be used for peaceful purposes, implements that policy by providing "the means for insuring that the policy is carried out." ("The best defense is a good offense.")

What is "offense" in space? Many things: orbiting nuclear bombs perfected to drop on target with pinpoint accuracy, manned military space fortresses; legions of spies in the sky; someday, perhaps, fortresses on the Moon and beyond—all the creations of the horror school of science fiction.

Is not Schriever merely being patriotic and hard-headed to propose that America strive for military preeminence in space? (If it doesn't somebody else will.) Would not mankind prefer a space umbrella to be made of "freedom" (i.e., United States policy) rather than "tyranny" (Russian, China, or some other nation)?

These are compelling arguments for Schriever's point of view. Still, does it really "benefit all mankind" to raise the potential level of destruction of the Cold War by another order of magnitude? First there were the long-range bombers; then came the missiles; and now we stand on the threshold of armed military satellites. Does it really make sense to take this next step?

Other questions, too, must be asked. Once the "umbrella" is up, how do you take it down? For example, if, in a moment of international crisis, the U.S. or the U.S.S.R. chose to put a nuclear bomb in a long-term orbit to win a "big decision," what would happen if and when the crisis passed? Would the satellite be disarmed, or would the other nation orbit a counter-bomb? And would agreement then be reached to disarm both nations' orbiting bombs? Perhaps, but how? And how could one nation be certain the other nation had done what it had claimed to have done? If it were not certain, would a nation then attempt to disarm the orbiting bomb itself, or bring it down, or blow it up? With what consequences?

The "protective umbrella" concept ignores still another reality of the future of the space age. It assumes the continuance of the two-sided nature (U.S. vs. U.S.S.R.) on the space race. And yet, Red China and the nations of Europe will enter the space arena also.*

In 1968 Mr. Webb saw that the most important concern of a majority in the Congress—space treaties or no space treaties— was the potential military applications of NASA research. For example, what does one "do" about such Soviet developments as FOBS (fractional orbital bombardment system), by which the Soviets had evidently stepped between the lines of both the 1963

* On November 15, 1968, a Reuters dispatch from Hong Kong reported that posters had been put up in Peking announcing the launching of China's "first man-made satellite." The posters were mysteriously covered over without further news. In its December, 1967, issue *Space/Aeronautics* magazine surveyed "Europe: Third Force in Space," and came to the conclusion that "Europe needs little further tutelage in space technology. Her space efforts are gaining more force and direction as she seeks to end traditional U.S. dominance . . . sometimes with Russian help." *Space/Aeronautics* pointed especially to the Toulouse-Bordeaux space launch complex in southern France.

"no bombs in orbit" UN resolution and the 1967 Treaty on Outer Space, "which prohibits the placing of nuclear weapons or other kinds of weapons of mass destruction in outer space as well as the establishment of military installations on the Moon and other celestial bodies." To side-step these treaties, the Soviets had (apparently) developed a warhead-carrying space weapon that would *not* make a complete orbit of the Earth. FOBS would make only a "fraction" of a complete orbit before dropping upon a selected target.

As described by Defense Secretary McNamara at a special press conference on Friday, November 3, 1967, the FOBS system differs from the "traditional intercontinental ballistic missile (ICBM), which normally does not go into orbit, but rather follows a ballistic trajectory from launch point to impact point. On this trajectory it reaches a peak altitude of about eight hundred miles." In contrast, the FOBS vehicle "is fired into a very low orbit about one hundred miles above the Earth. At a given point—generally before the first orbit is complete—a rocket engine is fired which slows down the payload and causes it to drop out of orbit. The payload then follows a reentry path similar to the reentry of a ballistic missile."

While admitting that a FOBS vehicle would give the U.S. a few minutes less warning time than a conventional anti-U.S. ICBM launched through the U.S. Ballistic Missile Early Warning System (BMEWS)—and that the U.S. had no really foolproof defense against such a weapon—Secretary McNamara downgraded FOBS on two counts: accuracy and payload. "The accuracy of the Soviet ICBM modified to a FOBS vehicle would be a fraction of the ICBM." He also pointed out that the U.S. had recently developed "over-the-horizon radars which possess a greater capability of detecting FOBS than do the BMEWS. These will give us more warning time against a full-scale attack using FOBS missiles than BMEWS does against a heavy ICBM launch."

Nevertheless, McNamara's announcement of the Soviets' "possible development" of the FOBS—made in the low-key, don't-get-excited press conference of November 3, 1967—marked another important turning point in NASA's image as a "peaceful" and "civilian" space agency. NASA's increasingly military pose can be dated almost from the very day of McNamara's press conference. Subsequent indications that the Soviets were developing a MOBS (multiple-orbit bombardment system) that would station a warhead in orbit that could be dropped on command— or retrieved when a crisis had passed—served merely to stimulate NASA's more militant look. The U.S. announcement that it was testing a "space bus," which could be equipped to carry multiple nuclear warheads, represented one more play in the scrimmage of threat-and-counter-threat engaged in by the U.S. and the Soviet Union from the fall of 1967 into the summer and fall of 1968.

Multiple warheads, quite obviously, multiply the level of over-kill dramatically. They also create a different kind of problem. As discussed earlier in this chapter, spy satellites have been cited as a "factor for peace" because they would make on-site inspection of another country's missiles unnecessary, and thus open the way for mutual disarmament moves. This argument assumes that a nation would not enter into, or abide by, any disarmament treaty if that nation could not be absolutely certain that the other nation wasn't somehow cheating. However cynical, this may be true. But how could a spy satellite tell whether a missile carried one nuclear warhead, or twenty (the capability of the U.S. Poseidon), or the thirty-five that the Russians' SS-9 missile can carry? As Ralph Lapp has said: "Unless you were capable of physically taking a screwdriver and opening the damn thing up, you couldn't tell."

In August, 1968, the U.S. moved into the lead of the deadly game of "Can you top this?" with the announcement of flight tests of the MIRV, a missile capable of showering up to ten hydrogen bombs, at a signal, each on a different target. More dovish voices, such as that of *The New York Times* editorial page, implored the military to stop the "'mad momentum' intrinsic in the development of all nuclear weaponry" and hold up the MIRV tests, at least until the direction of arms control talks was known. But, backed by President Johnson, the tests went ahead—based on the reasoning that MIRV's would strengthen the United States' bargaining position in any arms control discussions. Besides, said the military, MIRV's would not be operational for another two years; if arms control talks were successful, then the U.S. could simply stop the MIRV development. However, the last twenty years have shown that, once originated, development of new super weapons systems are not so simply stopped.

Once again, James Webb had read the handwriting on the wall. No longer was NASA quite so careful in concealing the military applications of its work; no longer were NASA officials quite so insistent that the agency's military role, "if any," consisted in surveillance and reconnaissance missions, and did not involve actual weapons systems. In April, 1967, Webb said in a nationwide TV interview:

> We wanted a complex that included Huntsville, the assembly plant at New Orleans, the Mississippi test [site], the Houston spacecraft [center] and the Cape for the launching site. We wanted this complex so that *if we ever had to fly big military payloads on these big boosters* here was an integrated system and the industrial system in the country could flow the materials toward this system. [Italics added.]

Congressman Ryan, ever alert to Webb's efforts to link NASA with "the big decisions as to the future" and thus obtain a bigger budget, sent off a letter to the Secretary of Defense. He asked for "a statement of [the Secretary of Defense's] position on the military significance of NASA's space program." On May 31, he received an answer from John S. Foster, Jr., DOD's Director of Defense Research and Engineering. The gist of Foster's reply, made at the request of the Secretary of Defense, was:

> . . . I do not believe that any special network of NASA space installations is necessary to assure that industrial input will flow with ease from all portions of the country into such plants in event of large-scale military operations. Should the need arise, the flow you suggest can readily occur within our present industrial structure. . . . I feel that the main contribution of NASA's space program to Defense is in the technology being developed rather than in major items of hardware. . . . Technology contributions from NASA programs in areas such as spacecraft power supply, life support, and attitude reference and control subsystems, for example, have been utilized in DOD space systems.

Questions of surveillance and weaponry are military in nature . . .

Ryan chose to believe Foster's central assertion that "the main contribution of NASA's space program to Defense is in the technology being developed rather than in major items of hardware." It was, quite obviously, exactly what Ryan wanted to hear, for it enabled him to criticize NASA without appearing to endanger "national security."

Yet this is not quite the end of the story, and perhaps one ought not to accept Foster's words quite so readily as Ryan did.

On March 29, 1968, the pilot program for a projected television space fiction series, "Star Trek," appeared on NBC. Its title was "Assignment: Earth." It dealt with, among other things, an orbital bomb. What was most interesting about the program, however, was the fact that it included on-the-scene footage of Cape Kennedy and the launching of the most powerful rocket "hardware" on Earth—the Saturn 5. This Saturn 5, in this episode, was equipped with a nuclear warhead.

Would one be overly suspicious to think that this was a clever plant, an attempt to show the public—by a kind of subliminal association—that the Saturn 5 could, indeed, carry "big military payloads?" We think not. NASA gave NBC permission to use the films of the Saturn launch. When asked how permission was received to use these films, an NBC official explained that it was a case of the "friendly cooperation" between NASA and the public media, which would "help create new public support and understanding of space exploration."*

Turning once again to the Apollo 204 disaster, it is easy to see that the tragedy only complicated an already dangerously entangled NASA-DOD relationship. The mismanagement and poor performance of NASA in events leading to the fire, and NASA's inadequate apologia after the fire, prompted renewed soul-searching on the urgent question: Who should control

* A similar decision by the U.S. Navy was announced on December 3, 1968. The Navy authorized its carrier, the *Yorktown*, to play the part of a Japanese aircraft carrier involved in the attack on Pearl Harbor, for the film *Tora! Tora! Tora!* The Navy's decision was based upon its desire to "increase public awareness of carrier airpower."

manned flight in the future? Representative Fulton strongly advised that the military had no business in space and that all manned flight should fall under the jurisdiction of NASA. Writers such as Erik Bergaust, on the other hand, felt that NASA had failed so miserably that it could not be trusted with a responsibility so tied to national defense. Clearly, the debate over AAP-MOL duplication is not over.

Before turning to the aerospace industry, that vast partner and supplier of both NASA and DOD, we pause on this haunting refrain of the U.S. space program in the 1960's, a refrain heavy with lost hope and lingering self-deception. The President's Science Advisory Committee (PSAC) made, in passing, in February, 1967, the following comment:

> The U.S. space program, in contrast to that of the Soviet Union, is predominately peaceful in character, operated outside of the Department of Defense, and conducted with full public disclosure.*

On August 6, 1968, a satellite was launched by an Air Force-industry team from Cape Kennedy's launch complex 13, the same pad from which NASA's lunar (Lunar Orbiter) and planetary (Mariner) probes have been launched. It was the first such launch from Cape Kennedy in five years. Secret shots are usually made from Vandenburg Air Force Base, California. According to John Noble Wilford of *The New York Times:* "An Atlas-Agena rocket shot into Earth orbit with a super-secret payload." Launching officials told reporters, "You wouldn't want to know what's on that bird. It's that secret."

Less than three months later, in the jubilant aftermath of the "flawless" Apollo 7 flight of Walter Schirra, Donn Eisele, and Walter Cunningham, a little-noted incident occurred. The refrain of a "space program . . . predominantly peaceful in character" receded even further back, seemingly irretrievably, into the nation's past. The incident had nothing to do with Apollo 7 signaling a new dawn for America's civilian space agency and its hope of a manned Moon landing, nor did it have anything to do with

---

* From a report by the joint space panels, entitled *The Space Program in the Post-Apollo Period.*

a reawakened public awe that man, in all his questing innocence and wonder, was back on the road to the stars. It had to do with weapons and targets, greed and secrecy.

On November 4, 1968, a thirteen-line news brief appeared in the "Washington Roundup" page of *Aviation Week & Space Technology*. It noted that some 700 photographs had been taken by the Apollo 7 astronauts. Then:

> The mission used a very high-resolution film developed for Air Force reconnaisance satellites . . . the Defense Dept., State Dept., Atomic Energy Commission and other agencies for the first time demanded seats on the NASA board selecting photographs for release . . .

One fear was that the photographs would reveal potential oil and mineral deposits and set off a "buying boom" somewhere. (In London the next week, British scientists and engineers referred to the U.S. refusal to release the pictures as the "strongest argument for a British and European satellite program independent of U.S. aid.") But a "buying boom" was of little concern to the powerful defense-conscious agencies that had bulled their way into NASA's photo-releasing process:

> . . . the State Dept. does not like to release photographs of foreign countries, the Pentagon is worried about views of military installations and the AEC does not want its nuclear facilities shown. NASA in the first week after the fire was permitted to release only 13 pictures . . . One NASA official doubted if many more would be cleared.

> *The U.S. space program . . . is predominantly peaceful in character . . . and conducted with full public disclosure . . .*

■ *The space program has become America's most
surprising poverty victim. . . . A famine of funds
and a dearth of public support are dire realities.*
FORBES
advertisement, February 1, 1968

■ *It's up to industry to say what needs to be said
to sell the program. After all, you don't sell
anything—not cars, not soap powder, not breakfast food—without convincing the public you
have something it wants.*
WILLIAM D. HALL,
Aerospace Daily, <i>February 19, 1968</i></div>

Chapter 11 ▪ To Mars and Beyond: Selling "The Spirit of '76"

In the spring of 1968, a full-page advertisement appeared in *The
New York Times* and the *Wall Street Journal* showing a grotesque
photograph of "Queen Isabella" of Spain (1451–1504) clothed
in a spaceman's costume. The ad was headlined: "If you think
it's a waste of money, it's a good thing you weren't Queen
Isabella."

It was part of a promotional campaign announcing a special
issue of *Forbes* magazine devoted to "The Case for Space." In
this special issue *Forbes* was to take up the drooping banner of
America's space effort and lift it high, once more, for the edification of its business-community readership.

When the special space issue was published on July 1, 1968,
"the case for space," as presented by *Forbes*'s thoroughly professional editorial staff, did not come off as an unmixed bag of
glowing testimonials. This was hardly surprising—but what about
Queen Isabella in her space suit?

The fact is that the Spanish queen who financed Christopher
Columbus's vogages, as well as other historical figures who
have backed similar schemes, have been turned by a wave of
the aerospace industry's magic wand into some of the staunchest
backers (were they alive) of America's space program. They
provide "historical precedents" for investing a lot of money with
little hope of realizing a return. In other words, the aerospace

industry has told America: "Don't let up on the cash, or we Americans might not discover the 'New World' of space." The theme was never so loudly proclaimed as when, with the help of Walter Cronkite and *The New York Times*, the Apollo 8 astronauts, Borman, Lovell, and Anders, were referred to as the mariners of the *Nina, Pinta,* and *Santa Maria* as they hurtled across the sea of space toward the moon.

One of the most ancient "historical precedents" created by the aerospace public relations team of historians is provided by Alexander the Great. History tells us that his unusual success was made possible through an appreciation for technological innovation. Alexander equipped his troops with a new, modified version of the traditionally short horseman's lance. The use of varied lengths of the lance so increased the efficiency of his infantry that he was able to launch a campaign of exploration and conquest that produced an empire vaster than any mankind had known before.

The aerospace storytellers display even greater relish, however, for the exploits of more recent adventurers. In the 1800's, for example, the tiny country of England launched a national program of exploration and colonization that resulted in an empire so vast its subjects could boast that "the sun never sets on the British empire." Britain's world domination, based on control of the oceans, continued for more than a century.

The storytellers then turn to the United States while failing to see the change in their own theme. Utilizing applications of technology spawned by the Industrial Revolution, the United States produced the first successful airplane. This faint beginning, at Kitty Hawk, has since yielded the vast aircraft industry, employing millions, and manufacturing the hardware that today dominates the international airways.

Each of these illustrations, characterized by an adventure into previously unknown regions, and putting the faith of one's dollar into the promises of new technology, seems, to many, to have much in common with America's newest adventure—the thrust into outer space. Exploration of space is likened to exploration of the Near East, the seven seas, and the atmosphere. It is the new arena in which the skills and techniques of future national excellence are to be tested, developed and honed.

There is an obvious and frightening flaw in these alleged historic parallels—the exploits of Alexander, the British, and the Wright brothers. Alexander and the British sought and achieved world domination through the use of their ambitious armies and navies. But as for the Wright brothers, theirs is quite another story. They were not poor. Neither did they enjoy a government subsidy. Their ultimate fame came only when, totally unappreciated in the United States, they took their product to France. Nor, one must hasten to add, were the inventors, like their predecessors or the present space lobby, dazzled by dreams of world domination.

The Queen of Spain, however, is by far the favorite of the aerospace historians. As President Lyndon B. Johnson once said, "the knowledge and products of space exploration are the modern counterpart of the gold and silver for which the Queen of Spain ransomed her jewels."

But the Queen of Spain did *not* mortgage her jewels. This myth —the quest of Christopher Columbus—needs reexamination. For it has become the symbol of the quest of America's aerospace-defense industry.

When Columbus first approached Isabella, she had no time or thought for his bizarre scheme. Her attention and funds were quite preoccupied by a full-scale campaign against the Moors. Furthermore, the expedition proposed by this adventuresome sailor was based on an outrageous supposition. He believed that the spices and other trade goods of Asia could be reached by sailing westward a mere three thousand miles. His figures were based on the concept that the Earth was a very much smaller sphere than scholars of the day had calculated. Indeed, he was very much mistaken. Nevertheless, Isabella knew that as long as there was any faint chance that he could be right, the booty would go to whoever supported him. The race was on.

Having thoroughly whipped the Muslims and broken their hold on Spain, Isabella changed her mind and decided to finance his expedition. Christopher, a sailor of peasant stock, having won the Queen's favor, drove a shrewd bargain which must have

tried Her Majesty's patience. Columbus wanted the full title of
Admiral, a vice-royalty in all lands discovered, and a 10 percent
interest in all gains won by trade or by conquest. This predecessor
of the modern "incentive contract" has been calculated, by Dr.
Joseph Shea, former Apollo program manager, to be valued at
about $14,000. In later voyages the bold mariner fared better,
however, and won possession of the island of Hispaniola (compris-
ing Haiti and the Dominican Republic), the title of Duke or
Marquise (whichever he preferred), an eighth of the gross, and
a tenth of the net profits of subsequent voyages.* History books
to the contrary, Christopher Columbus was no altruist.

Columbus also succeeded in bringing to the New World a
pattern of extortion known as, encomienda. This was a system of
tributary labor first instituted against the conquered Moors of
Spain. In Spanish America it worked as follows: worthy Spanish
subjects (such as Columbus) were "granted" territories in the
newly discovered lands. They were then permitted to exact tribute
from the inhabitants of the land, in this case the "Indians."
(Columbus insisted he had landed on a peninsula of India.) The
owner, in return, was responsible for the welfare of the subjects,
and charged with their conversion to Christianity.

The discoveries of Columbus, aerospace historians point out,
made it possible for Spain to rule the seas for more than a
century. It must be added, however, that Columbus himself not
only failed in his purpose (he did not find a short route to the
East) but to his death failed to understand that he had failed.
Furthermore, he was such a poor administrator of his titles, lands,
and new-found wealth that he was regarded as an eccentric by
some, a buffoon by others, and died in abject poverty.

Needless to say, Isabella had gambled and won, but the profits
enriched not all of Spain, but only those provinces held by the
Queen's family. Her husband, King Ferdinand II, unable to contribute, and thus having invested nothing, won nothing for his
family. The inhabitants of the New World, meanwhile, were
subjected to cruel and inhuman treatment by Columbus and the

---

* In the midst of these expeditions he was striken with the gout, became
lethargic, cantankerous, and downright inhuman. At one point, June 24, 1495, he
sent off five shiploads of Indians to be sold as slaves in Seville. The Queen was
shocked, freed the human cargo, and thereafter Columbus no longer enjoyed his
former favor.

Spanish conquistadores who followed during the more than hundred years of colonization that ensued.

This, then, is the noble venture with which aerospace stalwarts associate themselves. Unfortunately, there are numerous other similarities that go beyond the intentions of the aerospace storytellers. NASA's role in space began and has persisted as a race —with the U.S.S.R. It has been pursued on a crash-program, top-priority ("DX")* basis without letup, until 1968, in spite of the incredible burden of Vietnam.

Isabella's support of Columbus promised Christianity and civilization to conquered subjects. NASA and the aerospace industry have promised not only advanced technology, a higher standard of living for all, but better education and a new generation of space-age consumer goods. Idealists such as President Johnson insist that the gold and silver of "our space-age Columbus" is, in fact, real as well as symbolic. He maintains that "the funds going into space research are investments which will yield dividends to American lives, business, and professions, many times greater than the initial costs . . . For every nickel we put into it, we get a dime back."

In spite of such bullish appraisals, General Bernard A. Schriever, retired commander of America's military space projects, has said: "The exception has been found, it appears, to the rule, 'Nothing succeeds like sucess.' The exception is the American space program." NASA's fall from grace in 1967, was characterized by the fact that "the two justifications for [the U.S.] space program, universally accepted ten years ago—namely, that the nation's security and its prestige were at stake—[were] being reexamined." While both motives were still matters of great concern, General Schriever added, "other urgent matters [had] appeared to challenge the high position of the national space program." Among those problems vying for top priority were domestic problems and the "extremely costly war in Vietnam."

General Schriever found the lag in public and official enthusiasm, before the manned Apollo 7 mission, "very disturbing." The problem, he said, was that both the public and the Congress had

---

* The Executive Branch's designation for highest priority programs, usually associated with national security; "DX" programs have first call on the nation's resources.

failed to understand the importance of "new" criteria for judging progress in space. He was thoroughly convinced that space would once again enjoy its former stature and public support, if only Americans understood "the practical dollars-and-cents worth of this program to this country and the world."

In 1967–68 these assurances fell short because the Congress, if not yet the American in the street, had already observed that earlier promises of space-age fallout (or "spin-off," as it is generally called) had been grossly misrepresented. With the exception of occasional developments such as Teflon frying pans, a new bathtub caulking compound, and some remarkable but isolated advances in broader areas such as communications and medicine, there had been little for the foreseeable future. Specific rewards, according to an interview with John P. Rogan, general manager of Douglas Missile and Space Systems, McDonnell Douglas, were difficult to find, "except for the few large-scale artifacts that have emerged thus far—communications, weather, and navigation satellites."

To the contrary, Martin Goland, an authority on space research and engineering, and a frequent member of national scientific advisory groups, quoted in 1965 the conclusion of a study sponsored by NASA the year before at the Denver Research Institute:

> More subtle forms of technological transfer have had, and will continue to have, the greatest impact—not the direct type of product transfer which is most often publicized.

By 1968, it had become apparent that all predictions of tremendous practical benefits from space spending had been grossly exaggerated. Not only were the "gold and silver" conspicuously absent, but technology dividends seemed to be hiding as well. It appeared, as the editors of *Forbes* put it, that "the effect of all this spending has often been not so much to create new technology, as to accelerate trends that have long been in the making."

Indeed, assays of President Johnson's "gold and silver" yielded conflicting results. It all depended on who was making the analysis. One suspected that the ultimate benefits would be extracted not by the general public, or even NASA, but rather by the aerospace-defense industry alone. Conscious of this trend, NASA began deemphasizing economic spin-offs while pointing to the increasingly conspicuous spin-off of military benefits.

A NASA Moon landing, like Columbus' setting foot on a new landscape, would unquestionably uplift the spirit and reveal surprises; but the space agency will have failed to accomplish its main objective. That avowed purpose, in partnership with the aerospace-defense industry, was to pave the straight and narrow road to a better tomorrow. NASA was to be the prototype of a new breed of large-scale government management projects— after the Moon, the exploitation of the oceans, and solutions to the problems of polluted air and drinking water. Eventually, tangled cities and seething ghettos would be approached with the same gusto as NASA had met "space." The "systems-analysis" approach to mission-oriented research and development was to revolutionize the business world, resulting in better and more satisfying consumer goods. New concepts of communications and transportation were to emerge. Even the food and population crises facing underdeveloped nations of the world were to get their share of attention. Together, NASA and industry were to enrich science, health, education, commerce, and the minds and hearts of all mankind.

Not only had its systems approach to large-scale managerial problems failed to reap the benefits promised, but there was nothing particularly new about the approach itself.* In fact, the systems-analysis approach originated, not with NASA, but with the Department of Defense.

There had been no doubt that an upwelling of national pride and hope would occur after the first Apollo crew actually set foot on the Moon. That great moment, when the two men would step out of the Lunar Module, the "bug," as it is called, would be watched on live television the world over. Man would finally have broken a link in the chain that had held him to Earth.

But how long would that euphoria last? How long would it be

---

* In 1966, the National Commission on Technology, Automation and Economic Progress remarked: "The Systems approach is neither a new technology . . . nor a methodology reserved for the exclusive use of scientists and engineers of the aerospace industry . . . In most respects, [it] adds up to little more than the application of common sense, a trait not solely the possession of any single group in our society."

before Vietnam, Laos, or Cambodia captured, once again, our reluctant attention? How long would it be before the spotless, streamlined Saturn fades, and instead our dirty, depressing cities pass in review? We will soon know the answers to these questions, and it behooves us to prepare for the encounter. There are those who have felt that there was something obscene about men setting foot on the cold, barren Moon while American children suffer from malnutrition in Louisiana and Alabama, two states where the Saturn 5 had been built and tested. There are those who cringed when they looked from the Moon to Biafra, or to the future prospects in India. Getting to the Moon on a top-priority basis may already have hurt America more than she chooses to realize.

NASA itself had suffered considerably. Three project managers, Williams, Holmes, and Shea had come and gone. In the aftermath of the Apollo 204 disaster nearly the entire top berth of NASA executives have faded from view. Dr. Seamans was first, returning to MIT, although he remained affiliated with NASA as consultant and military liaison until his appointment as Secretary of the Air Force under President Nixon. Dr. Thompson was next. General Phillips, too, has implied that he might depart from the civilian program not long after the time of the Apollo Moon landing. Finally, Administrator James E. Webb surprised everyone by announcing his retirement even before the end of the Johnson Administration. His departure, effective on his sixty-second birthday and four days before the first manned Apollo (7) flight, was marked by the observation that "[the U.S. would] be in a second position [in the space race] for some time to come." He added that "a good many people had used the space program as a sort of whipping boy." Thomas O. Paine, who had replaced Robert Seamans as deputy administrator on January 31, 1968, took over the reins of NASA as acting administrator.

Within NASA and industry, the erratic record of the Apollo project, reaching a crescendo with the fatal fire, created such poor morale that countless other resignations were received for fear of an open military takeover of post-Apollo programs.

Even U.S. astronauts, whose devotion and dedication must necessarily be of the greatest intensity, had begun to yield to this widespread sense of disappointment. A whole generation of

scientist-astronauts, selected, after a hard-fought battle for rec-
ognition, to explore the Moon and beyond (once the old-time test
pilots had broken the ice) became potential drop-outs. The
crisis was temporarily stayed by granting most of them part-time
freedom from routine training so that they could maintain their
standing in the academic world. For many of them, their research
or professorships were the greater satisfaction at the moment.
Nevertheless, by September, 1968, three of the seventeen scientist-
astronauts had resigned and others were sure to follow.

NASA had not only lost much of its public support, but the
carte blanche support of the Congress as well. In mid-1968 *Forbes*
magazine even had the audacity to call the U.S. space program
"the other poverty program." Budget cuts, lay-offs, and countless
canceled scientific projects to Mars, Venus, and the rest of the
solar system, shelved until better days, were just part of the story.
For to date U.S. space efforts had not proved to be that greatest
of hopes, an alternative to war. Indeed, space had not turned
out to be all it was chalked up to be.

NASA, like the eccentric Columbus, insisted that it *had* laid
the foundation for a brighter future: the former NASA Administrator, James E. Webb, maintained that the space agency had
proven successful as a managerial model. However, one must
have serious doubts that NASA was such a glowing success. The
flights of Apollos 7 and 8 (discussed in the final chapter) cannot
erase the Apollo 204 tragedy, which was due to managerial
failures, the failure of NASA to maintain its budget and long-
range space projects, the failure of economic spin-offs to mate-
rialize, and the impending threat of a conversion of NASA, a
cilivian agency, to a lower berth in a growing military space
program.

Obviously, these apprehensions were not shared by the barons
of the aerospace industry and their proponents in the halls of
Congress. As Karl G. Harr, Jr., president of the Aerospace Industries Association, has said:

This industry almost alone is the possessor of the advanced
technology on which the future well-being of the nation depends. This is true not only in terms of military security, but
also applies to the myriad of other accomplishments that will

determine the prestige, power, and economic status of the United States in the world of tomorrow.

This tub-thumping statement is most disquieting when we take a closer look at just who comprises the aerospace industry. It is a complex of hundreds of corporations, large and small. These companies propose, design, and manufacture the launch systems, spacecraft, and satellites with which NASA conducts its exploration of space. But NASA provides only about 30 percent of the business and income of these companies. The other major client is the Department of Defense. Can one justifiably expect these militarily nurtured corporations to think in terms of "the benefit of all mankind" 30 percent of their time when they are very busy the remainder of their time dreaming up ways to harass, contain, or simply seek and destroy mankind? It just does not work. It never has; it probably never will—at least not as long as the American public continues to tolerate fictions like the Columbus myth. Nor will it work as long as NASA serves as a front for the rather ugly business of DOD, all of which is happily performed by the very same contractors.

One might reasonably ask why the defense-aerospace contractors are so anxious to do business with NASA if the space agency accounts for so little of their annual profit. The reasons are several, but three are perhaps most important.

The first of these reasons is that NASA contracts have vast public relations value.* Companies such as North American Rockwell, or McDonnell, providing billions of dollars worth of destructive apparatus for the U.S. government annually, can scarcely overlook the pleasant public image offered by "peaceful" contracts such as are associated with a trip to the Moon. Furthermore, space is the world of tomorrow. The company that has contributed to that journey has forged its place in the nation's destiny —it hopes. These companies very seldom place full-spread advertisements in The New York Times, Time magazine, and other popular media, boasting of their radar, laser, nuclear, and artillery systems. They do not advertise their bombers, fighters, and submarines.

* The makers of Tang, an orange-flavored breakfast drink, for example, use NASA footage on TV commercials to advertise the fact that astronauts will be drinking their powdered ("just add water") product.

They do, on the other hand, frequently place full-color two-page spreads dramatizing their role in putting Americans on the Moon, or in improving urban air and water. If nothing else, NASA has helped provide them with a welcome public image.

A second important reason why the defense-aerospace industry is happy to have NASA contracts is that defense contracts are highly competitive, winner take all, and usually provide a narrow profit margin per unit. NASA contracts, on the other hand, are for a handful of custom-made, hand-tailored units each worth many millions of dollars.* The Apollo project is a top priority national program as well. Time, not cost, is the important factor, so larger profit margins are permitted. And there are no penalties for failures such as the Apollo 204 disaster. The government absorbs the loss. It is always this way with crash programs.

The third reason, and by far the most important, is that the space program acts as a vast WPA project. It keeps thousands upon thousands of aerospace workers employed—a modern parallel of Spain's *encomienda*. For an average of about a dollar per week in taxes, each American can keep aerospace-defense employment on the upswing. If it were not for the space program, many a modest aerospace-defense corporation would long ago have been swallowed by merger or bankruptcy. The needs of World War II, Korea, and foreign aid had produced a huge aero-space-defense industry. After Korea they had less and less with which to occupy themselves. There were, after all, only so many huge, long-term military contracts to go around. Those who failed to land one of the big ones could always depend on NASA to take up the slack.

In the early 1960's, the aerospace industry was referred to as an "infant" industry clearly destined to become one of the giants. In 1962, for example, *Fortune* magazine predicted that government space expenditures would swell from the then annual $11.6 billion, to in excess of $20 billion by 1970. The growth has not been nearly that spectacular, but it has been surprising nevertheless. By 1964, the industry contributed about $24 billion to the

---

* Whether NASA or DOD contracts are more profitable depends on whom one talks to in the aerospace industry. David Demarest of TRW Electronics Systems favors DOD contracts because they often lead to big production runs of the same item.

gross national product. NASA's expenditures alone were about $4.4 billion. Department of Defense space expenditures, lumped together with missile activities, showed a total of $18 billion. DOD expenditures were restrained somewhat in these areas the following year, but NASA's budget grew proportionately. In 1965, it rose to about $5.5 billion. Total aerospace spending for the same period accounted for about 3.9 percent of the gross national product, or about 4.2 percent of total manufacturing employment. A rough yardstick is found in total expenditures, for the same year, by the American public on food and alcoholic beverages—only three and a half times greater than the total aerospace production budget.

Thus, one of the least advertised reasons for President Kennedy's endorsement of Project Apollo, "within the decade," was most certainly to stop a deflationary trend, in 1961, brought on by a slack in military hiring and spending. The trend had been produced, in part at least, by the conservative attitude of the Eisenhower Administration. Yet, while Eisenhower's policies may have been attractive in many ways, they made no provision for the unemployment that threatened the succeeding Administration. The tragedy is that once the trend was successfully reversed, Kennedy was unable to contain the aerospace-defense industry. Instead, it grew, and it grew, and it grew.*

While NASA officials bemoaned their misfortune at having suffered a budget cutback of about $1 billion in 1968, the aerospace industry as a whole was quite content. Military space

---

* In retrospect, it seems to have been a matter of investing too much, too fast, too soon. For example, President Kennedy may have had, among other motives already cited, the hope that full-scale involvement in an East-West race to the Moon would so deplete the Soviet GNP that our adversary would have to make the difficult choice of abandoning the missile race of the early 1960's. And it may well have worked the other way around. The U.S.S.R. has no doubt suffered much the same kind of economic strain as the U.S. (As early as October, 1963, Khrushchev implied that the U.S.S.R. was no longer interested in a race to the Moon.) There is no doubt that the popular appeal of manned space flight, and promises of "space travel," have served the Soviet Union and the U.S. equally as well. The U.S.S.R., too, must sell its costly space program to the Soviet man in the street, who has given up his butter for more guns more often than Americans have. On the other hand, the Soviets have (at least according to the Pentagon, in July, 1968) nearly closed the missile gap. Missile equality ("parity"), by 1970, will have eliminated the value of U.S. nuclear supremacy as a deterrent. By pursuing the moon, missiles, and Vietnam, and a host of other international gambits, the United States seems to have depleted its own funds to a large degree.

spending had filled the gap,* and civilian aircraft continued to boom. New aerospace projects and Vietnam seemed to promise months of continued growth. In fact, Gerson Chanowitz, chief economist for the Aerospace Industries Association, could boast in *Aviation Week*, July 8, 1968:

> The aerospace industry is the largest manufacturing employer in the U.S., with well over 1.4 million people. One in 50 people employed in the nation works for the aerospace industry.

Chanowitz observed, with evident pride, that in 1948, just twenty years before, sales of aerospace companies were only a little over $1 billion. In 1967, they had risen to well over $27 billion. This remarkable growth occurred in industrial areas once limited to the production of aircraft and related products. Consequently, those regions of the country that once flourished almost exclusively on aircraft production during World War II had become even more prosperous during the "Cold War" peace.

The state of California is a classic case of such a captive industry, tied to government economy. In an article in the *Pacific Historical Review* (November, 1968), Dr. James L. Clayton, assistant professor of history at the University of Utah, pointed out that wages and salaries paid to aerospace employees in California, since World War II, had exceeded all state and local public welfare expenditures throughout the entire nation. They had nearly equaled all U.S. foreign aid to Europe and the Far East during that same period. From 1951 through 1965, $67.2 billion, or about 20 percent of all DOD prime defense contracts for supplies, services, and construction, were received in that one state. An additional $5.3 billion was spent there by NASA, from 1961 through 1965. This amounted to about 41 percent of NASA's total spending during those years.

California is but one of thirteen Western states, containing one-sixth of the nation's population, that in recent years has received one-fourth of all DOD military contracts, one-third of prime military contracts, and two-thirds of all missile contracts. Aerospace-defense spending in California and these other Western states have been the major factor in the extraordinary rapid

* See Chapter 10.

expansion of industry and population on the West Coast. It has shifted the entire population density of the nation.

It is this kind of striking growth and overwhelming dependence of whole sectors of the economy on government contracts that has changed the character of the government-business relationship. This is particularly true since the related growth in electronics and automation had caused a parallel decline in the need for manpower. Today, for every million dollars spent on missiles and space activities, the number of persons employed is considerably less than was required just ten years ago, when the contracts were devoted to tanks, ordnance, and propeller-driven aircraft. It is not surprising, then, that California, New York, Texas, Alabama, and a host of Southern states demand more and more in the way of aerospace-defense contracts. NASA naturally is expected to contribute its share, as flag-bearer of the nation's space effort.

The following observation concerning the effects of this trend has been made by economists J. S. Dupre and W. E. Gustafson of Harvard University:

> The government has had to devise new standards in its contractual relationships with business firms. Essentially, the government now assumes the financial risk involved in innovation. Free competition no longer characterizes the process of bidding for government contracts. While private firms have thus been freed from the restraints of the open market, they have acquired new public responsibilities. They are no longer merely suppliers to the government, but participants in the administration of public functions.

Thus, the aerospace industry, which devotes two-thirds of its effort in the military sector and the remaining one-third to NASA or other "civilian" space efforts, has one customer. That customer is Uncle Sam. Yet it is the government and not the industry that takes the risks. The aerospace-defense industry occupies a unique role in the history of economics. It is, in the strictest sense, a publicly owned industry. It enjoys all of the privileges and few of the risk-taking responsibilities of private industry. The situation has advanced to the point where the industry no longer sees why it should train new and unskilled manpower. Recent overtures by the aerospace community to help relieve the job shortage in the ghetto areas of the country have come only after the government agreed to pay the corporation a profit after paying the cost of training. The aerospace industry, once accused of taking government funds away from social welfare projects, has moved into the business of social reform itself—at a profit.

The peculiar status of the industry has never been more openly exposed or more vulnerable than it was just after the Apollo 204 disaster. NASA, under fire in the Congress, found that the burden of responsibility had to be shared with the industry that had built the faulty spaceship. One anonymous NASA spokesman is reported to have complained that the North American Aviation Corporation "gave us a black eye." NASA submitted to its Apollo 204 Review Board, among other documents, a report prepared by Major General Samuel Phillips, in 1965, on the shortcomings and disappointments of the performance of the prime Apollo contractor—the North American Aviation Corporation. His notes, compiled during a series of briefings, noted faulty workmanship, schedule slippages, cost discrepancies, and an overall attitude that seemed, in his view, to threaten the entire Apollo project.

During the Congressional hearings dealing with the fire investigation, copies of that report were circulated among at least some of the senators and congressmen. At least as many more were in the hands of reporters representing the major public media. The Phillips Report was so damaging a document that the House and Senate committee chairmen agreed that it should not be released to the public. The members of the press were not satisfied; to them, the Phillips Report represented the first hard "space" news in weeks. According to at least one reliable source, a copy fell into the possession of Senator Mondale of Minnesota. Aware of its significance, he reportedly took it to Chairman Clinton Anderson of New Mexico, of the Senate Aeronautical and Space Sciences Committee, who informed him that the document was not to be released.

What even an indulgent congressman cannot ignore, however, is an affront to Congressional intelligence and dignity. NASA's and North American's handling of the "alleged" Phillips Report could not have been better designed to do exactly that. NASA's first response was that it knew of no such report—perhaps, NASA officials suggested, the congressmen were confused. In the February 27 hearings, before the Senate Committee, Senator Mondale asked NASA Associate Administrator Dr. George Mueller about the Phillips Report. Mueller answered: "I know of no unusual General Phillips report."

Further questioning elicited similar dissembling from NASA.

Over a month later, on April 11, before the House Subcommittee, North American president John Leland Atwood was asked by Representative Ryan about the Phillips Report. This exchange followed:

MR. ATWOOD: The Phillips Report to whom?
MR. RYAN: Has not that been discussed with you?
MR. ATWOOD: I have heard it mentioned, but General Phillips has not given us a copy of any report.

Pressure was put on NASA in both the House and Senate space committees to release the Phillips Report. James Webb refused, giving as one reason NASA's need to respect the confidential nature of its contractor dealings. He also cited Title 18, U.S. Code, Section 1905, which is designed to prevent, under penalty of fine or imprisonment, an unauthorized government employee from stealing, selling, or giving out trade secrets or financial information. Webb's position, to say the least, was curious. As NASA administrator, he was specifically obliged under the NASA charter *not* to withhold information from the public or the Congress.

Representative Ryan, who had obtained a copy of the Phillips Report* from (as it was later described by Senator Walter F. Mondale of Minnesota) "an unofficial surreptitious source," felt he had no other choice. On April 26, he released selected passages from the Report, pointing out that Major General Phillips had reached many of the same conclusions—fully thirteen months *before* the Apollo fire—as the Review Board reached two months *after* the fire.** The implication was clear. NASA and its prime contractor had known about many of the problems and

* Others (Mondale) had it.
** See Appendix H.

dangers "uncovered" by the Review Board long before the Apollo fire, but apparently had done nothing about them until the tragedy struck.

Ryan also quoted from Major General Phillips' covering letter of December 19, 1965, to North American President J. L. Atwood:

> I am definitely not satisfied with the progress and outlook of either program second-stage Saturn rocket and the command module . . . Even with due consideration of hopeful signs, I could not find a substantive basis for confidence in future performance.

Such was the tenor of the report President Atwood forgot he had received.

Webb had been, to say the least, outspokenly defensive about the Apollo contractor. As he told the Senate Committee on February 27: "I want to add one other thing, since you have raised the question of contractor performance. There is nothing in the preliminary findings or recommendations of the Board that points to the cause of the Apollo 204 accident or fires as being generated by any contractor."

A month and a half later, at the April 11 House hearings, J. L. Atwood, the North American president, was being questioned about any personnel changes that might have occurred at North American since the Apollo disaster.* Representative Roudebush asked:

> MR. ROUDEBUSH: Mr. Atwood, in your prepared statement you referred to personal pride and excellence of workmanship. I think you referred to a program in your plant which you call PRIDE. Has there been any reassignment of personnel at your plant since the accident?

---

* During this time, North American Aviation was maneuvering toward a merger. Its corporate reputation and public image were severely damaged by the Apollo disaster and more especially by the Phillips affair. Eventually a merger was accomplished with Rockwell Standard Corporation. The change became official on September 22, 1967, when the two companies combined their names in "North American Rockwell." The new corporation renegotiated its Apollo contracts with dispatch. Now apparently approaching the end of a difficult period of transition, the new company showed a slight upturn in profits in its fiscal year ending September 30, 1968. The company's management predicted that 1969 sales will remain at about the same level as 1968, or $2.64 billion.

MR. ATWOOD: Not in any major executive positions.

MR. ROUDEBUSH: I am referring to even a lesser level. Have any of the personnel working on the individual wire packages been changed or shifted within the plant?

MR. ATWOOD: We have quite a turnover. I don't know whether anyone in my group can answer it.

MR. ROUDEBUSH: Has anyone's employment been discontinued as a result of the accident?

MR. ATWOOD: I don't know of anyone who has been discharged.

Early in the dispute, North American was reportedly approached by at least one of the Congressional committee chairmen concerning the wisdom of voluntarily releasing the document to the public. The decision was presumably left to the management of North American. North American, quite unwisely, apparently declined this opportunity in order to avoid the loss of face—which resulted anyway. The withholding of information from the Congress by government contractors, such as North American, has thus been challenged—but not resolved.

The issue cannot be ignored however, for as Martin Goland has said: "Such an industry is public industry, even if served by private corporations. The criteria which govern the performance of the aerospace industry are not those of the free marketplace, but those of the conference room, the negotiating table, and the ballot box."

Dr. Ralph Lapp, during his radio interview with Representative Ryan on March 25, 1968, was even more outspoken: "It seems to me that when a company like Lockheed Aircraft does 10.6 billion dollars worth of business in the past seven years—so that 88 percent of its total sales are with one customer, the U.S. government—that's defense socialism . . . I guess we ought to transform defense socialism and call it aerospace socialism, because the aerospace corporations which do an annual business of twenty-seven billion dollars with the U.S. government . . . [are] certainly one of the buoyant forces tending to keep the space budget up. Once you've got companies like Boeing, North American Aviation, and others, with huge contracts, they want to keep the program going."

North American, of Downey, California, is without doubt the classic example of Lapp's "aerospace socialism." Ninety-seven percent of its business in 1961 was with the U.S. government. However, that year it lost the huge B–70 aircraft contract. Shortly thereafter North American became the dominant corporation in the new space arena when it was selected over Martin-Marietta, a tried and true spacecraft builder, as the primary space contractor. NASA Administrator Webb and a select committee overruled the decision of a professionally staffed contract-evaluation board that had recommended Martin-Marietta. There is some reason to believe that the nod to North American was a compensation for the lost B–70 aircraft contract.* Such a loss could have pressured the huge, one-customer corporation out of the market. In its favor, on the other hand, was a series of record-breaking flights with the experimental X–15, the high-flying aircraft that had gathered most of the data NASA needed to man-rate its spacecraft.

North American has several subsidiaries, most prominent of which is probably the Rocketdyne Division. Rocketdyne, one of three or so big rocket-engine producers, won contracts from NASA in the construction of Wernher von Braun's huge Saturn engines, the F-1's and the J-2's. The two-hundred-thousand-pound-thrust J-2 was originally designed for the Saturn 1, for Earth-orbital flights. The million-and-a-half-pound-thrust F-1 was designed for clusters of eight to boost the Nova vehicle. However, since the Nova was dropped, both have been incorporated in separate stages of the Saturn 5, the rocket used to launch U.S. astronauts toward the Moon. It is not difficult to see that North American stood to lose a great deal if the Phillips Report meant losing a contract; but the Moon mission was far too advanced for NASA to switch contractors. Instead, NASA chose to chastise North American by assigning Boeing to do "integration analysis" of the Saturn 5 rocket, the Apollo spacecraft, and the Lunar Module.

North American's merger, in 1967, with Rockwell Standard Corporation, one of the nation's leading manufacturers of auto-

---

* The controversial F-111 (TFX) award to General Dynamics is explained, in some quarters, in the same fashion.

motive components, was an attempt to diversify and thus get away from the business of total dependence on its one customer, the U.S. government. It had also evidently convinced itself that the consumer goods that would come from the fringes of the space business, the so-called "spin-off" products, were close at hand. *Forbes* magazine, interviewing the chairman and president of the year-old merger found that things were not as rosy as had been hoped. Aside from the loss of prestige due to the Apollo 204 fire, it had been found that "a real payoff" in spin-off was further away than had been hoped.

Yet before the merger, according to *Forbes*, North American's executive vice-president, John Moore, had convinced the Rockwell people that they could "get rich on the stuff in [North American's] wastebaskets." In July, 1968, Willard F. Rockwell, chairman of the new corporation, noted, however, "If you're building an item for the space program, you have to have it and the cost doesn't matter . . . But if you want to make money out of that item on the commercial market, you have to spend weeks and months trying to figure out how you're going to get the damned costs down so that you can turn a profit . . . a lot of space stuff is just too complicated for civilian use." *Forbes* and North American Rockwell agreed that while the future looks promising, actual output of most spin-off products is many, many years away.

Sperry Gyroscope, Lake Success, New York, has found the same to be true. On June 21, 1968, the company announced that 450 workers would be laid off immediately as part of a broad reorganization under the direction of Charles S. Rockwell. The North American subsidiary had found it increasingly difficult to hold its own in defense contracting. A final blow was its failure to apply aerospace-defense techniques and know-how to the unfamiliar but beckoning civilian market. Sperry had been contracted by the city of New York to produce a central traffic control system for New York's automobile-glutted streets. The final product failed to function, and was canceled. Hundreds more blue- and white-collar workers at Sperry, as well as at many other corporations around the country, were expected to be dropped as well. The reason was twofold: a general restraint of aerospace-defense spending, and a need for new, young blood. Most of the

Sperry workers that were dropped were in their fifties. It is a situation that presents an unusual problem. The aerospace-defense industry has for years been a sort of glorified parallel to the truck-farming business. Its blue- and white-collar workers are skilled migratory workers. They are constantly moving from one contractor to another, and in and out of NASA or defense projects. A large percentage have either gone to work for, or come from the ranks of, NASA itself. Their executive offices are often manned by former NASA or Pentagon strategists. NASA, too, is heavily manned by former industry or Pentagon personnel.

Thus, after ten years of flourishing space business, with the production curves beginning to come down, as had been predicted, thousands of people are faced with unemployment. Huntsville, Alabama, headquarters for the Marshall Space Flight center and home of the Saturn 5 rocket, is losing scientists, engineers, and technicians in droves. As the Apollo project neared its end, these men, with no follow-on projects to keep them back, were leaving Huntsville—and many were quitting the aerospace business for good. In spite of their skills, they often have nowhere to go. In fact, often it is their specialized skills that make them unemployable outside the aerospace-defense industry. Said one Huntsville employment agency operator who was switching to accounts outside the aerospace industry, "They'll be making bicycles, toys, refrigerators and TV sets a hell of a long time after we get to the Moon." The space WPA project, which had been advertised so widely, seems to be showing signs of wear. For this reason, among others, the nation's economic experts were predicting that the national unemployment rate would rise from the 1968 level of 3.6% to 4% or even 4.5% in 1969. Only time would tell how President Nixon would cope with the threatening decline in employment. He had already suggested two conflicting goals: the need to restrain the NASA budget until long-range goals had been delineated; and the promise to keep NASA "first in space."

Industry's response, and the major reason for the general sense of contentment, was that new large-scale "make-work" projects were fast filling the gap left in the wake of Apollo. The Super-Sonic Transport (SST) is presently the one which seems to offer the most immediate relief.

The function of the SST was clarified, in unusually frank and candid fashion, in response to an article, "Apollo and the Decay of Technical Excellence," written by Congressman William F. Ryan and published in the January, 1968 issue of *American Engineer*. A letter by John D. Alden, Executive Secretary for the Engineering Manpower Commission was published in the April, 1968 issue of the same journal. In his rebuttal to Ryan, Alden said: ". . . you keep blaming engineers for decisions in which they had absolutely no say. You cite the decision to proceed with the SST, overfunding of the space program, and the performance shortcomings of the F-111." Alden asserted that none of these decisions were made by technical people. In fact, he said, "The space program and the SST were adopted for political and economic reasons, while the F-111 decision was made by an accountant against unanimous recommendation of the engineers involved." Alden, obviously distraught by the implications of Ryan's attack, added, "Don't blame these people [i.e., professional engineers] because they fail to challenge the wisdom of their client's [i.e., the Government's] decision. Do you expect a doctor [an engineer] to tell the patient [the Government] his life isn't worth saving? I wouldn't be surprised if a majority of engineers voted against the SST, if you put that question to them, but you haven't."

A much-beleaguered project, then, the SST has gone through the hands of several contractors, has suffered innumerable major design changes, including a change from swing-wing to fixed-wing design—the very feature with which Boeing had won the contract away from its competition at Lockheed—and in fact faces opposition in many quarters simply because no one is certain what the human and economic consequences of such an aircraft will be.* There is some question whether, because of the great sonic boom that will everywhere accompany the craft, it will ever be possible for passengers of the SST to travel anywhere other than over the oceans and deserts. Those who pooh-pooh the consequences of sonic booms have been set back somewhat by federal and private studies that show the frequent exposure to the thunder of an SST will be psychologically nerve-wracking

* And yet ambitious plans are already forming for a successor to the SST: the Hyper-Sonic Transport, or HST.

and a potentially dangerous and unpredictable irritant to the general public. A demonstration flight of military supersonic jets, at the Air Force Academy in Colorado in the spring of 1968, did not help either. Several of the planes buzzed the campus, breaking nearly every one of the thousands of glass window panes in the gleaming new buildings. Further, recent investigations indicate that sonic booms may produce Earth-rippling seismic waves comparable to those created by a large pile driver from a distance of some 200 feet.

Aside from these factors, which are admittedly difficult to evaluate in quantitative fashion, the SST (of which Boeing is major contractor) is a response to the Soviet SST,* now airborne, and the Concorde, which first flew on March 2nd, 1969. Although it was originally a joint Anglo-French project, England found it impractical to continue in the partnership, and so France went it alone. The American SST is, in large part, another case of trying to beat someone else to the punch. American industry just cannot bear to see another nation, ally or adversary, have something that it hasn't got. The American SST is being developed at nearly total cost to the government, that is, the public. Yet industry, which has yet to show a practical need or use for the gigantic machine, will as usual show a great profit—in dollars and in technology learned. Every citizen is being taxed to build this new Trojan horse, but if it is ever completed and allowed to fly, it will never carry more than a very small portion of the population. In fact, it may never be used to transport the public at all. The Pentagon is showing increasing interest in using it as a troop transport.

If this turns out to be the prime use of the SST, it will become obsolete almost as soon as it becomes airborne. Other minds are busy at this very moment, together with industry, designing and researching a means of troop transport that will make the SST look like a biplane. These individuals, most from military ranks, include NASA's associate administrator, Dr. George E. Mueller.

Philip Bono, of McDonnell Douglas Corporation Space Systems

---

* The U.S.S.R. flew its prototype SST the last week of 1968—followed two months later by the Anglo-French Concorde, many years ahead of the time the U.S. entry would be airborne.

Center, has recently unveiled the newest offspring of Apollo. His prodigy is dubbed "Pegasus." Disclosed in the July-August issue of the military trade journal *Ordnance*, Pegasus shows a remarkable disdain, on the part of the military and the aerospace industry, for the efforts presently being made to keep space nonmilitary. According to Bono, the futuristic vehicle "could revolutionize all previous concepts of transportation—if [it] were designed with the basic versatility to satisfy government, military, and civilian mission objectives alike."

Pegasus, a bell-shaped rocket transport, 114 feet high (one-third as tall as Saturn 5) and forty-nine feet wide at its largest diameter, would weigh over three million pounds (half as much as Saturn 5). "Initially," Bono said, "it was evolved as a reusable-booster concept capable of delivering Saturn 5 payloads (100 tons) . . . for post-Apollo missions. It could also be used for resupplying space stations in orbit . . . landing on the Moon with massive cargo payloads for use in the construction of a lunar base. Modified versions could be used for manned expeditions to Mars."

The author makes it quite clear, however, that space missions of this sort could not alone warrant its development. Obviously, "a vehicle of this kind should be designed for adaptability to military missions." This then, is the hope of the aerospace-defense industry: *NASA and the military blended into one indistinguishable operation, capable of a steady stream of billion-dollar make-work programs.*

And why not, ask the aerospace-defense people. Pegasus could transport 260 soldiers (or thirty-six tons of military payload) to any point on the Earth. Traveling, in orbit, at about seventeen thousand miles per hour, it could reach any war zone on Earth in thirty minutes—whereas in some instances the SST would take at least three and a half hours.

Besides its military value it could be used to transport 170 "high income" passengers and eighteen tons of cargo from continent to continent—with no sonic boom problem. And NASA could use it to go to Mars.

One day soon, NASA will no doubt openly support the Pegasus, or some similar project, not only because Pegasus is the logical successor to the Saturn 5—just as Saturn was to the expendable

ICBM's of the 1960's—but also because both NASA and industry are very interested in carrying the space race from the Moon out to the planets. Mars, for example, has been the topic of discussion for many years now. It is a logical target, especially since the Soviets are well on their way to a second successful soft-landing exploration of Venus. The red planet offers not only the promise of discovery, greater understanding of our Solar System and of the Earth itself, but to some die-hards it still seems a likely place for extra-terrestrial life. NASA, while complaining loudly and ruefully that the Congress and President Johnson abandoned the planets to Russia, denies that a manned trip to Mars is the next major objective of the U.S. space program. Lack of funds and Congressional support have prevented plans to progress much beyond a few small-scale unmanned efforts. This does not make it any less of an objective. If NASA cannot pursue it openly, industry can.

The attitude of the aerospace-defense industry on this matter is clear. Mr. Douglas E. Serrill, of Boeing's Advanced Program Group, Huntsville, Alabama, spelled it out on July 29, 1966 to the staff of the House Subcommittee on NASA Oversight.* "Manned planetary exploration," Serrill said, ". . . should be our long-range program. The manned fly-by with a manned Mars landing then becomes the next long-range national space goal." He elaborated by explaining the shortsightedness of our first national goal, the lunar landing. He declared, "The requirements for a permanent lunar base disappear, because there is no potential application of it that is of any advantage over a large space station [AAP-MOL]." In going to Mars, he added, we will "not only use the technologies developed on the Apollo program, but will extend them. National security is still involved [Pegasus?], as is national prestige and pride, and international competition. These never cease to exist."

Mr. Serrill concluded in the following memorable fashion: "I would like to leave these two thoughts with you. One—what

---

* Serrill's discussion was published in March, 1967, as part of a House Subcommittee report on the status of the Apollo lunar landing program. The report (Apollo Pace and Progress—Serial F—prepared by James E. Wilson) was completed in December, 1966, prior to the Apollo disaster. It included, however, a preface which stated: "the basic conclusions" and "analysis provided . . . remain unchanged," in spite of the tragic accident.

will the next generation think of us if we don't take this opportunity to press on into space? Second, wouldn't it be fitting to take advantage of the launch opportunity that exists late in 1975 to announce to the world in 1976 the successful fly-by of Mars as a demonstration that the 'Spirit of 1776' still exists in America?"

Slogans such as those inspired by Alexander, Isabella, and Columbus just don't seem to go away. Someone is always dreaming up a new one.

■ *I don't think that we—that Congress really has supervised NASA as closely as it should or could.*

REPRESENTATIVE
JOSEPH E. KARTH
NBC-TV interview, April 5, 1967

Chapter 12 ▪ Congress: NASA's Reluctant Watchdog

During his first dramatic and exhilarating six years as chief administrator of NASA, James E. Webb's greatest personal annoyance seemed to be the required annual pilgrimage to Capitol Hill for budget presentations. Each year, however, he managed to return with the better part of his request and with renewed affirmation of his ability to handle himself as well as the Congress.

On January 25, 1967, just two days before the Apollo disaster, Webb had occasion to remind a Senate hearing on aeronautical research and development policy of the virtual autonomy of his office and of the space agency. Likening himself first to the Secretary of Defense, he then said: "It's not possible within the government to stop me as administrator of NASA, if I am sure an important course should be embarked on and I want to present it to your committee, without a good deal of noise being made about it."

A Cabinet member in fact if not in title, Webb was confident that his ability and authority would go unquestioned by an awed and respectful Congress. The one-sidedness of the NASA-Congress relationship, however, had produced an increasing number of potential opponents of NASA policies. Only the prestige of the space agency, its highly publicized successes, and the apparent weight of public opinion prevented Congressional critics from denting Webb's armor.

The Apollo 204 disaster, for which no one in NASA's management—and especially its public relations staff—was prepared, suddenly left Webb and his entire organization quite vulnerable to the pent-up grievances of the critics. Nevertheless, shocked as he obviously was by the tragic loss of the three astronauts, Webb had no intention of allowing himself to be offered up as a sacrificial lamb. This fact was made quite clear during his first statement before the opening session of the House investigation. Addressing himself to Olin Teague and the Subcommittee on NASA Oversight, Webb said: "Mr. Chairman, if any man in this room wants to ask 'for whom the Apollo bell tolls,' I can tell him. It tolls for him and for me as well as for Grissom, White, and Chaffee . . . It tolls for government and industrial executives and legislators alike. It tolls for an open program continuously evaluated by opinion-makers with little time for sober second thought." The committee was reminded that both NASA and the Congress had created and supported the American space program, and together, they must share the blame and set it right.

Webb, in that dramatic performance, managed to block any effective thrusts by the few mavericks determined to show that the Review Board Report had been less than adequate. The Senate and House committee chairmen were solidly behind him, and it was recognized that further scandal could only injure the Congress as well as the space agency.

A reading of the lengthy proceedings of the two Congressional investigations makes it quite clear that the congressmen generally asked only those questions which would serve to erase doubts from the minds of potential skeptics. The questions and answers, in adhering closely to the guidelines established by the Apollo Review Board, were, for the most part, well orchestrated, and rarely deviated from the score. In some instances the efforts to constrain the dialogue were particularly obvious, as when astronaut Colonel Borman began an impromptu elaboration on a key point made in the Review Board Report. He was interrupted by the Apollo Review Board chairman, Dr. Thompson, who suggested that it was doubtful he could add anything to the Report. Thompson said, "I think you just stand on what is presented here." On another occasion, James Webb asked Congressional indulgence, saying, "Dr. Berry is *supposed* to differ with me a little bit here, or say a word . . . I want to be sure we are accurate [italics added]."

While NASA representatives and the various other speakers readily accepted their share of the blame, most of their answers were direct quotes from the Review Board Report, and identical answers were read in response to many different questions. Impetuous congressmen were impatiently cut off when their time had run out, or they were otherwise detoured. When Representative Daddario of Connecticut, for example, asked Dr. Berry if in fact attempts to revive the astronauts might not have saved them, House Subcommittee chairman Olin Teague told Berry: "You may comment. You may say it is [an] inappropriate [question] and we will submit it to the Board in writing for an answer." In this instance, Dr. Berry disregarded Teague's offer of asylum and testified, with some degree of confidence, to the negative.

Teague unwittingly defined the situation quite appropriately during an interview, on April 16, 1967, with ABC's Jules Bergman of "Issues and Answers": ". . . what we have tried to do is paint as honest a picture of the whole situation as we could by holding hearings . . . But I would doubt very much if there are any facts that come out." Teague was so predisposed to keeping the facts from getting out that he had once said the House would not conduct its own investigation. "It would be an insult to NASA," he said. The very fact that he appeared on both ABC's "Issues and Answers," and NBC's "Today" show, reveals the lengths to which he, personally, was willing to go to reassure the public that everything was in good hands.

With the exception of the battle over the Phillips Report, released by Representative Ryan in an instance of insubordination, Teague's approach worked very well indeed. Ryan's move, in fact, only demonstrated the futility of challenging NASA and Webb on matters that they did not wish to discuss. Webb flatly refused to release the Phillips Report by virtue of "executive privilege"—a privilege that is clearly denied the administrator by NASA's own charter. It made no difference how loudly the congressmen complained. The only alternative to acquiescence was a more unsavory scandal than already existed.

During the fiscal 1968 budget authorization hearings, Webb was occasionally asked questions relating to the Apollo accident.

Representative Larry Winn, Jr., of Kansas, for example, said: "Many people in the country are concerned about a possible whitewash by the Board Review, particularly since some of the recent news releases say we may never know the cause of the Apollo accident."

Webb reassured Winn by reminding him that "this nation will be exposed to precisely what this Board has done and what its findings and recommendations are. Your committee will be one of the instruments in doing so. And I cannot believe that anyone will believe that there is anything behind the scenes when that is done . . ." The Senate similarly was informed that a complete investigation with thorough hearings had placed all the facts before the public. Nothing had been left undone. Nor had these efforts gone unnoticed. Among a host of others who extended their thanks, Senator John Stennis of Mississippi made a special effort to express his particular gratitude. Speaking in the most glowing and reverent terms, he said: "I want to say this for the record, not so much for Mr. Webb, that I have been tremendously impressed, favorably, with the way he has handled the most unfortunate accident concerning the loss of the lives of these fine men. It was done by NASA and Mr. Webb in an atmosphere of extreme regret and compassion, but at the same time, there has been a candor and a frankness, I think, with the public and with the Congress that has not been exceeded since I have been here. I think he has set a very high and a very wholesome standard in coming up with the real facts. Certainly, we cannot accuse NASA of any kind of a gap with respect to the facts."

While the House Subcommittee, abiding by the decision of Olin Teague, considered the Apollo disaster a closed issue and refused to draw up the final report, which had once been mentioned, several members of the Senate Committee—Senators Mondale of Minnesota, Brooke of Massachusetts, and Percy of Illinois, in particular—did not agree that the job had been finished. Some repudiation of NASA and its administrator seemed, in their view, required by virtue of the stand-off over the Phillips Report. All but that effrontery had been forgiven.

The remaining members of the Senate Committee were thus forced to attempt to draw up some sort of summary report that would satisfy everyone. The task was taken up in the fall of 1967, but no general agreement on wording or the extent of criticism could be reached. A confidential Committee print of the draft circulated for months while efforts were made to overcome these difficulties. According to William Hines, then staff writer for the *Washington Star*, "Mondale was in Russia and Brooke in Africa when a draft report was sent to members for their scrutiny and comments." Mondale and Brooke, upon their return, attempted to delay a Committee meeting designed to consider the revised report which had been drawn up in their absence. On January 25, Hines noted, the Senate Committee staff director, James Gehrig, told the *Washington Star*, one day before the committee was to meet, that "there probably would never be a report issued on the accident." But, as Hines said, "on January thirtieth the report was deposited with the Senate and was printed overnight—as a Senate, not a Committee document." The maneuver thus avoided the usual advance distribution to Committee members of Committee reports.

The report was, in fact, once again composed primarily of well-known facts and direct excerpts from the Apollo Review Board Report or prepared statements offered by NASA spokesmen during the hearings. The three senators, unwilling to be dismissed so easily, had expressed their views, in their own language, as separate, dissenting statements.

Mondale's additional statement,* while by far the stronger of the two (Percy and Brooke had submitted a joint statement), failed nevertheless to expand much beyond the most notorious revelation of the Congressional hearings—the Phillips Report. He said: "NASA's performance—the evasiveness, the lack of candor, the patronizing attitude exhibited toward Congress, the refusal to respond fully and forthrightly to legitimate Congressional inquiries, and the solicitious concern for corporate sensitivities at a time of national tragedy—can only produce a loss of Congressional and public confidence in NASA programs." Mondale noted that NASA had shown no indication that it intended to review or change its policies and practices "brought to light by the Phillips Report incident." He added, "Instead, there have been indications

* See Appendix I.

from the highest level of NASA management that such policies and practices will continue."

Congressman Ryan, whose role in the Phillips Report incident not only went unmentioned by the senators, but was cast by innuendo in an unfavorable light, angrily branded the Senate report a "whitewash." Newsman Hines, no doubt equally displeased, called it "nearly a whitewash." In view of the countless omissions and gratuitous language of the report one must certainly agree that the report was, at the very least, a whitewash. The Congress, by bending to the pressures of NASA, had effectively abdicated its responsibility as a legislative, investigatory, and supervisory body. Another irrevocable chapter in the Apollo disaster had been written.

It might have been otherwise. NASA officials might have found themselves, for once, accountable for their acts and for their decisions. There might be an avenue for the sort of recourse open to irate citizens in Italy and Great Britain. For example, in February, 1968, according to *The New York Times*, "nine persons [were] ordered to stand trial on charges arising from the Vajont dam disaster in October, 1963 . . . the nine persons, most of them engineers or officials involved in the construction and operation of the dam . . . are charged with involuntary homicide. They are accused of having failed to take precautions against the possibility of 'catastrophic' landslides." The citizens of Aberfan, Wales, took similar action when a coal tip buried a schoolhouse and most of its students. Responsible officials, it was charged, had failed to inspect properly the site that turned into a murderous mudslide. Why, one must ask, is it that Congress has not provided a recourse for American families such as the Grissoms, the Whites, the Chaffees, the Bartleys and the Harmons, whose losses were also due to involuntary homicide due to negligence?

In spite of the whitewash, relationships between Administrator Webb, other NASA officials, and most members of the Congress were no longer so cordial as they had once been. This atmosphere made budget cutting, a clear national requirement in fiscal year 1969, an easier if not pleasant task for congressmen. Webb fought vigorously to fend off cuts, but to no avail.

These cuts were anticipated as early as 1966, when James E. Wilson and other members of the advisory staff of the House

Subcommitee on NASA Oversight spent many weeks traveling from one NASA facility to another for conferences with representatives of NASA and of the major Apollo contractors. Wilson's task was to identify future goals and the problems that remained to pace the Apollo program.

On behalf of Olin Teague, Subcommittee chairman, Wilson expressed concern about the effect on the public of NASA's future plans, especially since a budget reduction, because of Vietnam, was expected in the next year or two. A member of the Boeing team had pointed out that social impact was one of the considerations behind the choice of a large orbiting space station (AAP) as immediate successor to the lunar landing. Coming right to the point, he had said: "It is a good immediate goal to keep the momentum and public interest in space up while pursuing your long-range goal, which may be too far out in time to hold the public interest."

During a conference in New Orleans, Louisiana, on July 29, 1966, Boeing's Douglas Serrill had introduced the "spirit of '76," the Mars fly-by, as the first step toward that long-range goal—a manned landing on Mars. Serrill also expressed the dilemma facing NASA, industry, and the Congress: "Well, I think to land a man on Mars before 1985 as the climax to an integrated space program and within the budgetary constraints previously discussed, you almost have to make a crisis program out of it, rather than a logical evolutionary program. I don't think that in terms of the overall space program that this would be politically or publicly acceptable."

Manned exploration of the planets, the natural follow-up of the lunar landing, could prove so expensive that even the Congress would find such a program difficult to accept. On the other hand, government and industry had, over a few brief years, created a bureaucratic giant, NASA, which seemed to have nowhere to go. A vast system of aerospace-defense socialism had been created, yet it lacked a future rallying point—a new long-range national commitment. Post-Apollo plans were very uncertain, to say the least.

Webb, in 1967, countered with the following strategy: while NASA's budget need not go up, it must not go down, otherwise even a minimum of new projects, necessary to keep the space agency and the industrial work force together, could not be launched. Not everyone understood the necessity of continuity. Of what value, Senator Allen J. Ellender of Louisiana, asked, is a mission to Venus to the Apollo project? Noting that NASA probably had plans for other planets as well, he said: "that is what the scientists want you to do, I am sure." Webb replied in the affirmative. All semblance of the unanimity of earlier years was gone, and only the Moon mission remained untouchable.

Senator Ellender observed that there was no end to NASA's demands. Webb replied, "Well, there is no end to the universe, Senator, and unless we understand the universe in which we live . . ."—whereupon he was interrupted with a thought that must have been on many minds. Said Senator Ellender, "We have lived here for many years now, without the space program."

James Webb, however, would not budge, stating his own position as follows: "I would like to try to do the thing that is best for the United States and best for the human race. Even with the difficulty involved I want to try it."

Nevertheless, cuts were to be made in the fiscal 1968 budget, in at least one and possibly both of two specific projects. The first of these was NERVA, an experimental nuclear rocket project conducted jointly by NASA and the Atomic Energy Commission. (NERVA, in addition to its potential military use, is, in the view of most of NASA's planners—as well as Chairman Clinton P. Anderson, in whose state, New Mexico, the nuclear rocket is being developed—the logical and most economical successor to the Saturn rocket. NASA views nuclear-powered space vehicles as the key to long-duration missions around the Earth, or to Mars, Venus and the distant planets.) The other area facing a cut, in 1968, was the Voyager project—the proposed unmanned Mars probe and successor to the Mariner IV satellite that secured the first photographs of the Martian surface.

Webb felt that a cut in either category, a failure to capitalize on a major investment, was "as serious as the placing of missiles in Cuba was." He added that knowledge of the solar system "can be used for many purposes to serve mankind or for military power." Senator Spessard L. Holland of Florida, quite put out by the trend of the discussion, asked Webb again which of the two, NERVA or Voyager, he would prefer to see cut. After a lengthy exposition on the part of the administrator, Holland congratulated Mr. Webb on his use of "several hundred words" without answering the question. Holland observed that either the Voyager project or the NERVA *would* be cut, and Webb would have to show a preference. It was a stalemate. Webb stood firm, saying: "I don't want to give any aid comfort to anyone to cut a program. I think it is essential that we do both."

Rattling the saber and the missile once again, Webb declared:

When the Russians can start putting payloads of very large size over your head every hour and a half, I think you have got a situation here which we should not close our eyes to— that there will be very large things going over your head every hour and a half.

Senator Holland did not see any connection between post-Apollo missions and the Russian payloads (Webb was referring to the Soviet FOB's—he did not mention the U.S. MIRV's). Senator Magnuson interjected: "I thought we had a treaty," and was quickly echoed by Senator Ellender who said, "That's what I thought, we had a treaty about all of this." The senators referred to the flexible treaty between the U.S. and the Soviets which bans orbiting bombs from space.

Administrator Webb spelled it out for the senators: "The same booster does both [military missions and peaceful exploration of space] and the ability to understand the forces at work in the solar system gives you a technology that you can use in both areas . . . In my view the chief enforcer of treaties is an advancing broad-based technology. If we lose our momentum in technology, treaties do not have the same effect."

Pressing his point, Webb further informed the Independent Offices Subcommittee of the Committee on Appropriations, during this trying session on July 26, 1967, that international cooperation in space is unlikely because the Russians believe they are out in front and don't need the United States. He added: "They have beat us on every single major thing, including the first soft landing on the Moon; the first orbit of the Moon; the first pictures of the back side of the Moon; the first man in space; the first multimanned space vehicle. We beat them in the first rendezvous."

Webb had, in fact, made this same admission before, noting that the Apollo lunar landing represented the *first* opportunity to beat the Russians in something big. Abandoning the planets and military supremacy of space was unthinkable after all the great effort of overcoming the initial advantage of the Soviets.

Nevertheless, the senators were startled. Said Senator Holland: "I am surprised to hear Mr. Webb, in a public statement at a public hearing, state that they [the Russians] have exceeded us in every major competition, because this differs so very greatly— if I may say so—from the testimony that they [NASA] offered us in the Authorization committee." Holland expressed great disappointment that Webb could not suggest criteria on which painful but necessary budget cuts would have to be made, especially since they only meant a delay of a year or two in either project. "I think," the senator said, "he should be helpful to us rather than evade our questions."

While Webb's handling of these discussions was aimed at blocking further attempts at budget cutting, it exasperated rather than silenced the already ruffled congressmen, most of whom were openly concerned. If intelligent cuts were not made, something vital to future progress might inadvertently be eliminated. Webb was only making their job harder. Rather than healing the rift though, the Congress only succeeded in playing word games. No means of handling NASA and its articulate administrator had been developed over the years. Rather, it was always Webb who handled the Congress.

Naturally, at times things got out of hand, as when NASA submitted a new set of mass proposals—to replace the deleted Voyager. Ranking members of the Congress were infuriated to learn that the 1973 flight was the same old Voyager test flight. Only the name had been changed. As the editors of *Aerospace Technology* observed; "a rose by any other name does not always smell as sweet . . . Key House Appropriations Committee members indicated, however, that they are not going to buy the name change and will not approve funds for the 1973 mission."

Isolated attempts were made by some congressmen to solicit the cooperation of Webb without engaging in bitter oratory. Representative James G. Fulton of California and House minority leader Representative Gerald R. Ford of Michigan sent a letter to Administrator Webb. In it they requested Webb's advice as to how various potential cuts would affect NASA programs. NASA's response was as follows:

Dear Mr. Fulton: Responding to your joint request with Congressman Gerald Ford regarding the effect on NASA programs of a reduction in the fiscal year 1969 budget of $200, $400, $600, or $700 million, you are advised that under the provisions of the Budget and Accounting Act of 1921 NASA is not at liberty to answer such questions.

The letter was signed not by Mr. Webb, but by one J. S. Brown *for* Robert F. Allnutt, Assistant Administrator for Legislative Affairs. A very reasonable and indeed necessary question, by two congressmen, had been shunted off to a lesser office and denied an answer.

It is quite clear, then, that the Congress has little hold over NASA other than the power to cut the budget. And, in the face of public opinion, it may often lose that crude weapon. The fact is, until the Apollo disaster had altered the flow of events, the Congress rarely made any attempt to manage NASA at all. Having once abdicated such responsibilities, how could it expect, overnight, to reclaim them?

Then, too, there are countless less conspicuous spending anomalies which together swell into a major problem. Far too few congressmen have been willing to open this Pandora's box. Representative Lester L. Wolff of New York was an exception. He pointed out that NASA had been doing business with a company cited by the Congress in August, 1967 as having charged the Department of Defense fifty times their published price on catalogue items. According to *Aviation Week*, March 11, 1968, Representative Wolff complained that "the same slipshod prevailing practices that were going on in DOD were widespread over a number of NASA centers." Noting that NASA's Goddard Center had bought a $3.29 dial for $32.90, and a $14.95 clutch for $44.95, Wolff suggested: "as with an iceberg, there is much more below the surface."

A combination of unfortunate realities of the NASA-Congress governmental relationship has led to Congress' abdicating its responsibility to supervise NASA. First, it must be realized that those Congressional committees that deal with the space program grew into some of the most prestigious and glamorous committees on which a senator or congressman could serve. NASA had been an agency with almost unlimited funds that attracted the attention of vast segments of the nation's industrial constituency. Congressmen from those states that were deeply involved in the space program, such as California, enjoyed great power and respect, both at home and in the Congress. As NASA grew in size and became more successful the space committees increased in importance.

There is little doubt that many congressmen have been dazzled by the thought that as NASA's laurels increased, their place in history was also elevated. Space *was* the new frontier. To be associated with the space program was to be part of history. One who supported NASA, the self-styled spearhead of science and technology, was certain to be recognized as a modern patron of human progress. A kind of renown by association had developed, not unlike the situation often exploited by the most unlikely commercial enterprises. One frequently sees on television, for example, orange drink, wristwatch, or toothbrush advertisements stating that the product will accompany the astronauts to the Moon. The screen meanwhile is engulfed in smoke as a Saturn 5 blasts off its pad. Neither NASA nor the astronauts have personally endorsed the product, but it is comparable to the old British practice whereby a manufacturer is permitted to include as part of his presentation the notice, "by appointment to Her Majesty the Queen."

Had Senator Anderson or Representatives Miller and Teague, all of them committee or subcommittee chairmen, allowed NASA to be besmirched by the Congressional hearings, they would have brought the wrath of their colleagues and their constituents crashing down upon their heads. Furthermore, they would have diminished the significance of the committees which they headed. No one wants to be chairman of a declining committee.

The analyses of NASA and its contractors and recommendations for the committees are made not by the congressmen, but by the working staffs of the separate committees. Usually the voice of the staff is that of the majority party. Thus, a conscientious and even well-informed minority member may have no easy avenue of expression. The staff members, as well as the committee members, are always interested in promoting the advantages of the space program to the industrial sector. Considerable effort has been made to get influential members of the business community to support publicly NASA's goals. And, when NASA's goals have been slow in developing, the staff members have sought ideas from the business community itself. Sometimes the results are disappointing.

Early in 1968, for example, the staff conducted a poll of leading businessmen. The survey polled 750 of the largest corporations included in *Fortune* magazine's June, 1967 listing. Four hundred and forty-nine responded. Eighty-one of those queried were among the top hundred DOD and NASA contractors. Of those who responded:

- 57.4 percent thought $5 billion was a budget level appropriate to NASA.
  37.0 percent thought it was too much.
- 54 percent thought lunar landing in this decade should be maintained.
  27 percent thought it should be changed.
- 69 percent thought the space program had contributed "much" of scientific value.
  27 percent thought "some."
- 22 percent thought the space program had contributed "much" of utilitarian value.
  54 percent thought "some."
- 47 percent favored the same budget level on the basis of national security in the context of the Vietnam War.
  43 percent favored a decrease.
- 37 percent felt the relative effort of DOD and NASA should be maintained "about the same."
  30 percent felt that DOD effort should be greater.
- Ranking national priorities, respondents said: (1) defense 96 percent; (2) education 70 percent; (3) space 44 percent; (4) poverty 40 percent; (5) medical research 31 percent.

Obviously, leading business executives, as well as the man in the street, had cooled on the space program. It is interesting, but not particularly surprising, that the poll revealed the main support for NASA was drawn from those who saw its defense link. The poll also shows how difficult it is to generate sufficient support for social programs such as poverty, medical research, urban renewal, or anti-pollution.

During James Wilson's field study on Apollo Pace and Progress, in 1966, the question he most frequently directed to NASA's contractors and representatives, to Joseph Shea, to the Apollo managers, and to Major General Phillips, NASA headquarters, was, "How will this affect the schedule and the budget?" Teague's committee, for whom Wilson spoke, was definitely interested in cutting tests, check-outs, even flights, almost anything to get the lunar landing accomplished on time and at the promised cost. So much so, in fact, that Major General Phillips, even in 1966, complained quite candidly that from the point of view of testing and safety the program had been "cut to the bare bones" and further restraints would not be "prudent."

The situation, which transcends the plight of NASA, was expressed most articulately by Elmer P. Wohl, an administrative vice-president of the North American Rockwell Corporation. Writing in the defense-oriented journal *Ordnance*, July-August, 1968, he said: "We are indeed in a crisis, and we do not yet fully understand how, or why, or where, or what to do." Wohl added, quite succinctly: "When Government says it is managed by objective, when industry says it is managed by objective and when both fail to achieve objectives, it becomes apparent that we don't understand sufficiently the processes, the economic forces, the technology, the dynamic, changing balances that are involved in the Government/defense industry effort." He observed that the "alliance" between government and industry, while it had acquired a sinister appearance, in the eyes of some, was often "governmentally stimulated."

In the present difficult period, Wohl urged, government and industry must: wage a constant battle against erosion of standards of excellence; courageously examine old assumptions; join the best talents of government and industry in basic efforts, unshackled by distracting management techniques, toward understanding and accomplishment; select and communicate objectives appropriate to our time. Wohl concluded that his readers must "move vigorously toward [the accomplishment of these goals], as though our lives depended on it," for, "one day they *may* depend on it."

Unfortunately, these glowing recommendations raise more doubts than they settle. For, if these were not the very challenges of the past decade, then what in the world has the space program been about? How is it that problems such as those basic to any successful enterprise are only being addressed today, so late in the game?

More specifically, what effect has this belated concern for co-ordination had on the present space objective—the lunar landing? And what does it imply for America's space program after Apollo astronauts land? It has been—it is now—the Congress' duty to explore and ultimately to answer these questions. Congress-men must ask themselves if it is really in the national interest to continue to base their decisions on the ups and downs of the space program's "image," whether, indeed, they wish to guide America's space program or be guided by it.

I am certain that as future generations look back on our incredible decade, they will be unanimous in their belief that the treasure that we have dedicated to sending man to explore the stars was the most significant and important investment ever made by any people . . . There will be little men with poison pens, without vision, who will seek to scrub your great efforts. But they will not prevail . . . we will not forget you.

PRESIDENT LYNDON B. JOHNSON,
*Manned Spacecraft Center
Houston, Texas, March 2, 1968*

Chapter 13 ■ The Future in Space

When James Webb announced his retirement as NASA administrator on September 16, 1968, he made some extremely pessimistic remarks about the future of America's space program. "We are going to be in a second position," he said, "for some time to come." Webb's sense of timing was extraordinary. The day before, as usual without an official announcement, the Russians had launched their unmanned Zond 5 spacecraft on a journey destined to take it around the Moon and back to Earth for a splashdown in the Indian Ocean on September 22.

It was a dramatic Russian "first" in space. Never before had a vehicle swung around the Moon and been brought back to Earth. As an added fillip, the Soviets later announced that Zond 5 had carried a "zoo," including turtles, mealworms, and wineflies, as well as various types of plant seeds and buds. Zond 5 did not go into lunar orbit; and its round trip to the Moon only brought it within 1,200 to 1,500 miles of the lunar surface.

But the Russians did not hold the space headlines for long. On October 11, the United States launched Apollo 7 into Earth orbit, carrying astronauts Schirra, Eisele, and Cunningham. It was the first manned flight of the three-man Apollo capsule. The astronauts were America's first men in space since, twenty-three months before, James A. Lovell, Jr., and Edwin E. Aldrin, Jr., had flown Gemini 12 in November, 1966.

The safe return of Apollo 7 on October 22, 1968, inspired *The*

New York Times the following day to state in an editorial entitled "Atlantic Splashdown":

The precision that characterized every phase of the long voyage brings much closer the possibility that men will be able to fly to the moon almost as readily as they now orbit the earth.

This sparkling feat demonstrated above all the utility of the incredibly painstaking work done in the 21 months since the flash fire that killed three Apollo astronauts. The accent on foreseeing and making provision for every conceivable safety hazard was reflected in the equipment that enabled the astronauts to right their capsule easily when it landed upside down in the Atlantic.

Many more things might have gone wrong on this trip than on any earlier American manned space voyage simply because the rockets were far more powerful and the crew consisted of three men, as against the two in the earlier Gemini flights. That millions of components functioned so smoothly testifies to the quality of the planning and of the workmanship that went into the flight.

NASA's reaction to such new expressions of public confidence and enthusiasm was swift and predictable. The space agency's plans became suddenly both more ambitious and more flexible. Miraculously, months were cut out of previous schedules. The boldest of plans were chosen, and "warm-up," or practice missions, previously described as essential, were canceled.

After the Apollo 7 mission, NASA had three principal choices for its next mission, Apollo 8. The space agency could run what would have been essentially a "repeat" mission to iron out the problems that showed up during the preceding mission—and, contrary to the barrage of self-praise and superlatives that followed the Apollo 7 mission, real problems had occurred during that "101-percent-perfect" mission. These will be discussed below. NASA's second option was to send Apollo 8 on a loop-around mission to the Moon and back.

After less than three weeks of deliberation, however, NASA chose to proceed with the third, the most daring and dangerous, of its options: a mission that called for ten orbits around the

Moon. Based on the seven previous flights of the Apollo program, described below, the decision to make the Apollo 8 mission a ten-circumlunar-orbit flight must rank as one of the most audacious gambles ever taken in an area reputed to have over-whelming significance for national prestige. As will be seen, the series of previous Apollo flights had by no means fully justified the decision to proceed with the most ambitious of Apollo 8 objectives. Apparently, according to *Time* magazine, the pro-posal could be traced back to August, 1968. The idea originated with the manager of the Apollo spacecraft program, George M. Low. Said *Time* (Jan. 3, 1969): "Last August, when it became apparent that the Earth-orbiting December flight would be de-layed by problems with the Lunar Module [LM], he [Low] pro-posed a bold plan: an Apollo 8 Moon-orbital mission—without the LM. He was more than convincing, and that is why Apollo 8 got the go-ahead for its historic trip."

Even the members of the press who had remained sympathetic to NASA through its trying days seemed surprised by NASA's audacity. It was overwhelmingly evident that never before had a bigger gamble been taken in manned space flight. In *The New York Times*, John Noble Wilford, three days before the launch, termed it "the most daring flight of the space age." About four weeks before, *Time* had said "Apollo 8 involves greater risks than any of the previous manned space flights." *Newsweek* (Novem-ber 25, 1968) concurred: "There is no question that Apollo 8 is a riskier flight than any staged before by the U.S."

Some voices were much more outspoken. A sometime critic of the space race, Sir Bernard Lovell, director of England's Jodrell Bank Observatory, denied reports that he had said the Apollo 8 mission "sickens me" and that he had called it "just damn silly." The famed British radio astronomer, who had once been quoted as saying the U.S.-Soviet space rivalry was "one of the deepest follies of all time," ultimately claimed he had been quoted "out of context," a month before the Apollo 8 flight, on the statement: "On a scientific basis, this project is wasteful and silly. We've reached the stage with automatic landings when it's not necessary to risk human life to get information about the Moon."[*]

---

[*] After the Apollo 8 mission, Sir Bernard paid a lavish, if somewhat generalized, compliment to the Americans. "The entire enterprise," he said, as quoted in *The*

In late November, the British weekly the *Economist* joined in Sir Bernard's alleged criticism, calling the American Moon-landing deadline "a foolish goal." The *Economist* continued: "One trouble with a goal is reaching it. Especially if the goal is arbitrary, like becoming Miss World or landing a man on the moon, there is just no logical next step. . . . NASA, instead of insisting that the budget cuts be spread equitably, has fought hard to prevent practically anything at all being taken from Project Apollo. As a result disproportionate reductions have had to be made in everything else."

Not all criticism and pleas for caution came from abroad. In the *New Republic* in early December, Dr. Ralph Lapp urged that Apollo 8 be postponed until Apollo 9 could be readied as a "rescue ship" in the event the Apollo 8 astronauts were unable to return to Earth. "We are pushing our luck, gambling that everything will work perfectly," said Dr. Lapp. "At the very least we ought to be prepared to attempt a rescue."*

It bears repeating here—as discussed in Chapter 5—that the Lunar-Orbital Rendezvous (LOR) landing profile, which has

---

New York Times on December 28, 1968, "is magnificent and an amazing tribute to the present excellence of American technology and organizational procedures."

* NASA has belatedly begun to give serious consideration to the problem of space rescue. Cursory attention had been given in 1966, resulting in a House staff study entitled *Space Flight Emergencies and Flight Safety—Series E.* The report, published in 1967, considered a host of possible crises and solutions. Its lack of thoroughness, however, is indicated by the fact that nowhere did it consider the possibility of a cabin fire. Toward the end of May, 1968, more deliberate discussions were being considered. NASA told the House Committee on Science and Astronautics that it planned to study several space escape and rescue systems. As noted by *Aerospace Technology,* however, "nowhere in the report . . . did the space agency indicate that it was studying a real rescue system for Earth orbital or lunar surface operations." Nor did it indicate that it was ready to develop a system. During the second day of the Apollo 7 flight, the astronauts performed what was described as a "simulated rescue of two astronauts stranded in orbit around the Moon." What the astronauts actually did was to maneuver within seventy feet of the fuelless shell of their second-stage rocket (a Saturn 4-B) that had been passively orbiting within about one hundred miles of the Apollo spacecraft since the day before. Finally, as one more tardy nod to safety, NASA announced in mid-December, 1968, that it had given contractors nine weeks to submit proposals for a back-up propulsion system for the LM, in case of failure of the engine designed to lift the astronauts back off the lunar surface to a docking with the orbiting command module. It was doubtful, however, that this move, reported in *Aviation Week & Space Technology,* December 23, 1968, would provide such a back-up system for the first Moon landing. It would take time for NASA to evaluate the proposals, and months more for the chosen contractor to develop and test the system.

become America's blueprint for the Apollo landing, is probably the most hazardous of the three choices that NASA considered in 1961. According to LOR critics, it is most hazardous because all of the necessary docking and rendezvous maneuvers between the spacecraft and the Lunar Module, the LM, are conducted in orbit around the Moon. (See Fig. 7.) The more conservative method, Earth-Orbital Rendezvous (EOR), they say, would have seen more of the required maneuvers executed in Earth orbit. A malfunction in Earth orbit need not end in disaster because the astronauts could more easily return home. In orbit around the Moon, it is another story altogether. A malfunction in any of several systems necessary for a safe return flight would mean certain death.

Moreover, the LOR mission profile was predicated on the concept of simultaneous design and construction of all flight hardware and systems by a vast host of independent contractors and subcontractors. More than twenty thousand separate corporations, four hundred thousand workers, and two hundred colleges and universities have participated in the race to the Moon. The problem of coordination of these many contractors has proved to be an extremely difficult task. In fact, this was one of the problems which came to the attention of the public only as a result of the Apollo 204 fire. It was learned that NASA and North American Aviation had been persuing different design specifications in wiring and other layout situations.

Undaunted by all these challenges, NASA forged ahead go-for-broke, seemingly hypnotized by George Low's bold plans. NASA worked diligently to downplay the hazards of the Apollo 8 flight. Astronaut Lovell testily countered the reported criticisms of Lapp and Sir Bernard Lovell by describing the mission as no more dangerous than a combat tour in Vietnam. (Lovell's personal courage was admirable, but he did not seem to realize that an astronaut's value to the nation depends on his staying alive.) In a nationwide television interview, the Apollo 8 crew of Borman, Lovell, and Anders called the forthcoming mission a "conservative" one. Associate Administrator Dr. Mueller proclaimed the official NASA attitude: "We are taking no undue risks in flying a lunar-orbital mission." The question naturally arose:

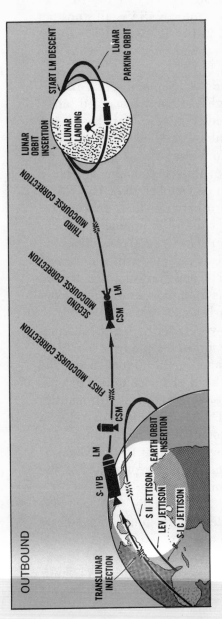

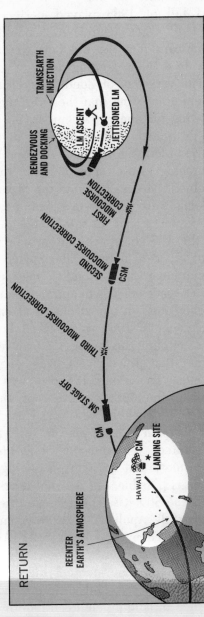

Fig. 7: Lunar-Orbital Rendezvous (LOR) Method of Landing
Men on the Moon and Returning Them

would a "combat tour in Vietnam" pose an undue risk for an astronaut?

No doubt, the flurry of Soviet space activity in the summer and fall of 1968 played perfectly into NASA's all-stops-out strategy. Once again, NASA could justify its haste by warning Americans that the Russians were on the verge of beating the U.S. to a Moon landing.

The very day of Zond 5's splashdown, September 22, rumors began circulating that the U.S. "might" attempt a manned lunar-orbiting mission in December. Speculation rose that the Soviets would quickly follow Zond 5's flight by sending cosmonauts on a Moon-looping mission. As Apollo 7 was being groomed for launching, word spread that "the Russians might launch a manned spacecraft around the Moon on October 15 or 16." NASA officials were portrayed as being torn between their concern for the utmost astronaut safety and their desire to uphold the honor of the U.S. in space. An article in *The New York Times* on September 23 noted: "The Soviet Union's successful unmanned circumlunar flight Zond 5 may put new pressure on United States space officials to approve plans for a more ambitious moon-circling mission by astronauts as early as December."

October 15, 1968, was marked, however, not by Russian cosmonauts circling the Moon, but by a report of a top Soviet scientist's denial that Russia was even engaged in a Moon race. The scientist, Dr. Leonid I. Sedov, was head of his country's delegation to the 19th Congress of the International Astronautics Federation, held in New York City. Dr. Sedov claimed that Russia did not plan to send men to the Moon "in the near future." He elaborated: "The question of sending astronauts to the Moon at this time is not an item on our agenda. The exploration of the Moon is possible, but it is not a priority."

As the Soviet scientist spoke, the United States' "101-percent-successful" Apollo 7 flight was entering the fourth day of its mission. Then, four days after Apollo 7's return, the Soviets launched a man into space in their Soyuz 3 spacecraft. It was the first Russian manned flight since the death of Vladimir Komarov, which had occurred when his Soyuz 1 spacecraft crashed in landing eighteen months before.

Reaction in the U.S. was practically unanimous. It was summed up in a *New York Times* editorial the day following the Soviet manned launch.

Both the American and Soviet manned space programs were temporarily halted by tragedies early last year; *now the space race is back in full stride . . .* The current Soviet exploit, coming only a few weeks after an automatic Soviet space capsule circled the Moon, indicates that Moscow is as eager as Washington to be first to put a man on the Moon . . . (italics added)

Once again, the press was interpreting a Soviet space flight as a sign that the Russians were racing America to the Moon.

However, as the details of the Soviet manned launch became known, American space experts, as well as the press, became somewhat less certain that the Russians were really back in the Moon race. The flight seemed to have demonstrated absolutely nothing new; the Soviets appeared to have made few, if any, significant advances in space technology. *Newsweek*'s reaction, dubbing the flight the "Soviet Unspectacular," was typical. The Soyuz 3 spacecraft, piloted by a single cosmonaut, Colonel Georgi T. Beregovoi, was launched into Earth orbit from the Russian space center at Baikonur, in the plains of Kazakhstan in Soviet Central Asia. The day before, an unmanned spacecraft, Soyuz 2, had also been launched. Western observers predicted that the Russians were about to achieve their first manned docking in space. (This they achieved with their manned Soyuz 4 and Soyuz 5 spacecraft on January 16, 1969. On this mission, the Russians also achieved a space "first" when two crewmen transferred in space from one capsule to the other. Russia had already accomplished docking of unmanned spacecraft, but it had never carried out manned link-ups such as those performed in the U.S. Gemini program.) But no successful docking was announced; the most that Russian authorities claimed was that Colonel Beregovoi had piloted his Soyuz 3 to a "rendezvous" within 200 meters (656 feet) of the pilotless Soyuz 2.

Another mystifying "unspectacular" aspect of the flight was the fact that it carried only a single crew member. The newer, redesigned Soyuz spacecraft had been reputed to be the Soviet counterparts of the three-man U.S. Apollos. One possible explanation for Colonel Beregovoi's solo performance was that

Soviet space scientists, still edgy from cosmonaut Komarov's death in the Soyuz 1, thought it best to risk only one man—rather than three—on the Soyuz 3 mission.

Thus, despite the speculation outside the U.S.S.R. that Beregovoi's flight fell far short of its programmed objectives,* the mission may have been planned simply as a test of the new Soyuz hardware. In any case, on October 30, 1968, after sixty-four orbits and just one hour less than four days in space, Colonel Beregovoi guided his ship down safely to a soft landing in the vicinity of Baikonur. Soviet authorities were reported to be "jubilant" that everything had gone so well.

The Soyuz 3 flight evoked a strange two-sided response from the U.S. space establishment. While in one breath space officials were describing the mission as "not very spectacular" and "really rather unimpressive," they also found it necessary to suggest that the Russians were on the verge of some truly great super-spectacular. The time was now early November, and the an-nouncement of Apollo 8's great gamble was coming up. It was vitally important to make the Soviets' space plans seem as im-pressive as possible. One rumor was repeated again and again: The Russians were going to launch a manned circumlunar journey before Apollo 8, possibly as early as December 2.

The Russians did launch a circumlunar flight, Zond 6, on November 10, but there were no cosmonauts aboard. The mission was essentially a repeat of Zond 5, with a "crew" of biological specimens. It was a noteworthy flight in some respects. It utilized the Earth's atmosphere for an aerodynamic "skipping" reentry that slowed its speed before it returned through the atmosphere to a soft Earth landing; and Soviet scientists announced that the flight had dispelled their worries about coping with radiation dangers in space. These were indeed noteworthy achievements—but hardly spectacular.

One other significant Soviet launch occurred in mid-November, the day before Zond 6 returned to Earth. The "heaviest automatic

---

* A Czech astronomer, Dr. L. Krivsky of the Czechoslovak Academy of Sciences' Ondrejov Observatory, claimed that a "very dangerous" outburst of radiation from a solar storm had forced the Russians to end Colonel Beregovoi's flight prematurely. "This was obviously one of the reasons why Cosmonaut Beregovoi in Soyuz 3 did not fulfill some of the other programs that had been planned," Dr. Krivsky stated.

space station ever launched," called Proton 4, was lifted into Earth orbit. According to Tass, the official Soviet press agency, the purpose of the Proton 4 was to investigate the "nature of cosmic rays of high and super-high energies and their interaction with nuclei of atoms." Weighing approximately 37,500 pounds, Proton 4 indicated that the Russians possessed a booster capable of developing up to three million pounds thrust—more powerful than the U.S. Saturn 1B, but dwarfed by the Americans' 7.5 million-pound-thrust Saturn 5, which had launched as much as 280,000 pounds into space.

At this point, after the launch of Proton 4 on November 16, a curious change occurred in the Russians' announcements about their space plans. Quite suddenly, they began to drop broad hints that they were ready to send men around the Moon—and "soon." December 8 was mentioned as the most likely date in the Western press, and the flight could carry one, two, or three cosmonauts.

On November 23, Tass declared for the first time that Zonds 5 and 6 were designed as test flights to precede a manned flight to the Moon and back. Two days later, *Izvestia*, the government newspaper, announced that the Zond spacecraft, with certain modifications, were capable of carrying men to the Moon. (Previously only Soyuz spacecraft had been mentioned in connection with manned flights.) The next day, a UPI report from Moscow said: "The Soviet Union is preparing to launch its most spectacular manned space flight by dispatching shortly at least two, and probably three, men on a circumlunar flight. The Moon flight, sources said today, may be undertaken before the launching of the American manned craft, Apollo 8, set for December 21." Finally, on November 29, Tass proclaimed: "Automatic space probes always precede manned flights . . . The space route earth-moon-earth has been opened."

What was the explanation of this sudden indication of an intense Soviet desire to put men on the Moon? One guess is that the Soviet Union was simply blustering, knowing it was going to be beaten. Another hypothesis worth considering is that the Russians had no intention of attempting to beat the Apollo 8 flight, but were simply trying to push the U.S. into all-out haste—toward, perhaps, a tragic miscalculation. The Soviets had always taken a more cautious and conservative approach to space exploration than the U.S. They had, for example, proceeded with unmanned automatic rendezvous and docking (a feat that had yet to be accomplished by the U.S.), and sent two unmanned Zonds on around-the-Moon missions before committing cosmonauts to these spacecraft. It was extremely doubtful that Russia would send cosmonauts to a Moon landing before first landing an unmanned craft and bringing it back. Morevover, the Soviet space program has always seemed to place emphasis on building Earth-orbiting space laboratories from which relatively small rockets could be launched to explore the Moon and planets. The U.S. was reminded of this fact when, on January 5 and January 10, 1969, the U.S.S.R. sent its second and third soft-landing probes (Venus 5 and Venus 6) on twin four-month, 155-million-mile trips to the surface of the planet Venus. In terms of space hardware, moreover, the Russians did not have a booster that could make a direct Earth-Moon manned trip (although they were reported to be developing a rocket in the fifteen-million-pound-thrust class), nor had they demonstrated a lunar landing craft.

All these characteristics of the Russian space program were known—or should have been—as NASA prepared for its Apollo 8 flight. Yet not until December 17, four days before the Apollo 8 launch, did Russia finally concede—and the Western press and space officials accept the fact—that the Soviet cosmonauts were not going anywhere near the Moon in 1968.

Thus, the American manned space program stood, unchallenged, on the verge of its greatest triumph.

It is time to investigate more thoroughly the Apollo program's achievements since the Apollo 204 fire. Can the American people, with *The New York Times*, take pride in the "sparkling feat[s] [that] demonstrated above all the utility of the incredibly painstaking work done in the . . . months since the flash fire that killed three Apollo astronauts"?

Whether intentionally or not, NASA created some confusion as to the sequence of the Apollo flights by changing to a new numbering system after the Apollo 204 fire. Prior to the disaster, all Apollo missions, manned and unmanned, that would utilize the Saturn 1B booster were designated as the "200 series." Three successful unmanned Saturn 1B flights preceded the abortive 204 manned mission; these were termed Apollos 201, 202, and 203.*

Then followed these Apollo missions:

Apollo 4, November 9, 1967: This unmanned mission was the first launch of the 7.5-million-pound-thrust Saturn 5 (its first stage utilizing five 1.5-million-pound-thrust engines), the booster designed to send men to a landing on the Moon. Of all the Apollo tests, before Apollo 8, this one was perhaps the most genuinely successful. The fact that the first launching of the most powerful rocket ever built—thirty-six stories tall, weighing 6.2 million pounds and capable of placing an unprecedented 140 tons in orbit—went off so smoothly seemed to surprise even space agency officials. Apollo program manager Major General Phillips remarked: "Yesterday I would have said that I think we have a reasonably good chance of accomplishing a lunar landing before the end of 1969. Today I think that reasonably good chance may be a notch above reasonably good." In the next few days, Phillips' and other NASA and industry officials' reserve all but disappeared. At a "splashdown party," one North American Rockwell engineer chortled: "Our slate's clean now, baby! We showed them who knows how to fly a bird." Said Phillips: "We're really moving again." Such exuberance was understandable; but it should be pointed out that the eight-and-a-half-hour Apollo 4 mission demonstrated two significant achievements. One was the fact that the Saturn 5 could fly. The other was that the unmanned Apollo spacecraft appeared to be able to withstand the unprecedentedly high reentry heat a command module would encounter when returning, at about 25,000 miles per hour from a Moon trip. However, the Apollo 4 spacecraft reentered at somewhat less speed than would a craft, such as Apollo 8, returning

---

* In this same system, all flights, manned and unmanned, utilizing the more powerful Saturn 5 booster were identified as the "500 series." Thus, the first unmanned launch of the Saturn 5 (November 9, 1967) was to be known as mission AS-501. However, in the thick sheaf of press releases that NASA issued in commemoration of its tenth anniversary (October 1, 1968), AS-501 had been transformed into "Apollo 4." From that point on, the Apollo missions have been numbered sequentially 5, 6, 7, 8, 9, etc. Mission 204 is not cited in the "Apollo Flight Program Summary" contained in NASA's tenth anniversary special report—the rationale being, perhaps, that it never did get off the ground.

from an actual Moon trip. Nor was the mission utterly perfect. The vital third-stage rocket had begun to spill liquid hydrogen fuel during flight. Furthermore, a computer had shut down at the Bermuda tracking station, and started up again only moments before the lift-off.

These problems, "not considered serious," were premonitions of the major flaws that would mar succeeding Apollo missions.

Apollo 5, January 22, 1968. This unmanned Earth-orbital mission was the first to test the "spacecraft systems performance, ascent and descent stage propulsion firings and restart, and staging" of the Apollo Lunar Module. This was a stripped-down, incomplete version of the "bug" which, when completely equipped, would carry two U.S. astronauts to the surface of the Moon and back to the Apollo mother ship remaining in lunar orbit. This version of the LM was not equipped to carry men. Nor, because it lacked many components, could it have landed on the Moon.

Because, among other factors, the pull of gravity on Earth is six times greater than it is on the Moon, Moon landings cannot be exactly duplicated on Earth. Therefore, both manned and unmanned tests of the LM for a Moon landing cannot be simulated in Earth-orbit. This means that the only way to test the capabilities of the LM would be by sending an unmanned lunar module, guided by instruments, to and from the lunar surface. Such a test has never been part of NASA's plans.

The Apollo 5 mission was rated a success by NASA. Perhaps the best description, offered by *Science News Letter* (November 2, 1968), was that Apollo 5 was a "qualified success."

After a four-hour delay on the launching pad because of mechanical difficulties, the unmanned LM was lifted off by a Saturn 1B rocket (incidentally, the very same Saturn that had been "mated" to the Apollo 204 capsule a year before). After the LM was separated from the Saturn, the flight plan called for four firings of the LM's rockets. However, the 10,500-pound-thrust rocket designed to brake the astronauts' descent to the Moon's surface failed to fire properly. This rocket had been programmed to fire for thirty-eight seconds at up to 90 percent of its maximum thrust. Instead, the descent engine fired for only four seconds at 10 percent of its maximum thrust and then simply cut off completely. A strange "success" indeed—what if astronauts had been aboard this LM?

Part of the reason why the fiction of the Apollo 5 "success" went largely unchallenged was the fact that mission controllers altered the flight plan on the spot, thus averting a mission abort. By changing the flight plan, a 12.5-minute second firing of the descent engine was eliminated. This firing, which would have been the longest continuous firing of any U.S. rocket engine on an actual mission, had, until Apollo 9, yet to be performed in space. Furthermore, as has been pointed out, "there [had] been many other difficulties [with the LM] including troubles with major engine components [unrelated to the descent engine misfiring]. A particular woe is weight. The LM was to have weighed 32,000 pounds, including fuel, but is now so heavy that it may have to leave as much as 2,200 pounds of fuel behind" on the Apollo 9 mission.

In the light of these facts, a comment that appeared in *The New York Times* (January 28, 1968) less than a week after the Apollo 5 mission had a strange air of unreality.

> . . . hopes for a moon landing were bolstered earlier this week by the *successful* initial test flight of the landing craft in which two astronauts are to go to and from the Moon's surface.

In the same article, by the *Times'* John Noble Wilford, Major General Phillips was quoted as saying "I'm bullish." And Wilford himself wrote of the "new optimism" of the space program in describing a "gradual emergence out of the shadow of disaster which was affirmed in a series of interviews and visits to launching, testing, and manufacturing facilities this week."

The fact is that the LM program has been plagued by troubles from its very conception. The windows in the Apollo 5 LM mysteriously ruptured during launch preparations. The "bug" flew with aluminum replacements. An LM was meant to be aboard what became the Moon-orbiting Apollo 8 mission; instead the Apollo 8 astronauts had to be given a dummy section representing the Lunar Module. This meant that the LM's first manned flight would have to be aboard Apollo 9, with Colonel James A.

McDivitt scheduled to command "one of the most headache-producing pieces of equipment in the Apollo program" for the first time.

"Lunar landing simulators," vehicles designed to give astronauts experience in piloting the LM, have been in difficulty. A lunar landing training vehicle, designed to simulate procedures in the LM's touchdown on the Moon, crashed in flames at the Manned Spacecraft Center in Houston on December 8, 1968.* The test pilot ejected safely, but the $1.9-million vehicle was a total loss. It was the second crash of the year of a lunar-landing simulator. In the earlier crash, Gemini 8 veteran Neil Armstrong had also escaped by using his ejection seat, while the Moon landing trainer was reduced to a pile of rubble.

Clearly, the Apollo 5 mission and its "successful" test of the LM gave one little cause to envy astronaut McDivitt and those who were to follow him in flights of the Lunar Module.

However, it is all too apparent why NASA had to term the Apollo 5 mission successful. The day before the flight, Wilford reported from Cape Kennedy: "If the test is successful, the lunar module will probably be declared ready for manned operations later this year. The lunar module is the only remaining untested vehicle in the Apollo man-to-the-moon project. A failure would force the space agency to repeat the test this spring with a backup vehicle. A serious failure, requiring major redesigning of the engines, could set back the nation's plans to send astronauts on a round trip to the moon by the end of the decade."

NASA, once again, was back in the business of turning failures into successes in order to beat a schedule.

Apollo 6, April 4, 1968: This was the second unmanned, Earth-orbital test of the Saturn 5 rocket. It is NASA's claim that this "launch vehicle development flight . . . demonstrated Saturn 5 rocket performance and Apollo spacecraft subsystems and heat shield performance."

If the Apollo 5 flight could be described most charitably as a "qualified success," the Apollo 6 flight must be described as a

---

* A month prior to the December 8 crash, following a series of ground tests, astronaut McDivitt expressed growing confidence in the LM. He declared, "My confidence level has gone up a lot. I just hope it flies as well as it performed in tests."

"qualified disaster." Yet six months after this Apollo 6 flight, in its tenth anniversary press kit, NASA declared that "Apollo 6, launched April 4, 1968, [has] not been officially declared success or failure, pending further evaluation." Later in the reports, where missions were designated as to their success or failure, Apollo 6 is defined as "unrated," both in the category of vehicle performance and the category of accomplishment of mission objectives.

Quite simply, what happened during the Apollo 6 flight was that two of the Saturn 5 rocket assembly's five second-stage engines cut off prematurely. Moreover, the third-stage engine, the rocket designed to push the spacecraft out of Earth orbit and on its way to the Moon, failed to reignite at a critical point. The Apollo spacecraft went hurtling into the wrong orbit, and eventually splashed down in the Pacific Ocean northwest of Hawaii.

The Apollo 6 mission was specifically designed to "man-rate" the Saturn 5 rocket. As *The New York Times* pointed out: "The Saturn 5 moon rocket apparently failed to qualify for manned missions without further testing . . . A flawless launching would have qualified the super-rocket for use in a manned flight this fall [1968], one of the primary steps in preparations for landing men on the Moon."

The test was a failure. It was acknowledged as such by none other than NASA's associate administrator, Dr. George Mueller. "We're all disappointed," said Dr. Mueller. "This will have to be defined as a failure." When a reporter asked Dr. Mueller whether another unmanned test flight would be required, the NASA official replied that this was "probably the decision that would be reached."

*But this was not the decision that was reached. NASA committed astronauts Borman, Lovell, and Anders to a Saturn 5 rocket assembly, as yet unproven as a man-lofting vehicle, for Apollo 8, a mission involving "greater risks than any of the previous manned space flights."**

Incredibly, as they had done with the badly flawed Apollo 5-

---

* The Apollo 7 manned mission, which orbited Earth for eleven days, was launched not by a Saturn 5 but by a Saturn 1B rocket. Previously other Saturn 1B's had been successfully tested.

LM mission, NASA officials transformed clear "go slow" warning signals into a mandate to accelerate the Moon-landing schedule. Perhaps the most lucid description of this remarkable approach occurred in *Science News Letter*, December 21, 1968:

> Until last April, space officials were not sure they wanted a crew to go along on Apollo 8. On April 4, however, *the second unmanned flight of the Saturn 5 proved to be such a success* that it was decided to entrust astronauts to the mighty booster. [Italics added.]

And then came the clincher:

> This also moved the scheduled lunar landing up from Apollo 12 to Apollo 11, which could put men on the Moon as early as next summer [1969].

One further example of NASA's ability to confuse press and public alike about the significance of its missions and their results can be found in an editorial in the *Christian Science Monitor*, November 5, 1968. In describing the success of the Apollo 7 mission, the editorial made the remarkable statement that "the Saturn rocket is moonworthy." The point that seems to have escaped the *Monitor* editors is that the Apollo 7 utilized a much smaller Saturn 1B rocket in an *Earth-orbital* mission; indeed, a Saturn 1B is simply not powerful enough to send three Apollo astronauts to the Moon. A Saturn 5 rocket assembly would have to be used for the first trip to the vicinity of the Moon. Thus, by no stretch of the imagination had either Saturn rocket been proved "moonworthy."

Apollo 7, October 11-22, 1968: This was the "flawless," "101-percent-perfect" manned flight that prompted NASA to resume its go-for-broke race to the Moon. Its objectives were approximately the same as those that had been programmed for the Apollo 204 mission twenty months before; the mission even lifted off from the same launch pad 34. Major design changes had been made in the command module and other units of the Apollo spacecraft; it was, in essence, a brand-new capsule, including a hatch that the crewmen could open in seven seconds, enabling them to complete their exit during a ground emergency in approximately thirty seconds. The five miles of wiring in Apollo 7 had been coated with stainless steel; the men's space suits had been redesigned, utilizing glass-fiber Beta cloth that withstands temperatures up to 2,000° F. The redesign of the suits had made them far bulkier. Two of the suits, those designed for the astronauts who would make the descent to the Moon's surface in the LM, weighed fifty-four pounds; the suit of the navigator, who would remain in the lunar-orbiting Apollo capsule, weighed twenty-five pounds. In addition to the more fire-resistant suits, some twenty-five other fireproof or fire-resistant materials had replaced more easily ignitible materials that had been aboard space capsule 204. As for the pure-oxygen cabin environment, as has been mentioned earlier, the following procedure was adopted for Apollo 7:

> To reduce the ignition and fire-feeding hazards [of pure oxygen], engineers . . . substituted a gas mixture of 60 per cent oxygen and 40 per cent nitrogen for use in the capsule during ground tests and at launching time. After launching, the oxygen-nitrogen mixture [would be] slowly released into space and gradually replaced by oxygen. After about five hours of flight, when the most dangerous phases of the early mission [had] been completed, the capsule's atmosphere [was] expected to be about 95 per cent oxygen. From the start, the astronauts [would] breathe pure oxygen from a separate supply system that feeds [oxygen] directly into their helmets.

Most interestingly, these new safety measures had added approximately 650 pounds to the weight of the capsule. *It will be remembered that one of NASA's oft-repeated reasons why more safety features had not been designed into the Apollo 204 capsule was that the weight penalties simply could not be paid.*

The bare facts of the Apollo 7 mission are these: At 11:03 A.M., Eastern Standard Time, October 11, 1968, a Saturn 1B rocket lifted Captain Walter M. Schirra, Jr. (U.S. Navy), Major Donn F. Eisele (U.S. Air Force), and R. Walter Cunningham (a civilian and former U.S. Marine pilot) into Earth orbit. Just under eleven days later, at 7:11 A.M. EST, after 163 Earth orbits, the Apollo 7 capsule dropped into the Atlantic Ocean 325 miles south of Bermuda. At a news conference that morning, Lieutenant General Phillips* made the following remarks: "Apollo 7 goes in my book as a perfect mission . . . In my experience this is the first space operation that has accomplished more than one hundred percent of its preplanned objectives. Our official count is that we have accomplished 101 percent of our intended objectives."

A more dispassionate view of the mission appeared in *Science News Letter* some ten days later: "Despite some fifty acknowledged mishaps, three nagging colds and an upside-down landing, space agency officials have declared the flight of Apollo 7 to be a 'more than 100 per cent success.' "

The problem of sick astronauts tended to be shrugged off after the safe return of the Apollo 7 (but it was to turn up again among Apollo 8 astronauts Borman, Lovell, and Anders). The respiratory infections that plagued Schirra, Eisele, and Cunningham fortunately were minor. Nevertheless, there was cause for alarm that the astronauts' eardrums would rupture during re-entry because of the combination of clogged respiratory passages and the rapid pressure build-up within the capsule during its descent. (Pressure would approximately triple during the six-and-a-half-minute drop into the sea.) Schirra's repeated requests to make the reentry without helmets—so that the three astronauts could follow the familiar steps of taking a deep breath, holding their noses, shutting their windpipes, and "popping" their ears in order to equalize the pressure between the ear and nasal passages and the pressure in the cabin—were finally approved, and none of the astronauts suffered ear injury. It appears that only through Schirra's insistence was the danger of this injury averted; the flight controllers were reluctant to approve a procedure that had never before been used during reentry.

Although much publicity was given the "upside-down" landing of the Apollo 7 capsule, this was really a relatively minor mishap, a contingency that was recognized from the start and easily dealt with by activating a series of three inflatable flotation bags. However, among the "fifty acknowledged mishaps" of the Apollo 7 flight, there were some that, while far less dramatic than an upside-down landing, might have brought a premature ending to, or even spelled disaster for, the entire mission.

Before describing some of these "anomalies," we should note

---

* On May 28, 1968, Phillips had been promoted to lieutenant general.

that something did go splendidly right with the Apollo 7 flight. This was the testing of the crucial 20,500-pound-thrust rocket engine located in the service module behind the command module. This so-called SPS (service propulsion system) engine had to operate perfectly in order subsequently to send the Apollo 8 spacecraft into a lunar orbit, to push that spacecraft out of orbit around the Moon and on its way back to Earth, and finally to make any major correction necessary so that the Apollo could pass through its narrow "reentry corridor" to an Earth landing at exactly the right angle. During the Apollo 7 mission, the eight planned firings of the SPS engine went off virtually without a hitch. There is little doubt that the performance of the SPS, more than any other single factor in the Apollo 7 mission, emboldened NASA officials to go for broke on Apollo 8.

And yet how, considering the following mishaps—only a few of the fifty acknowledged by NASA—could the Apollo 7 flight be termed "101 percent perfect"?

■ Just before lift-off, after the astronauts had strapped themselves into their couches and the spacecraft hatch had been sealed, "someone on the launching tower," according to *The New York Times*, "pushed the wrong button and caused an electrical malfunction of the high-speed elevator running between the ground and the platform adjacent to the spacecraft. The elevator was planned as the astronauts' first route of escape in case of trouble. But mission officials decided the elevator could still be used on a limited basis, or else the astronauts could, if necessary, rely on the slide wire running from the top of the tower to the ground. So the countdown continued without pause . . ."

■ About one hour and twenty minutes after lift-off, there was a power failure in the Mission Control Center in Houston. Emergency back-up power allowed the crucial mission computer to keep operating; but for about two minutes mission controllers could not follow the flight on their consoles. Only dull red emergency lamps burned in the semidarkness of the control room, which is the main decision and command area of Building 30, the three-story, windowless Mission Control Center.

■ On the second day of the mission, Major Eisele discovered a malfunction in the navigational guidance and control equipment that would be needed to guide an Apollo spacecraft to the Moon. The equipment consists of a telescope, a sextant, and related components linking these units to a computer and inertial guidance system. When he moved the shaft of the telescope, Eisele reported, "A lot of sandy white particles flutter out and they obscure the field of view. Also, at times when the sun is more direct on the side where the optics are, it appears to be either a lot of light leak or absolute sunshine reflecting down inside the optic assembly." He added: "You just don't see anything when you look out there."

■ Late into the third day of the mission, the spacecraft's electrical distribution system experienced a temporary circuit failure. Moreover, the back-up system, designed to take over if the main electrical distribution system should go awry, did not cut in and take over. The system was eventually reactivated from the ground. Flight controllers were sufficiently alarmed to order the astronauts to fire their SPS engine in order to bring the spacecraft's orbit about thirty miles nearer to the Earth's surface. From this point, the astronauts could more easily have been brought back to Earth using a minimum of power.

■ During the fifth day of the mission, the astronauts encountered a series of "minor" malfunctions, including a sticky control handle by which Captain Schirra was meant to be able to fire manually the spacecraft's maneuvering rockets. Also during this fifth day, a curious anomaly occurred in the motion of the spacecraft. Schirra reported: "The spacecraft is actually torquing —it's pitch—a certain surge effect . . . This is what we had a heck of a time trying to explain to ourselves." This peculiar torquing motion was apparently never adequately accounted for.

■ A week into the mission, another communications blackout occurred on the ground, lasting approximately nine minutes. This caused the loss of about two minutes of coded data from the spacecraft, but according to NASA flight directors the lost data "were not considered essential."

■ On the eighth day, the astronauts reported difficulties with the biomedical sensors attached to their chests to give information on heartbeat and respiration. Some of the connecting wires had actually snapped, and Major Eisele reported that his wires were heating up. Not until after the completion of the mission did NASA announce just how serious this problem had been: *Three days of medical monitoring of heartbeat and respiration rates were lost.*

■ Another significant problem was not mentioned until after the Apollo 7's splashdown: on-board electrical battery chargers failed to perform up to par.

Before the Apollo 7 flight, NASA officials had stated that unless everything went well, there would have to be a repeat of the mission. It seems evident that "fifty acknowledged mishaps" do not represent perfect performance. If deficiencies in the electrical power system in the command module, loss of biomedical data, and two blackouts in the mission control center—plus a host of other malfunctions—did not, when taken together, warrant a repeat of the Apollo 7 mission, then what would?

There was no repeat of the Apollo 7 mission.

Apollo 8, December 21-27, 1968: This manned flight, carrying astronauts Colonel Frank Borman (U.S.A.F.), Captain James A. Lovell, Jr. (U.S.N.), and Major William A. Anders (U.S.A.F.) must go down in history as one of the most miraculously successful ventures ever attempted by man. The three astronauts "broke free" of Earth's bonds of gravity for the first time in history, traveled a quarter-million miles to the Moon, orbited it ten times at altitudes as low as seventy miles above the lunar surface, fired out of lunar orbit, and returned to a safe splashdown in the Pacific, about one thousand miles southwest of Hawaii near Christmas Island in the predawn hours of December 27, 1968. The capsule landed about three miles from the primary recovery vessel, the carrier *Yorktown*, and the astronauts were promptly picked up by recovery teams from the carrier. The Apollo 8 mission was truly a technological miracle—a "miracle" in the most profound sense.

Throughout the entire Apollo 8 mission, there were four difficulties that might be considered significant. First, on December 11, during a countdown rehearsal, there occurred a macabre reminder of the Apollo 204 disaster. According to UPI: the

astronauts *"spent an extra two and a half hours in their cabin because of some ground communications problems* [italics added]."
A second malfunction occurred in the two-and-a-half-hour period
after lift-off, as Apollo 8 orbited the Earth waiting for the "go"
or "no go" signal from the ground for "TLI" (Trans-Lunar In-
jection), that is, the decision to move out of Earth orbit and head
for the Moon. During this time, there occurred a "minor glitch"
—the oxygen flow-rate within the capsule was temporarily too
high—but this appeared to be corrected, and the craft received
orders to shoot for the Moon. Thirdly, Colonel Borman experienced nausea accompanied by vomiting and diarrhea; the
other two astronauts, though not so severely as Borman, were
also experiencing some queasiness. Finally, toward the end of
the flight, the spacecraft's larger windows had become so fogged
that the astronauts could barely see outside their capsule.

In the light of Apollo 8's substantial accomplishments and its
safe return, it is perhaps simply nit-picking to challenge NASA's
assertion that these and other trouble-spots were "minor." They
are, indeed, minor when one considers the overwhelmingly major
gambles that NASA took—and miraculously won—in launching
Apollo 8 at all on December 21, 1968. The three most glaring
gambles were these:

■ The Saturn 5 rocket assembly had never been man-rated.
Its previous unmanned launching test (Apollo 6, described
earlier) had been close to a fiasco.

■ The 20,500-pound-thrust engine, which had to work flaw-
lessly in order to prevent a mission failure or, at worst, the
deaths of all three astronauts, had no duplicate ("back-up") parts
for three of its essential components: the combustion chamber
itself; the nozzle through which the engine's flame escapes; and
the extension of the nozzle that protrudes nine feet from the
back of the spacecraft. If any of these units failed, the engine
would have malfunctioned. NASA explained away its failure to
provide these three SPS back-up units by pointing first to the
fact that all the engine's other components and subsystems were

"redundant" or duplicated,* and second to the fact that the engine had been fired over three thousand times (but only eight times in space, aboard Apollo 7) without malfunction.

■ The Apollo 8 plunged back into the Earth's atmosphere at nearly twenty-five thousand miles per hour, at a steeper angle and some seven thousand miles per hour faster than any astronaut had ever made a reentry. This was faster, too, than the unmanned Apollo 4 spacecraft, which had "proved" it could be done. The dangers—in terms of the men's physiology, reentry heat, parachute-braking, and effects on communications—were far greater than those of any previous manned reentry. Apollo 8 had to reenter the Earth's atmosphere at an angle no greater than 7.5° nor less than 5.1°. This meant that the spacecraft had to hit a "corridor" less than forty miles wide. Reentry at too steep an angle (greater than 7.5°) would have caused a sudden shock of deceleration. The force on the astronauts might exceed 20 g's. Friction with the atmosphere would have heated the spacecraft much above its design limits. According to a preflight briefing by Lieutenant General Phillips: "There would be a structural breakup and loss of the spacecraft and the crew." On the other hand, if Apollo hit the atmosphere at too shallow an angle (less than 5.1°), the spacecraft would bounce off the atmosphere and soar into an elongated elliptical orbit about the Earth, much like a flat stone skipping on the surface of a pond. The astronauts would have had only enough oxygen and electrical power left to survive for a few hours. Said Lieutenant General Phillips: "It's a crew-loss kind of situation."

And yet, one day into the Apollo 8 mission, a report from Houston Manned Spacecraft Center hinted that because of Apollo 8's performance, NASA might try for the actual lunar landing in May, 1969, on the next mission but one—Apollo 10.

As Apollo 8 sped toward the Moon, a Soviet space scientist, Georgi I. Petrov, while praising the mission, pointed out: "The Apollo 8 system is distinguished by the fact that the crew ap-

---

* The Soviet Soyuz 3 craft contains in its rear compartment (equivalent to the Apollo's service module) two complete rocket engines and fuel for both. One engine is a back-up for the other, in case of a failure. This is yet another example of the Soviets' more cautious approach to manned space travel.

parently plays the main role in controlling the ship. Soviet scientists and designers have been working on systems in which man's control of the spaceship is completely duplicated by automatic devices capable of returning the ship to earth and landing it even if the astronauts are incapacitated. It seems to me that such a control system and the preliminary testing of the entire flight program by automatic stations before sending off a manned spaceship ensures greater safety."

Apollo 9, officially scheduled on February 28, 1969, but then delayed because the crew came down with colds. As much as NASA might have wished, this flight could hardly have been tagged for the lunar landing, since it was the first manned flight ever of the Lunar Module, and the first time it had been launched by a Saturn 5. Before the Apollo 7 flight, NASA had indicated that the Apollo 9 mission would probably occur no earlier than March, 1969. By the time the Apollo 8 mission was over, there had been talk of launching Apollo 9 as early as February 20. NASA's schedule-telescoping was once again in evidence.

It is ironic that the glories and tributes that were heaped upon astronauts Borman, Lovell, and Anders after their lunar-orbiting feat would not fall equally on the crew of Apollo 9: Colonel James A. McDivitt and Lieutenant Colonel David R. Scott of the Air Force; and Russell L. Schweickart, a civilian astronaut. No less courage or professionalism was demanded of the Apollo 9 astronauts, even though their scheduled ten-day, Earth-orbiting mission was "far less spectacular" than Apollo 8.*

McDivitt, Scott, and Schweickart were slated to test a vehicle that had failed badly in its initial, unmanned test flight (Apollo 5) and had not been retested. The mission required Scott, pilot of the command module, to nose his spacecraft into a collar on the LM, which, attached to the third stage of the launch vehicle, had already been separated from the command and service modules. This coupling achieved, McDivitt and Schweickart were to crawl through the tunnel-like hatch and take over control of

---

* This fact was confirmed, just before the Apollo 8 flight, by NASA's director of flight operations at the Houston Manned Spacecraft Center, Christopher C. Kraft, Jr. He told a *New York Times* reporter that the Apollo 9 mission "is even more dangerous than Apollo 8."

the LM. They would then fly the LM for five or six hours in its first manned test, concluding with a final rendezvous and docking, in which the LM would rely exclusively on its own engines for the crucial maneuvering, while the command module remained "passive."

During this time, Schweickart would climb out of the LM, grope his way to the command module and back—a "space walk" whose primary purpose, according to NASA was to demonstrate that if the two vehicles failed somehow to dock, the two LM astronauts could still get back to the command module. Schweickart's adventure also had two other purposes: to take pictures of the Earth and the two spacecraft, and to check the illumination provided by a floodlight (on the service module) used in docking. All three astronauts would make their return in the command module, leaving the LM in orbit.

It was not, however, the hazards of the Apollo 9 LM mission that most impressed NASA officials, but the fact the LM project was running almost two years behind schedule. In late July, 1968, NASA Associate Administrator Dr. Mueller and Apollo program director Lieutenant General Phillips delivered a scathing, closed-doors lecture to contractors and suppliers at the home of LM's builder, the Grumman Aircraft Engineering Corporation in Bethpage, New York. Unlike the Phillips Report of December, 1965, the Bethpage lecture had nothing whatsoever to do with quality or performance standards. It had to do with something quite different. As reported by John Noble Wilford in *The New York Times*, August 15, 1968:

> In an effort to hasten the landing of astronauts on the moon, Apollo project officials are pressing contractors to stop making many small engineering changes and get flight-ready vehicles . . . [to Cape Kennedy] . . . on schedule. Dr. George E. Mueller . . . was reported to have said that the disregard [by contractors] of planned delivery dates for Apollo equipment amounted to a "disease" in the project. "This is the disease relating to everyone . . . [trying to be] . . . a program manager and deciding that they know best about how to schedule deliveries," Dr. Mueller reportedly said. "This has got to stop . . ."
>
> "I've never heard a government agency talk to a contractor

like that," commented a representative for one major Apollo contractor . . .

More than ever, the dozens of contractors in the $24-billion program are under strong and conflicting pressures to achieve the nation's goal of landing men on the moon by the end of the decade. They are being urged to meet tough specifications for mission safety and success at the same time they are being pushed to meet rigid delivery deadlines. As a result of the fire that killed three Apollo astronauts . . . in January, 1967, the contractors are said to be obsessed with checking and double-checking all systems . . .*

Referring to Grumman's lunar landing vehicle the LM, General Phillips is supposed to have suggested that "we quit trying to make them better and get a few in orbit so we can be sure we know where our flight problems lie."

Joseph G. Gavin, Jr., the Grumman vice president for space work . . . said the purpose of the remarks by Dr. Mueller and General Phillips "was aimed at the idea of freezing configurations"—that is, going with current equipment.

Apparently, Dr. Mueller and Lieutenant General Phillips had forgotten that it had been precisely this kind of attitude—"going with current equipment"—that had contributed to making the Apollo 204 Block 1 spacecraft a death trap.

Apollo 10: In the wake of the Apollo 8 mission, this flight was tentatively scheduled for May 17, 1969. For many weeks, the mission had been described by NASA as "all but" a lunar landing. Astronauts Colonel Thomas P. Stafford, Commander John W. Young and Commander Eugene A. Cernan were to repeat Apollo 8's history-making trip. However, this time the Apollo spacecraft would be carrying an LM capable of everything but a landing on the Moon's surface. The plan was to enter lunar orbit and then launch the LM—with astronauts Stafford and Cernan at the controls—toward the Moon's surface. Apollo 10's LM would stop short of an actual landing. It would descend to an altitude of approximately fifty thousand feet above the lunar surface and

---

* Before a House Authorization hearing, in the spring of 1967, Dr. Mueller had shrugged off these nervous Nellies. "Some people will even complain about the color of the paint," he said.

then ascend again to rejoin Commander Young in the orbiting Apollo 10 command module. NASA officials had stated that this "all but" flight was necessary to erase any doubts about the LM's capability before the actual Moon landing was attempted.

And yet there remained the suspicion that NASA just might try to go all the way on Apollo 10—despite a firm denial by Lieutenant General Phillips in late December, 1968. He pointed out that the LM that had been attached to a Saturn 5 for the Apollo 10 mission was not equipped to land. Furthermore, the Apollo 10 LM is several hundred pounds heavier that the LM earmarked for the next mission, Apollo 11. So heavy is the Apollo 10 LM, in fact, that there was real doubt whether its ascent engine could lift it back off the lunar surface if it did make a landing.

It was evident, however, as 1969 began, that some strong voices, somewhere in the NASA organization, were not giving up the idea of landing with Apollo 10. There was, for example, the hint of a "May landing" that came out of Houston in the first exuberant days of the Apollo 8 flight. An Associated Press dispatch from Houston on November 13, 1968, had reported that "officials of the National Aeronautics and Space Administration have said privately that the mission [Apollo 10] might be changed to a lunar landing." On December 6, *Time* suggested that Apollo 10 "may even try for a landing." *Newsweek* had mentioned it; *Science News Letter* kept mentioning it despite Lieutenant General Phillips' denial. Rocket and space expert Willy Ley, in a guest column for *The New York Times* on December 28, 1968, wrote that "Apollo 10 might accomplish the actual landing."

But even if it dared, how could NASA possibly do it? There was one very simple way. That was to remove certain components of the Apollo 11's LM and install them in the LM atop Apollo 10. Both Saturn 5 rocket assemblies (for Apollos 10 and 11) stood in the huge Vertical Assembly Building at Cape Kennedy. Someone in NASA—or several persons—seemed to be thinking of these two towering rocket assemblies and asking: Why not make the switchover? The price was to delay Apollo 10 for perhaps a month—to allow time for alterations to its LM. A Grumman official explained: "Some of the electronic components aboard the LM 4 vehicle [the one presently assigned to the Apollo 10] were not designed with a lunar landing in mind." It would take time; yet, even so, it might beat the Apollo 11 flight, tentatively scheduled for mid-July, by at least the better part of a month.

The idea of sending two astronauts to a Moon landing in a patchwork LM was so incredible that NASA would hopefully stick to its announced decision and keep Apollo 10 an "all but" flight—a mission dangerous enough as it is.

Indeed, when astronauts Neil A. Armstrong and Air Force Colonel Edwin E. Aldrin, Jr., go for the Moon landing in the Apollo 11 LM, while Lieutenant Colonel Michael Collins (U.S.-A.F.) awaits their return in the lunar-orbiting command module, they will be taking the most daring risks. Were it not for the "end-of-the-decade" deadline, this recklessness would not be required of them, for there is no reason why the Lunar Module could not have been adapted for an unmanned, remote-controlled flight to the lunar surface and back. Even though similar remote-controlled soft landings of the Surveyor spacecraft have proved that the lunar surface is less hazardous than had been expected, it does seem strange that the very first attempt to walk upon another celestial body should not have been preceded by at least one full-scale unmanned testing of the systems designed to bring about the historic feat.

It is extremely difficult to find in the LM any basis for confidence in its safety and performance. There is no provision, for example, for repairing a crack in the LM armor if an uneven landing should cause a buckled or punctured wall. Furthermore, the oxygen back-pack for lunar walks outside the LM spacecraft —or for mid-flight extracurricular activity which might be required in a docking emergency—is limited to about four hours. It has only a thirty-minute reserve. Especially since the LM will never be given an unmanned landing test, these seem to be very chancy limitations. Indeed, a great many corners have been cut just so that Grumman's lunar "bug" can get off the ground.

Because of weight restraints there were indications of a very narrow margin of fuel for the LM. In June, 1968, it was learned that expected increases in the weight of the lunar "bug" might provide a fuel margin of only 2 percent to 4 percent for the first manned lunar landing. Since a minimum margin of 5 percent is considered acceptable for aircraft, astronaut Ed Mitchell was reported as saying: "No test pilot in his right mind is ever going to go out on a first mission like that with no more reserve for error than a couple of percents; that's cutting it awful fine."

"Cutting it awful fine" would serve as a fitting motto for the entire Apollo program. Once, on January 27, 1967, NASA had cut it a bit too fine with safety and lost three astronauts. The space agency reeled, but recovered, and resumed its spectacular, death-defying performances. And so, two Americans might be on the Moon by June, 1969, or if not then, perhaps the next month, on Apollo 11—at the end of the race to "beat the Russians" and beating the "end-of-the-decade" deadline by several months, thus paying a magnificent tribute to the memory of a martyred President and three fallen astronauts.*

The scientific experiments aboard the Apollo 11 LM have been cut to the bare minimum. Current plans indicate that the Apollo 11 astronauts will spend only three hours outside the LM during its approximately twenty-two hours on the Moon's surface. The rest of the time will be spent largely in preparing the LM for its return trip to the orbiting command module—and, incredibly, eight hours of sleeping. During their three hours on the lunar surface, the two astronauts will pick up a selection of random rocks and deploy three simple pieces of scientific equipment, all within about ten yards of the LM. The three pieces of equipment are: a "passive seismometer," designed to pick up tiny tremors from the lunar interior and radio them back to Earth; a "multiple-corner reflector" at which scientists on Earth will beam a laser and time the returning signal in order to measure more accurately the distance between the Moon and Earth; and finally, a piece of aluminum foil (one foot by three feet, and weighing less than three ounces on the Moon) which will trap particles of the inert gases (argon, helium, neon, krypton, and xenon). The astronauts will unroll this piece of foil when they first leave the LM, and then carry it back to Earth, where scientists will use a mass spectrometer to measure the number of trapped inert gas particles. Apollo 11 was originally designated to carry the elaborate "Apollo Lunar Surface Experiments Package (ALSEP)"

---

* NASA's official scheduling of a Moon-landing attempt in July, 1969, suggests that the space agency might well have been considering a "miraculous" lunar landing in 1967. The fire and LM complications delayed manned flights by about twenty months. Twenty months subtracted from July, 1969, would have been December, 1967!

containing several hundred experiments, but this has been postponed for Apollo 12. Many scientists are worried that the rock samples brought back by the astronauts, whose oxygen supply will not permit them to travel much more than thirty feet from the LM, will be contaminated by the spacecraft's exhaust as it descends to the Moon's surface.

It is perhaps not unwarranted or impolitic to remind NASA, at this high point in its history, that the entire Apollo program—indeed the very future of the U.S. civilian space agency—depends, at this time, not upon making lunar landings by certain dates, but upon putting men on the Moon and bringing them back to Earth—*alive*.

This is not Cassandra talk. Although the possibility of space tragedy, because of human error and consequent equipment malfunctions, should never be ignored, no ghastly portents of a similar disaster are hinted here. To speculate darkly of other tragedies to come in the space program would be not only unseemly but ghoulish.

Yet the parallels between the current period of euphoria and that following the Gemini flights must not be overlooked. It is at such times that great miscalculations are made, that fundamental problems are overlooked, and questions that should be asked are not asked.

A great human outpouring of pride and gratitude, awe and hero worship, swelled during the Apollo 8 mission and became a gush of almost world-wide praise when astronauts Borman, Lovell, and Anders returned safely form their historic Moon-orbiting trip. The demonstration of wonder and affection for the achievement of Apollo 8 and its astronauts has rarely been equalled. It would be difficult to imagine a warmer response for those astronauts who actually achieved the Moon landing and returned to Earth.

Yet not everyone was dazzled. A few voices—some of them almost apologetically—refused to join the chorus of hosanahs. In his December 29, 1968, column in *The New York Times*, Tom Wicker noted: "Apollo 8 had scarcely made its marvelously accurate landing in the Pacific before two of the most distinguished American scientists—Dr. Harold C. Urey and Dr. George B. Kistiakowsky raised difficult questions about the intrinsic value of the moon voyage." Dr. Urey, Wicker reported, did not believe that the $24 billion spent on the Apollo project could in any way be justified in terms of value to science. Wicker then went on to preview the remarks that would be made by Dr. Kistiakowsky, Science Advisor under President Eisenhower, on a CBS radio interview that day. Dr. Kistiakowsky was described as favoring unmanned flights, rather than the Apollo "adventure" and "spectator sport," because instrumented flights promised more scientific knowledge. While appearing to deride "the euphoria . . . [that followed] . . . earlier [space] triumphs, to satisfy the Walter Mitty instinct, or . . . the why-did-you-climb-Mount-Everest syndrome ('Because it is there')," Wicker may have felt a bit uncertain about criticizing the U.S. space program's latest accomplishments: "It may seem ungracious and tasteless," he wrote, "even to raise these questions on the morrow of the astronauts' great performance, and in view of the incredible achievements of the men who developed and controlled the space program . . . it may well be that Drs. Kistiakowsky and Urey are only old-guard scientists who had never caught the excitement of space exploration . . ."

Disgruntlement over the Apollo 8 spectacular and the entire Moon-landing goal was also evident in a New York *Post* editorial during the flight, and at a symposium that took place shortly after the flight at the Explorers Club in New York City.

An especially trenchant, almost bitter, letter concerning the Apollo 8 mission was written by chemist and university professor John N. Cooper to *The New York Times* on December 27, the day of the spacecraft's splashdown. Headed "Prestige and Apollo 8," Cooper's letter read in part:

I am dissatisfied with the [Apollo] program not only because it seems to have so mean a product—prestige—and little enough of that, but also because with so many useful worthwhile projects to spend our nation's resources on—poverty, overpopulation, urban decay, etc.—the Congress and the country can only be mobilized massively to support this sort of glittering bauble of technological problem-solving.

We have known all along we could solve this one and we have been ten years working out the fine details. But for the really important national objectives, for which no pat answers are evident, we have hardly begun to define the questions . . .

Such was the type of comment that provoked *Time* magazine to single out "students and intellectuals" for blame in taking the bloom off Apollo 8 and the rest of America's space program. According to *Time* (January 3, 1969), "Many students and intellectuals, inveighing against the 'power structure' and the 'Establishment,' have been loud in their condemnation of America's commitment to space."

Time apparently chose not to ask the opinions of some of the people-in-the-street that correspondents for *The New York Times* were interviewing at the close of the Apollo 8 mission. A young Negro woman in a Detroit office commented: "You want to know the truth? It [the Apollo 8 flight] didn't impress me at all. I don't see any purpose in it. There is something else they could have done with all that money, something they really need." A Detroit Negro postman thought Apollo was "a wonderful project, but," he added, "I think all that money being spent for it could go far in other projects, any of the domestic problems, alleviating the problems of the poor, housing, clothes, schools." NASA's bugbear—indifference—was also evident among some citizens. "I think people are taking this so calmly," an Atlanta, Georgia, woman remarked. "I think they're getting used to it really." And a seemingly naive comment by a Staten Island, New York, housewife posed a question that had bewildered a great many knowledgeable scientists, "students and intellectuals," for the better part of a decade. "I wanted to understand why they're doing it," she said. "I couldn't."

One might ask *Time*, also, whether it included football fans among the "students and intellectuals [who] have been loud in their condemnation of America's commitment to space." When on December 22, CBS-TV broke away from the NFL Baltimore Colts-Minnesota Vikings game for two-and-a-half minutes to televise the first live pictures of the Apollo 8 astronauts on their way to the Moon, "several thousand people swamped the CBS switchboard" with calls of protest.

Time to the contrary, the students and intellectuals seemed to be divided in their reaction to the Apollo 8 flight. A great many of them seemed to be thrilled—and they were joined, if not by a Detroit postal clerk and a Staten Island housewife, then by a glittering array of national and spiritual leaders as well as eminent figures in both the sciences and humanities. The press and TV networks reacted with massive coverage both of the flight itself and the acclaim that followed it. Estimates of the number of Americans who watched the final moments of Apollo 8's flight ran from forty to seventy million viewers. Jack Gould of *The New York Times* wrote, "With live broadcasts [relayed by satellite] and taped summaries, the total global audience for Apollo 8 has run into the hundreds of millions."

Astronauts Borman, Lovell, and Anders were *Time* magazine's "Men of the Year," their faces appearing on *Time*'s January 3, 1969, cover. Not only were journalists inspired by Apollo 8's flight, but poets, too. One of America's most eminent literary figures, Archibald MacLeish, wrote "A Reflection," that appeared on the front page of *The New York Times* on Christmas Day. In his piece, MacLeish expressed the hope that Apollo 8's flight would give mankind a whole new perspective of itself and its planet, so that "man may at last become himself." *Life* magazine went to the American poet James Dickey for celebratory verses, which it published, illustrated with color shots taken on Apollo 8, in its special issue "The Incredible Year '68," on January 10, 1969.

In its next issue, *Life*, which ever since the start of manned space flight has had contracts with the astronauts, printed personal commentaries by astronauts Borman, Lovell, and Anders on their historic mission.* The same week, *Look*, in association with the science staff of *The New York Times*, put out a $1.25 "special" issue entitled *Apollo 8: Voyage To The Moon*. This was little more than a glossy reprinting of *Times* articles that had appeared during the days of the mission, together with several of the Apollo 8 photographs, a few diagrams, and a fold-out, full-color Norman Rockwell rendering of the moment two astronauts climb out of the LM and onto the lunar surface.

* After the Apollo 8 mission, there were indications that some lucrative "spin-off" was coming—of direct benefit to the astronauts. *Life* was reported to be eager to extend its contracts with the astronauts beyond the Moon landing, an arrangement that could mean $400,000 to the astronauts as a group. Moreover, MGM was considering a documentary film that would add an additional $3 million to the astronauts' coffers. All this was added to paid-up $50,000 life insurance policies purchased in the name of each NASA astronaut.

Thus did the American public media embrace the Apollo 8 astronauts. The response of most of the rest of the world's press was hardly less enthusiastic.

Pronouncements by "free world" national leaders indicated the prestige-building success of the Apollo 8 flight. A congratulatory cable from British Prime Minister Harold Wilson stated Apollo 8 "had added a new dimension to our appreciation that this is indeed one world." Chilean president Eduardo Frei hailed "the greatest human adventure of our century." Similar messages came from Charles de Gaulle, Japanese Premier Eisaku Sato, King Hassan of Morocco, and many more. At a special appearance of the astronauts at the United Nations on January 10, 1969, U.N. Secretary General U Thant called them "the first true universalists," adding: "The legendary cow of the nursery rhyme never did make it, but these three men actually did jump over the moon."

Soviet leaders, scientists, and press were also gracious and unstinting in their praise. Soviet President Nikolai V. Podgorny cabled President Johnson: "Accept Mr. President, our congratulations on the successful completion of the flight of the Apollo 8 spacecraft around the moon, which is a new accomplishment in mastering the outer space by man." Soviet space scientist Leonid I. Sedov, often called "the father of Sputnik," said that the Soviet scientific community "rejoice at and appreciate highly the achievements of American specialists." Writing in *Pravda* on December 30, Boris N. Petrov, specialist in automatic space control systems, praised the "very high reliability" demonstrated by the Apollo 8 systems and the "great courage" displayed by the astronauts. Tass urged that "One should pay tribute to the courage and skill of Frank Borman, William Anders and James Lovell, who have accomplished this outstanding scientific and technological experiment . . . opening a new stage in the history of space research." At the completion of the Apollo 8 trip, the ten Russian cosmonauts who had made successful space flights wired the astronauts in Houston: "We followed very closely each stage of your flight and note with satisfaction the precision of your joint work and your courage, which contributed to the excellent completion of this important experiment. We are confident that the exploration of outer space will greatly benefit earthmen. We congratulate you on a successful step toward this noble goal."

Of course, the warmest of all the warm acclaim for the Apollo 8 astronauts came from American leaders and officials who had for years championed the Apollo program. One congressman, Representative Dante B. Fascell of Florida, proposed the award of the Congressional Medal of Honor to Borman, Lovell and Anders. Although the astronauts did not receive the Medal of Honor (the nation's highest award for *wartime* courage), they did receive almost everything else the nation's leaders could give them, including week after week of personal appearances, press conferences, ticker-tape parades and tours.

On the morning of January 9, 1969, at a ceremony at the White House, President Johnson presented gold medals to the astronauts. The citations accompanying the Distinguished Service Medals of the National Aeronautics and Space Administration read in part, for "significantly advancing the nation's capabilities in space." The President remarked that he was "proud to live in a country that has produced men like you and produced men who lifted you into space." Colonel Borman responded: "Mr. President . . . we know we are symbolic of the country's greatness, we feel inadequate . . ." The astronauts then traveled across Washington in an open convertible through packed streets to an appearance at the House of Representatives. As they entered the chamber, they were greeted by a standing ovation from House and Senate members, the entire Cabinet, the Supreme Court justices, foreign diplomats, and a packed House Gallery whose occupants included the wives and families of the astronauts, as well as Lady Bird Johnson and her two daughters.

Doubtless, the flood tide of emotion that greeted the Apollo 8 astronauts could be explained in part by the fact that theirs was an extraordinary act of heroism and that their flight profoundly touched man's spirit of adventure. One must also remember that 1968 will go down as one of the darkest in United States history, a year that saw the war in Vietnam drag on, the assassinations of Martin Luther King and Robert F. Kennedy, the brutal "police riot" at the Chicago convention, the problems of the seething urban ghettos seemingly without solution. Apollo 8—which, ironically, had little or no immediate bearing on any of these events—gave a Christmas-miracle-like finish to the sorry year. When the human spirit is low, it seeks passionately for something by which it can elevate and ennoble itself. Apollo 8—carrying, in the words of Vice-President Humphrey "the dreams of all men who have charted new courses and crossed new frontiers"—was seized upon.

In such an atmosphere, it is easy to forget not only more earthly problems but also certain fundamental and still unsolved problems of the space age.

One danger is that consideration of the values of manned versus unmanned flight tends to become distorted by the pioneering "Columbus" attractions of man in space. No clearer example of this tendency can be found than the words of NASA's Acting Administrator Thomas Paine in the wake of the Apollo 8 success: "Man has started his drive out into the universe," Paine proclaimed, marking "the beginning of a movement that will never stop."

A measure of what can happen is that NASA after seven years of manned spectaculars found itself with very uncertain support for programs to follow Apollo. It took the manned spectaculars, so NASA thought, to maintain support for any space program at all—a program that certainly could not be "sold" on the basis of its practical economic benefits. As a 1968 National Academy of Sciences report pointed out: "That part of the NASA budget that is directly aimed at developing practical applications of space technology is now about $100 million per year or about 2 per cent of the total [NASA budget]." Thus NASA performed its manned space dramas to drum up enthusiasm for the performances that would follow.

What, realistically, does "the future of man in space" mean?

The phrase may still conjure up, for some, visions of space hotels and vacations on the Moon. To others, it may hold out the hope of mankind moving out to populate the Moon and planets to escape an overcrowded Earth. These are lovely fantasies, but the time, cost, and space hardware required to make them come true are far beyond man's current reach. They will remain fantasies for many generations.

A number of reputable scientists believe that "man in space" is not only terribly expensive but something of an absurdity. In August, 1968, the Space Science Board of the National Academy of Sciences stated: "We are unable to identify a need in planetary exploration, in the foreseeable future, for the unique abilities of man." It recommended that "a substantially increased fraction of the total NASA budget be devoted to unmanned planetary exploration."

The Board's consensus was that in terms of scientific rewards, instrument-equipped space vehicles will produce as much or more information than manned flights. In at least one respect, this opinion was substantiated by the Apollo 8 flight. The color pictures that the astronauts brought back were indeed glorious, but they added little to the information already obtained by the unmanned Lunar Orbiters. Said Colonel Borman: "The site itself [the Moon's Sea of Tranquility] has been well documented by Orbiter because it was down at the altitudes we were at. Our photographic equipment did not produce in detail what we already had for vision or for instruction before we went on the flight."

The colds and nausea experienced by astronauts on Apollo 7 and Apollo 8 have been shrugged off as minor incidents. But is the problem of sick astronauts really so minor? In the closed environment of a space capsule, it is nearly impossible to prevent other crew members from picking up a contagious infection. This fact suggests a host of potential problems that lie at the heart of the controversy over manned versus unmanned missions. From an engineering standpoint, man is essentially a three-pound computer (the human brain), linked, rather inefficiently, to a group of not always reliable sensors (the human senses). In order to get this three-pound computer into space, the most elaborate systems must be designed to duplicate as closely as possible the environment to which a human being has become adjusted through the long process of evolution. Thus, the difficulties of sending a man into space are far greater than sending even the most sophisticated computer, or battery of computers and electronic equipment, into space. Besides, computers don't catch colds.*

---

* The opposing viewpoint was expressed by astronaut William A. Anders at a press conference before the Apollo 8 flight. Reacting to the reputed critical comments of Sir Bernard Lovell, Major Anders commented that while Apollo 8 was not intended as a scientific flight, it gave science its first opportunity to observe the Moon at close range with "an eyeball connected to a brain connected to an arm that can write or a tongue that can speak. We think that by having a man in space, you can do a job that you can't do with unmanned vehicles."

And what about the possibility of a severely debilitating illness spreading among the crew? NASA has belatedly come to recognize that it has perhaps not given adequate attention to the possibility of sickness in space. As Richard D. Lyons pointed out in *The New York Times* during the Apollo 7 flight:

> . . . the space flight surgeons here at the Manned Spacecraft Center have begun to wonder if flights of much longer duration than two weeks might not incur such risks to the astronauts' health that the middle parts of the missions would become as hazardous as either end.
>
> Such a threat might come from a lowered resistance to infection brought on by the slovenly condition of the crewmen, the lack of genuine rest for long periods, the deleterious effects on their cardiovascular systems brought on by lack of exercise, and a decrease in the number of their red blood cells, those that carry oxygen to the tissues.
>
> Another potential threat, they say, is the possibility that some of the bacteria and viruses aboard the men and their capsule at blast-off might, in a space trip lasting some months, mutate into more virulent strains of microorganisms.
>
> The chief space flight surgeon for the Apollo 7 mission, Dr. Charles A. Berry, says, "It is possible to have a mutation in the environment of spacecraft." The theories are that different levels of ionizing radiation in space may affect the genes of the bacteria and that the pure-oxygen atmosphere might change the metabolism of the germs in such a manner as to incite mutations.
>
> Scientific experiments performed by the Air Force also have shown that a spacecraft environment lowers resistance to disease.
>
> The National Aeronautics and Space Administration has prepared a little-circulated medical report stating that "infectious diseases represent an area of potentially serious concern for the health of the astronauts, both during and following space flights."

Then, too, there are serious reasons to doubt whether it is wise to rely on the astronauts to compensate for instrument failures, as they did in Gemini flights. Disturbing reports suggest that man in space is not as dependable as had been assumed. The fatal

November 15, 1967, crash of the X–15, piloted by Air Force Major Michael J. Adams, a top test pilot, was found to have been caused by his failure, under "some sort of disorientation," to read his instruments correctly.* Disorientation has also been produced in laboratory monkeys in simulated weightlessness. Reaction times were observed to have been quite retarded. These preliminary findings, part of the Biosatellite program, have prompted chief investigator Dr. W. Ross Adey, of the Space Biology Laboratory, University of California at Los Angeles, to say of those earlier medical tests which are the basis of NASA's great expectations for Apollo astronauts: "I have nothing but contempt for the sort of medical experiments that went into the Gemini program."

One might add that Biosatellite is a classic casualty of NASA's program coordination. It has been shuttled about and underfunded for years. The projected flights with primates certainly should have been accomplished *before* man was sent toward the Moon. Biosatellite has already shown various detrimental effects of prolonged weightlessness on plants. Since these findings did not seem in any way to apply to short-duration missions, however, they did not affect NASA's determination to put men on the Moon "by the end of the decade."

The Defense Department has been equally determined in its plans for man in space. The appointment of Dr. Robert C. Seamans, NASA's former deputy administrator, to the post of Secretary of the Air Force under President Nixon was an indication of the very high priority the military had given its space plans. To the Pentagon, manned space flight means MOL, its Earth-orbiting successors, and the commanding position in a potential new theater of war. The increased military space activity expected in the 1970's does not necessarily mean scores of Earth-orbiting thermonuclear bombs. What it can mean is twenty-four-hour-a-day surveillance of practically every object on the Earth's surface.

And what about NASA's plans for man in space? Several more Moon landings are planned after the first one, with increasingly longer stays by the astronauts, and a permanent lunar base will most likely be established—if only to keep money flowing into the

---

* The result of recent Air Force high-stress tests were reported in the February 17, 1969 issue of *Aviation Week*. Voice warnings had been found to be "the *only* effective means of alerting crews to on-board emergencies." Pilots repeatedly ignored or failed to notice tone signals or cockpit instruments.

aerospace industry. It is perhaps a vain hope that such a base will be truly civilian, scientific, and international. As *The New York Times'* C. L. Sulzberger has pointed out, the denationalization and demilitarization of bases in outer space would mean that "mankind would have to grow suddenly as wise as he is intelligent, and history indicates little probability of this."

Having found little support for its Apollo Applications Program (AAP), which would place scientific "workshops" in Earth orbit, NASA officials began to talk in late 1968 about a manned "space station," apparently striking "AAP" from their vocabulary. NASA's space station, according to the new concept, would carry out both civilian and *military* experiments.

Thus, NASA's post-Apollo manned space program was full of uncertainty. To some observers, it seemed the perfect time for NASA to embark upon an ambitious but sensibly coordinated unmanned program of planetary exploration. The booster capability and hardware already developed could be well utilized in this effort. Proposals had been drawn up to modify the Saturn 5 rocket to carry advanced space probes to the surface of Mars.

Over the next ten years, NASA revealed, it was considering four or five significant unmanned planetary probes. These included the Viking project, aiming for a soft landing on Mars in 1973, a Jupiter fly-by in the early 70's, Venus-Mercury fly-bys in 1973 and 1975, and finally, soft-landing instrument packages on Mars, utilizing Saturn 5's, in 1975 and 1977.

NASA Acting Administrator Paine was perhaps trying to add luster to these plans when he spoke in December, 1968, of "the nuclear rocket . . . that is coming along with an eye to flying in the late 1970's. There are a number of potential applications for this rocket. One of those is the unmanned, so-called grand tour of the outer planets that uses the extremely favorable position of Jupiter, Saturn, and Mars." In the 1980s', he continued, the nuclear rocket might lift "much higher, heavier payloads, perhaps even man loads . . . even out to Mars."

Just how much Congressional support Paine could count on to prepare for such ambitious missions was very much in doubt. The chairman of the Senate Aeronautical and Space Sciences Committee, Clinton Anderson, was singularly unimpressed. "I couldn't care less about Venus," he said. "I have not had nearly the pressure about a space program to Mars or Venus as I had about the Moon program. So I want to be darn sure this one job [the Apollo program] is done, then we may turn back to the Earth for a while. The Moon is of little military value, for one thing."

The euphoria inspired by Apollo 8 carried with it, too, a threat to the great American hope that its science and technology could promise all men an ever fuller and richer life. The threat was that, once again, space expenditures would dominate federal spending in science and technology, while other less glamorous, less single-goal-oriented programs would remain underfunded. Senator Anderson, for one, was eager to increase space expenditures. "I hope to see the space budget grow a good bit," he said in early January, 1969.

As chairman of the Senate space committee, Senator Anderson could not be blamed, perhaps, for thinking first of space. But one might hope that, as a United States senator, he might have been paying at least some attention to other areas that called out for enlightened leadership and direction by the Congress of America's vaunted science and technology.

The pollution of the Earth's air, land, and water was a dominant theme at the annual meeting of the American Association for the Advancement of Science in Dallas during the last days of December, 1968. At the meeting, scientist after scientist spoke out against the "technological affronts" to man's environment, such as the ever-growing menace from radioactive wastes and fallout, automobile smog, detergents, insecticides and herbicides, and chemical wastes. Said Dr. Barry Commoner, director of the Center of the Biology of Natural Systems at Washington University: "I believe that unless we match our technological power with a deeper understanding of the environment we run the risk of destroying this planet as a suitable place for human habitation." The distinguished anthropologist Margaret Mead added: "We are altering man's environment in ways we do not understand and in ways that may be disastrous."

Taking note of these frightening appraisals, a *New York Times* editorial clearly warned that "space" did not represent an escape hatch from problems on Earth:

Despite the latest major advance in space exploration, this planet is going to be the human race's chief habitat for many generations to come. *The time is overdue for a really major effort to insure that earth remains livable not only today and tomorrow, but also decades and centuries from now.* [Italics added.]

In mid-January, 1969, Dr. Thomas E. Bryant, assistant director for health affairs in the U.S. Office of Economic Opportunity, reported that twelve million Americans could not afford the seventy-five cents per day needed to buy enough food to meet minimum nutritional needs. In testifying before the Senate Select Committee on Nutrition and Human Needs, Dr. Bryant stated that lack of funds made it "impossible to implement an all-inclusive, in-depth program in every area of need in the country." Before the same committee, Secretary of Agriculture Orville L. Freeman estimated that it would take perhaps $1 billion per year to close this "nutritional gap" and bring an end to hunger in the United States. Is it not in the realm of science to study nutritional needs, and in technology's realm to develop methods to meet such needs? Can the Congress refuse to fund the needed research and development in favor of making "the space budget grow a good bit?"

As billions of dollars continued to pour into the Apollo project in 1968, the Johnson Administration, citing budget difficulties, all but withdrew support of U.S. participation in the fifty-four-nation International Biological Program (IBP). This program, "an attempt to investigate the biological basis for man's welfare on the planet," suddenly found itself without $5 million it had been all but promised for fiscal 1969. The chairman of the United States IBP committee, Dr. W. Frank Blair, found himself with only $700,000, or under 0.2 percent of NASA's budget.

For the Congress and recent Administrations, spending for science and technology has always tended to be an "all-or-nothing" proposition. Either a vastly expensive, extravagant program, such as NASA's Apollo program, is approved and funded, or, as in the case of U.S. participation in IBP, there is strong sentiment for no funds, and no program at all.

The all-or-nothing factions could benefit from studying a two-hundred-page report prepared by the Commission on Marine Science, Engineering and Resources and delivered in January, 1969, to Congress and the outgoing Johnson Administration. The report assesses the government's role—present and future—in the marine sciences and the exploitation of the oceans' vast resources. It does not recommend a crash government program to exploit the oceans' mineral and oil riches; in fact, it recommends little or no increase for the present in the approximately $500 million the government is spending for all marine sciences. It recommends the creation of a new, independent agency (suggested name: the "National Oceanic and Atmospheric Agency") to coordinate the marine and atmospheric research now scattered among a score of federal agencies. Such an agency could lay the base for a measured, long-term, step-by-step national effort in marine sciences and engineering when the time is ripe.

The report closely followed the recommendations of a similar study made for the National Council on Marine Resources and Marine Development by Economic Associates, Inc., with the support of Ocean Science and Engineering, Inc. and three University of Maryland consultants. This 520-page study saw neither the necessity nor the means for the economic recovery of ocean resources at this time. Instead, it urged the federal government over the next ten to twenty years to concentrate its efforts on basic research, such as undersea mapping, and the development of tools and techniques for underwater work.

Such concern for priorities and for a logical step-by-step progression in research and development efforts has been exceedingly rare in government-financed science and engineering projects. Witness NASA.

Yet orderly scientific and technological progress need not be a rarity in America. Now that we live in the age of science, technology, and space, all the scientific and technological activities of the United States government might well be considered as a whole and not as individual, competing parts. Had this been done earlier, NASA might not have reached the point, as it did in 1965 and 1966, where its funds for research dwarfed those of all other government agencies combined—especially since the work of those agencies was and is no less tied to the well-being of the nation. Dilemmas of this kind could be avoided in the future by acting on either one or two proposals made by eminent scientists as 1968 drew to a close.

The Congress and the President could be urged to create a new Cabinet post for a Secretary of Science and Technology. This office would give to one man fully integrated authority and a well-rounded, well-informed staff. It would necessarily embrace all national science agencies—speaking with one voice—in the national interest. Donald Hornig, Johnson's Science Adviser, addressed himself to the question at the 1968 meeting of the American Chemical Society. "The problem has to be opened," Dr. Hornig said. "It may be wrong to concentrate; science, like economics, is part of everything." But, he concluded, a Federal Department of Science "is sure to be an issue in the year to come." It is unfortunate that such a move has not yet been enthusiastically endorsed—and is probably dead under the current Administration. President Nixon has often announced his opposition to the idea of a "federal science czar."

Perhaps, however, the Nixon Administration would find a second proposal, advanced at the 1968 AAAS meeting, more appealing. Dr. James A. Shannon, former director of the National Institutes of Health, warmly supported by Dr. Philip Abelson, editor of *Science*, urged the formation of a national agency that would establish scientific and technological priorities "in terms of broad public policy." As described by Dr. Shannon, the new agency would be similar to the National Security Council, with direct access to the President. It would have a full-time staff of scientists and laymen "empowered to bring order and central purpose to the decentralized system by which scientific and medical research is now financed by the Government."

Dr. Shannon sharply criticized existing government panels, such as the President's Science Advisory Committee. "Bringing a board to Washington every few weeks," he declared, "hardly satisfies a need of this magnitude." Endorsing Dr. Shannon's remarks, Dr. Abelson said: "My criticism of science budgeting is that everything is considered in isolation, so that there is no possibility of judging the potential social benefits of one area of science as opposed to another."

Either a "Secretary of Science" or a national science agency could rank scientific objectives in terms of their national priority, cost, and feasibility. It would be the task of the politicians in the Congress to sound out their constituencies and legislate funds and schedules for the national scientific priorities thus established. It would then be up to the engineers and technicians— constantly in dialogue with both scientists and congressmen—to execute the tasks required. As Representative Joseph E. Karth has said: "If science were to be left strictly to the scientists, engineering only to engineers, and politics exclusively to the politicians, then these specialists would communicate mostly within their own groups and in the end lose sight of the public interest."

It is unlikely that the Congress will act on any such proposals without decisive urging by the public and informed voices from all quarters of American life. Perhaps the motivation can be derived from a last, hard look at what NASA has become in its first decade.

The plain fact is that NASA has never been permitted, nor have its officials fought, to carry out the high promise or to meet the great challenge of its 1958 charter. NASA became a giant under a succession of Congresses that were swayed by the arguments of the aerospace industry. A sprawling, government-supported space establishment, aerospace officials never tired of suggesting, would be of immense benefit not only to the nation's economy, but to each and every congressman who could bring NASA money into his state. NASA became *the* space-age pork barrel. Also to gain congressional support, NASA found it necessary to stress its value to the military, thus becoming an appendage of the Defense Department. As Lee DuBridge commented in an interview following his selection as President Nixon's Science Adviser: "I think President Johnson said just the other day that some of the military satellites have been of sufficient value to pay for the whole space program . . . it is the judgment of somebody who knows what is going on."

So comprised, NASA was unable to fulfill its larger promise of demonstrating how large-scale technological endeavors can be organized and executed for the benefit of man.

It took a major disaster to make NASA design ships that were more spaceworthy. Then, after the "101-percent-flawless" Apollo 7 mission, the space agency reverted to the deadline-chasing haste that had almost dealt America's entire space program a death blow.

The courage of the astronauts is inspiring. Man's spirit of adventure could not permit him to forsake a landing upon the Moon. Indeed, man needed to achieve that goal, but not as a vastly expensive spectacular that has little, if any, scientific or economic value. The future space program must be considered, together with other national priorities, one technological and scientific endeavor among many others that are, important.

APPENDIX **A** The first official retracing of the chain of events leading up to and through the Apollo 204 fire was contained in the following memorandum from NASA Deputy Administrator Robert C. Seamans, Jr. to NASA Administrator James E. Webb, dated February 3, 1967:

NATIONAL AERONAUTICS AND SPACE ADMINISTRATION
WASHINGTON, D.C. 20546

OFFICE OF THE ADMINISTRATOR

February 3, 1967

MEMORANDUM

To: Mr. James E. Webb
         Administrator

From: Robert C. Seamans, Jr.
         Deputy Administrator

Subject: Report on Apollo 204 Review Board Discussions

I spent yesterday at the Kennedy Space Center with the Apollo Review Board and other key personnel involved in the current investigation of the causes and circumstances of the Apollo 204 accident.

First, there has been no determination of the specific cause of the fire that resulted in the deaths of Lt. Colonel Grissom, Lt. Colonel White, and Lt. Commander Chaffee. The retracing of possible, and then of probable, chains of events in such an accident is a complex task that is demanding the complete attention of the Review Board headed by Dr. Floyd Thompson, of the assistants and consultants to the Board, and of many of the elements of government, industry, and universities involved in the Apollo program.

The Board is taking full advantage of the extensive taped data available as well as records made prior to the accident, the present condition of the spacecraft, and the reports of those involved in the test. All the physical evidence and data concerned with the test were impounded immediately following the accident. This was to assure that no pertinent information would be lost and that no actions would be taken except in the full context of all the data available.

As I have stated, the preliminary review of this information has not provided any direct indication of the origin of the fire; the preliminary analyses point to the conclusion that a clear identification of the source of ignition or of its possible source will depend upon detailed step-by-step examination of the entire spacecraft and its related test support equipment.

At present, the spacecraft is still mated to the unfueled launch
vehicle at the pad. However, it is being prepared for removal to
our industrial area where it will be disassembled and where experts
in many technical and scientific areas can work with the physical evidence.
Prior to disassembly of the damaged spacecraft, an undamaged and nearly
identical (#014) spacecraft will be used to establish the conditions
existing prior to the accident. The 014 spacecraft was flown from
the North American plant in California to Cape Kennedy on February 1.

The current plans are to go through a parallel, step-by-step disassembly
process, first working on the undamaged vehicle and then repeating as
closely as possible the procedure on the damaged vehicle.

In addition to analyses of recorded and physical data and equipment,
the Board is defining a series of investigative tasks and is assigning
these to teams for execution. For example, a team is charged with
the chemical and spectrographic analysis of damaged elements aimed at
identifying the propagative history of the fire. Another is working
on relating the propagation history to the flammability characteristics
of the spacecraft materials. Another is dealing with design analyses
and experimental tests to help establish possible ignition sources.
As work progresses and a pattern of information emerges, additional
tasks, analyses, and reviews will undoubtedly be instituted by the
Board.

From information now available to the Board, I had an opportunity to
learn more about certain specific aspects of the simulated mission
and the test sequence itself than we had previously had before us in
a clearly related pattern.

At 6:31:03 pm EST the fire was first detected. The mission
was holding at T-10 minutes. Up to this time there had been
only minor difficulties with the equipment. The purpose of
the hold was to provide an opportunity to improve the communications between the spacecraft and the ground crew.

Up to this time the cabin pressure, the cabin temperature, and
the oxygen suit supply temperature were nominal. The oxygen rate
of flow into the suits had shown an increase 4 seconds prior to this
time but we have not been able to relate this to the accident.

Lt. Col. White was the only astronaut instrumented for heart rate
and respiration. His heart rate had shown an increase 40 seconds
prior to this time, but at 6:31:03 his heart was at the normal
level for him when in a relaxed prone position.

The spacecraft was operating on external power. Earlier in
the day, at 9:30 a.m. EST, the system for transfer from external
(ground) power to simulated internal (spacecraft) power had been
tested, and operated normally. The fuel cells in the service
module were not in use, and the so-called internal power was
being supplied by batteries having the same characteristics as
the fuel cells but located external to the spacecraft. If the
accident had not occurred, the transfer from external to simulated internal power would have taken place on resumption of the
count.

 At the press conference on Saturday morning, Apollo
 Program Director S. C. Phillips was asked whether the
 spacecraft was on internal or external power when the
 fire occurred. At that time he did not realize that
 the spacecraft was still on external power since he had
 in mind primarily the eyewitness reports. Subsequent
 examination of the data has established the above power
 supply sequences. There is no evidence up to this time
 that the source of power whether simulated internal or
 external was related to the accident.

Lt. Colonel Grissom was the command pilot, sitting in the left
seat; Lt. Colonel White, the senior pilot, sitting in the middle
seat; and Lt. Commander Chaffee, the pilot, was in the right seat.
In the event of emergency, the procedure is for the senior pilot
(White) to reach high over his left shoulder to actuate the inner
hatch release handle. The command pilot (Grissom), after lowering
the center headrest, aids the senior pilot in lifting the inner
hatch and removing it to the floor of the spacecraft. The main
duty of the pilot (Chaffee) during this procedure is to maintain
communication and assist in the removal of the inner hatch if
needed. From the following data, you will note that the crew
appeared to follow the correct procedure.

At 6:31:03, Pilot Chaffee reported that a fire existed in the
spacecraft. At about this time Senior Pilot White's heart rate
started to increase. At 6:31:04 the inertial platform in the
capsule gave an indication of a small amount of motion which may
have been caused by movement of the crew. At 6:31:05 the cabin
temperature began to rise. At 6:31:09 Senior Pilot White repeated
the previous report saying that there was a fire in the cockpit.
At the same time the cabin pressure commenced to rise and a larger
amount of motion was indicated by the inertial platform. This
means that the crew were commencing their emergency egress procedure.

At 6:31:12, or nine seconds after the first indication of fire, the cabin temperature started to increase rapidly and pilot Chaffee reported that a bad fire existed in the cabin. Also at this time pilot Chaffee increased the illumination of the cabin lights and actuated the entry (internal) batteries. No other intelligible communications were received although some listeners believe there was one sharp cry of pain. Loss of radio signal occurred a few seconds later.

The oxygen supply to the astronaut suits, which had been holding nearly constant, pressure and temperature started to fluctuate at the time of signal loss. At 6:31:17 or fourteen seconds after the fire was first detected, the cabin pressure reached a level of approximately 29 psi and the cabin ruptured.

One and one-half minutes after the start of the fire, the ground power was switched off. Various command module systems continued to operate on the entry (internal) battery power until about 12:30 am EST on Saturday when the batteries ran down.

The official death certificates for all three crew members list the cause of death as asphyxiation due to smoke inhalation due to the fire.

I would like to emphasize that this report is based on preliminary information. This information has not as yet been extensively analyzed by the Apollo Review Board under Dr. Thompson. Since the data were recorded at a number of different stations, the time sequences may not be perfectly synchronized, possibly giving rise to errors of one or two seconds.

During my meetings with the Board a number of other items of information were discussed but I believe that the data I have outlined include all events having a significant bearing on an understanding of the accident.

Robert C. Seamans, Jr.

Robert C. Seamans, Jr.

---

* Some errors of a few seconds (later corrected by NASA) were made in Seamans's memorandum. For example, Grissom's (?) cry of "Fire!" or "Hey!" was later determined to have occurred at 6:31:04.7, rather than at 6:31:03.

B1

The fatal plugs-out test of the Apollo 204 spacecraft on January 27, 1967, was monitored by hundreds of technicians and engineers. Some of the most revealing information came from "logs," such as the following by C. G. Eybel and J. M. Rubino of the General Electric Company. Their sequence of notations was included in the *Report of Apollo 204 Review Board*, Appendix B, pp. 169–171. (Note errors in dates in introductory statement and in heading of log.)

C. G EYBEL
AND
J. M. RUBIO

On January 22, 1967, Mr. C. G. Eybel and Mr. J. M. Rubio, General Electric Company, Apollo Support Department, observed tests on AS-204 Space Vehicle in performance of a task assigned by NASA. They were physically located in the CIF Building and observations were made from 0800 to 1920. The purpose of the assigned task was to make observations in support of the NASA program to reduce human and procedural errors during pre-launch operations. The notes taken during the observations are as follows:

January 26, 1967 (Friday)
Test Plugs-Out Drop Test
1-20015-SA-204

	Test Pickup at 0600
0800	Begin Monitor
0820	T-5 hrs. 40 min. 00 sec.
	Begin Power Transfer - Prior to Spacecraft (S/C)
	Going on Internal Power
	Lou is Pad Leader
0825	Communications adding items (equip) to S/C - POWER IS ON Also S/C is through with command Carrier - RF Checks O.K.
0900	T-5-00-00
	TC and EPS
	S/C confusion as to what 100 AMP circuit breaker "On" will do to S/C (5 mins. - No hold)
	TC wants breaker on and voltage reading taken (it was 31.5V yesterday)
	They must take off rear cover of GSE unit
	Pad Safety - Thundershowers this P.M.
	31.2V Reading
0938	Close Circuit Breaker (100 AMP)
	Prepare for S/C Internal Power Transfer
	Pad Safety - Stop Grinding Operation on Service Structure
0945	Main Bus B dropped to zero during power transfer on S/C-trouble shooting - Potential Serious Problem (TP)
1003	Procedure was wrong - rewrite
1033	S/C Inst. Test complete
1035	S/C is down 1 hour - Problems with ECS
1040	Suit Compressor Check Complete (S/C)
1100	T-3 hours estimate 1 hour hold so ECS can support crew ingress (suit technician sets up S/C but can't if crew is in) holding
1110	S/C move switch position check list up 15 minutes earlier so crew will ingress smoothly.
	Also a sequence in document was entered twice - Line one out
	S/C switches must be set before test is picked up (and will take approximately 20 minutes)
1135	Must let S/C cool down - TD and suit technician
	Discuss off net
1200	Extend hold +20 minutes (still waiting for ECS) - then suit technician must still set switches which will be approximately 15-20 minutes
1209	ECS Complete

1210	Begin setting switches in S/C (Confusion in switch setting)
1220	T-3:00:00 and counting
1233	Switch settings complete
1235	Suit technician out of S/C
1240	Astronauts departing for pad
1245	Crew leaving Astronauts Quarters on way to Pad 34.
1254	Couches almost set up crew approaching pad
1256	Crew at S/C level
1256	T-2-22-35 - Begin crew ingress Command Pilot (Grissom)
1303	Command Pilot - Smells funny odor in suit (like buttermilk)
1305	Command Pilot Secured
1306	Senior Pilot (Ed White) begin ingress preparation (Gus wants an air sample taken)
1308	Chaffee begin ingress
1318	Ingress Complete
	Bendix Environmental Engineer to take O_2 sample.
	Pad Safety - 20% probability of elect. activity in 2 hrs.
	Will hold at T-2:00:00 until air sample is taken
1320	T-2 hours and holding
	Chaffee is on board (over net - not TV)
	Crew didn't bring check lists with them - Pad Leader gave them set - its extensive
1330	Estimate 1½-2 hour hold to take air sample. Also O_2 sample to see it meets specification Type 11-B
1403	Per George Page - Send for second crew to take sample.
1405	Extend hold 20 minutes
	Found changes to be made in check list.
1414	Begin taking sample - (original crew)
	Take from Gus loop - through helmet fitting -
	Inflate the watermelon
1424	Sample Complete (Bendix)
	Reset Environmental Switches in S/C
	Begin suit circuit check
	Estimate 5 minutes
	C. Kraft and G. Page - Whose causing most holds -
	Houston or MSC - facetious
1430	Extend hold 10 minutes - ECS
1436	Begin suit circuit purge (sample) 98% - Go
1440	ECS Complete
1442	T-2 hours and counting
1445	Rain expected in 1 hour
1449	T-1:53:15 Closing Hatch
	Discrepancies between crew check list and S/C switch settings - Can't make run in present configuration
1458	Begin LV EDS Check
	Standby - Communication Problems - Very noisy and cutting out over net
	S/C VHF AM - Switch position was incorrect
1522	Begin Cabin Purge
1540	Abort light not received (S/C)
	Trouble Shoot
1542	T-60 and counting - EDS check not finished
1545	Abort light o.k. - Switches were not in correct position for test
1552	T-50 and holding estimate 15 minutes
1555	Did not get reset verify light in ECS check - standby

Information from a group of monitoring devices show a concurrent sequence of "anomalies" ("variation," "glitch," "drop out," "carrier drop out," "hi flow") several seconds before the first call of fire. These anomalies probably show the time the fire, otherwise undetected, actually began.

1557	EDS test is complete
	(off station)
1620	Still holding - Not getting right concentration - (Bad Analyzer) Cabin
1635	Start cabin leak check (purge is ok)
	Estimate 30 minutes for completion - including hatch closure - will then be in T-50 configuration.
1655	Ready for hatch closure. Leak rate is zero
1702	Hatch secured - Ready to pick up
1703	T-50 and counting
1736	S/C has communication problem
1738	T-15 and holding
1750	(Command Pilot's Cobra Cable) Suspect
1758	Command Pilot's transmitter and receiver VHF fuse switch appears bad
1800	Changed Comm Configuration in S/C
	It still isn't too good
1800	Trouble shoot after run
	Prepare Static Fire
1805	Set up switches in S/C and Static Fire
1813	Test complete -- Ready to pick up
1815	T-15 and counting
1820	T-10 and holding
	Communications Problem again
1832	Fire in S/C (Voice from S/C)
1835	3 arrive at White Room
	Masks on
1838	Pad Leader and crew can't see to get Astronauts
	Pad Leader can feel Astronauts but can't see them
1844	Pad Leader - I better not describe what I see
1845	Pad Leader - Ambulance is all I need at the White Room
1855	Pad Leader 2 - Pad Rescue have smoke casualties
	T/C - Several ambulances on way
1858	T/C - Batteries that couldn't be disconnected were ones that caused the problem
	Panel 150 could not be reached by Pad Leader to remove power from spacecraft
1920	Leave CIF

---

* Enclosure V–17 in summary volume of the *Report of Apollo 204 Review Board*, p. 5–47. Times are given in Greenwich Mean Time (GMT); thus 23:30:00 corresponds to 6:30:00 P.M. Eastern Standard Time (EST).

Information from a group of monitoring devices show a concurrent sequence of "anomalies" ("variation," "glitch," "drop out," "carrier drop out," "hi flow") several seconds before the first call of fire. These anomalies probably show the time the fire, otherwise undetected, actually began.

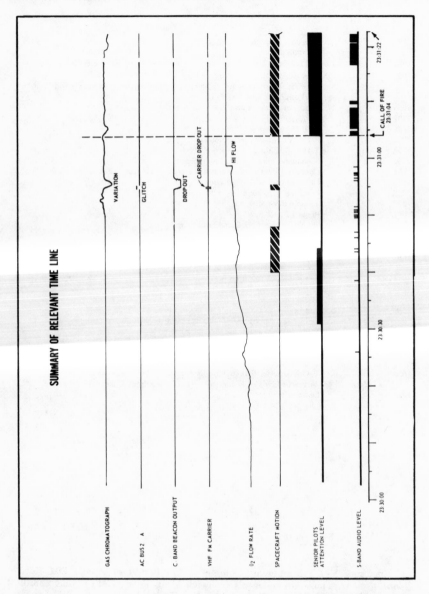

*Enclosure V–17 in summary volume of the *Report of Apollo 204 Review Board*, p. 5–47. Times are given in Greenwich Mean Time (GMT); thus 23:30:00 corresponds to 6:30:00 P.M. Eastern Standard Time (EST).

The official autopsy reports of the three dead astronauts (their names appear at the bottom left of each report) clearly show that the astronauts did not "burn to death," but were asphyxiated by toxic gases. Some of the burns, also, may have come after death. Note that Chaffee's report is incorrectly dated.

Standard Form 503
Revised August 1954
Bureau of the Budget
Circular A-52 (Rev.)

* U.S. GOVERNMENT PRINTING OFFICE : 1961 0—565587

CLINICAL RECORD	AUTOPSY PROTOCOL				
DATE AND HOUR DIED'	DATE AND HOUR AUTOPSY PERFORMED 1100 A.M.		CHECK ONE		
XXXX			FULL AUTOPSY	HEAD ONLY	TRUNK ONLY
27 January 1967 P.M.	28 January 1967 XXX		X		
PROSECTOR Charles J. Stahl Commander, MC, USN	ASSISTANT Colonel Edward H. Johnston./MC, USA				
XXXXXXXXXXXXXXXXXXXXXXXXXXXX	Latimer E. Dunn, Captain, USAF, MC				

CAUSE OF DEATH: ASPHYXIA DUE TO INHALATION OF TOXIC GASES DUE TO FIRE

CONTRIBUTORY CAUSE OF DEATH: THERMAL BURNS

MANNER OF DEATH: ACCIDENTAL

PATHOLOGICAL DIAGNOSES

1. ASPHYXIA DUE TO INHALATION OF TOXIC GASES DUE TO FIRE, MANIFESTED BY:

    a. CARBON MONOXIDE POISONING.

    b. SOOT WITHIN NOSE, ORAL CAVITY, TRACHEA AND BRONCHI.

    c. HEMORRHAGIC PULMONARY EDEMA, DIFFUSE.

2. THERMAL BURNS, 1ST, 2ND AND 3RD DEGREE, ESTIMATED 60% TOTAL BODY SURFACE AREA, as follows:

    1st and 2nd Degree: Estimated 24% total body surface area.

    3rd Degree: Estimated 36% total body surface area.

    4th Degree: None.
                (Continued)

APPROVED—SIGNATURE *[signature]* The Draft				8 March 1967	
JOE M. BLUMBERG, MAJOR GENERAL, MC, USA					
MILITARY ORGANIZATION (When required) Det. 1, 113/ USAF Special Activities Sq.	AGE 40	SEX Male	RACE Caucasian	IDENTIFICATION NO. FR 22450	AUTOPSY NO. AFIP 1232462
PATIENT'S IDENTIFICATION (For typed or written entries give: Name—last, first, middle; grade; date; hospital or medical facility)			REGISTER NO. --		WARD NO. --

GRISSOM, Virgil Ivan
Lieutenant Colonel, United States Air Force

Armed Forces Institute of Pathology
Washington, D. C, 20305

AUTOPSY PROTOCOL
Standard Form 503
503-104

Standard Form 503
Revised August 1954
Bureau of the Budget
Circular A-32 (Rev.)

* U.S. GOVERNMENT PRINTING OFFICE : 1961 O—588527

CLINICAL RECORD		AUTOPSY PROTOCOL			
DATE AND HOUR DIED		DATE AND HOUR AUTOPSY PERFORMED 1100 A.M.	CHECK ONE		
27 January 1967	XXXI. P.M.	23 January 1967 XXX	FULL AUTOPSY	HEAD ONLY	TRUNK ONLY
PROSECTOR COL Edward H. Johnston, MC, USA		ASSISTANTS Charles J. Stahl, CDR, MC, USN	X		
XXXXXXXXXXXXXXXXXXXXXXXXXXXXXX		Latimer E. Dunn, Captain, USAF, MC			

CAUSE OF DEATH: ASPHYXIA DUE TO INHALATION OF TOXIC GASES DUE TO FIRE

CONTRIBUTORY CAUSE OF DEATH: THERMAL BURNS

MANNER OF DEATH: ACCIDENTAL

PATHOLOGICAL DIAGNOSES

1. ASPHYXIA DUE TO INHALATION OF TOXIC GASES DUE TO FIRE, MANIFESTED BY:

   a. CARBON MONOXIDE POISONING.

   b. SOOT WITHIN NOSE, ORAL CAVITY, TRACHEA AND BRONCHI.

   c. HEMORRHAGIC PULMONARY EDEMA, DIFFUSE

2. THERMAL BURNS, 1ST, 2ND and 3RD DEGREE, ESTIMATED 48% TOTAL BODY SURFACE AREA, as follows:

   1ST and 2ND Degree: Estimated 8% total body surface area.

   3Rd Degree: Estimated 40% total body surface area.

   4TH Degree: None.
                (Continued)

APPROVED—SIGNATURE *Joe M. Blumberg* The Director AFIP					8 March 1967
JOE M. BLUMBERG, MAJOR GENERAL, MC, USA					
MILITARY ORGANIZATION (When required) Det. 1, 1137 USAF Special Activities Sq.	AGE 36	SEX Male	RACE Caucasian	IDENTIFICATION NO. FR 23567	AUTOPSY NO. AFIP 1232464
PATIENT'S IDENTIFICATION (For typed or written entries give: Name—last, first, middle; grade; date; hospital or medical facility)			REGISTER NO. --		WARD NO. --

WHITE, Edward Higgins II
Lieutenant Colonel, United States Air Force

Armed Forces Institute of Pathology
Washington, D. C. 20305

AUTOPSY PROTOCOL
Standard Form 503
503-104

Standard Form 503
Revised August 1954
Bureau of the Budget
Circular A-32 (Rev.)

* U.S. GOVERNMENT PRINTING OFFICE : 1961 O—582527

CLINICAL RECORD		AUTOPSY PROTOCOL			
DATE AND HOUR DIED	A.M. P.M.	DATE AND HOUR AUTOPSY PERFORMED A.M. 27 JAN 1967 - 1100 HRS P.M.	CHECK ONE		
27 JANUARY 1967			FULL AUTOPSY	HEAD ONLY	TRUNK ONLY
PROSECTOR L. E. DUNN, CAPT, USAF, MC		ASSISTANT C. J. STAHL, CDR, MC, USN	X		
~~XXXXXXXXXXXXXXXXXXXXXXXXXXXXX~~		E. H. JOHNSTON, COL, MC, USA			

A. CAUSE OF DEATH:

    <u>ASPHYXIA</u>, DUE TO INHALATION OF <u>TOXIC GASES</u>, DUE TO <u>FIRE</u>.

  CONTRIBUTORY CAUSE OF DEATH:

    <u>THERMAL BURNS</u> DUE TO <u>FIRE</u>.

  MANNER OF DEATH:

    <u>ACCIDENTAL</u>

B PATHOLOGICAL DIAGNOSES

  1. ASPHYXIA, DUE TO INHALATION OF TOXIC GASES, DUE TO FIRE MANIFESTED BY:

      (a) CARBON MONOXIDE POISONING
      (b) SOOT WITHIN THE MOUTH, NARES, AND TRACHEOBRONCHIAL TREE
      (c) HEMORRHAGIC PULMONARY EDEMA, DIFFUSE

  2. THERMAL BURNS:

      (a) FIRST AND SECOND DEGREE - ESTIMATED AS 6% OF BODY SURFACE
      (b) THIRD DEGREE - ESTIMATED AS 23% OF BODY SURFACE
      (c) FOURTH DEGREE - NONE

  3. OLD INJURY OF 7TH THORACIC VERTEBRA, CONSISTENT WITH OLD COMPRESSION
     FRACTURE.

APPROVED—SIGNATURE JOE M. BLUMBERG, MAJOR GENERAL, MC, USA		A-210 8 March 1967			
MILITARY ORGANIZATION (When required) 8th Naval District, New Orleans, Louisiana	AGE 31	SEX Male	RACE Caucasian	IDENTIFICATION NO. 564218	AUTOPSY NO. AFIP 1232463
PATIENT IDENTIFICATION (For typed or written entries give: Name—last, first, middle; grade; date; hospital or medical facility)			REGISTER NO. --		WARD NO. --

CHAFFEE, Roger B.
Lieutenant Commander, United States Navy

Armed Forces Institute of Pathology
Washington, D. C. 20305

AUTOPSY PROTOCOL
Standard Form 503
503-104

The following description of how NASA attempted to manage the release of information by its contractors after the fire was supplied, by James Webb, at the request of Representative Wydler of New York, to the House Subcommittee on NASA Oversight during its hearings on April 10, 1967.

On January 31, 1967, the following telegram was sent to Apollo contractors by Mr. John G. McClintock, Chief, Program Control Division, ASPO, Houston:

"Subject: Speeches and news releases on the Apollo program. As a result of the recent accident involving spacecraft 012 and in the interest of the Apollo program, contractors are asked to have their personnel refrain from participating in any of the following activities pertaining to the Apollo program until such time as the investigation has been concluded:

"Speeches (except currently scheduled courses of instruction or familarization).

"Presentation of technical papers.

"Publication of articles in periodicals or technical journals.

"Holding of news conferences.

"News releases.

"The above policy also applies to coverage on all systems, subsystems and operational methods. Immediately notify all subcontractors and confirm notification with Jack McClintock of the Apollo Spacecraft Program Office.

"Public information activities of the contractors in response to pressure from news media must be closely coordinated with MSC Public Information Office. Information release should be only in response to query and must not be or lead towards speculative conclusions concerning the accident. Responses by public information employees about systems should follow specifically documents already in the public domain."

When a copy of the above telegram was circulated at MSC, the MSC Public Affairs Office called NASA Headquarters. As a result, the following telegram was sent on February 2, 1967 to the Manned Spacecraft Center, Kennedy Space Center and the Marshall Space Flight Center:

"The following guidelines should be followed with respect to speeches, presentations and publication of technical papers, articles, news conferences, news releases, etc. This supersedes any earlier instructions issued following the AS-204 accident of these matters. Signed McClintock.

"1. During this period of time, we realize that all Apollo associated personnel will be questioned about the 204 accident. This matter is in the hands of the Review Board and no speculation on causes or probable cause is proper. However, we feel that speeches per se should not be forbidden. The speaker must stay away from those areas about the accident which speculate on causes or probable causes, but dissertations about the program in general and specifically the role of the individual contractors is all right. Discretion must always be exercised, but there is no blanket embargo.

TECHNICAL PAPERS

"2. There should be no embargo on technical papers now scheduled. However, again we do not want to speculate on 204. Presentations, such as on one-gas versus mixed gas atmospheres, which could tend to have contractors or NASA de[f]ending a position should be looked at carefully and coordinated with Apollo Office.

ARTICLES IN JOURNALS OR PERIODICALS

"3. All of these papers come to NASA for clearance for technical accuracy and will continue to be examined in that context. Contractors should not stop present commitments and should continue to prepare such articles for publications in the normal course of its work.

NEWS CONFERENCES

"4. None are presently scheduled. If there is a desire to hold news conferences, contractors should discuss with the center public affairs office.

"5. All news releases are presently cleared for technical accuracy [by] the Center Public Affairs Office. This continues and contracts [sic] should continue to submit news releases considered of public interest. There is no desire to stop the flow of public information in NASA or the Apollo program.

"6. Contractors understand the responsibility of the Review Board. The desire is not to hamper the Board in its work, and to refrain from speculation. We are keeping the doors of our contractors open to the press, responding to queries and demonstrating to media the equipment presently used and under development. This material is presently in public domain. Press relations should continue to be carefully coordinated with the center public affairs offices.

Signed George E. Mueller, Associate Administrator for MSF; Julian Scheer, Assistant Administrator for Public Affairs."

Readers of the following summary were impressed, and rightly so, with its engineering thoroughness and unflinching criticisms of specific technical shortcomings. But there it stopped.

SUMMARY OF BOARD FINDINGS, DETERMINATIONS AND RECOMMENDATIONS

In this Review, the Board adhered to the principle that reliability of the Command Module and the entire system involved in its operation is a requirement common to both safety and mission success. Once the Command Module has left the earth's environment the occupants are totally dependent upon it for their safety. It follows that protection from fire as a hazard involves much more than quick egress. The latter has merit only during test periods on earth when the Command Module is being readied for its mission and not during the mission itself. The risk of fire must be faced; however, that risk is only one factor pertaining to the reliability of the Command Module that must received [sic] adequate consideration. Design features and operating procedures that are intended to reduce the fire risk must not introduce other serious risks to mission success and safety.

1. FINDING:

a. There was a momentary power failure at 23:30:55 GMT.

b. Evidence of several arcs was found in the post fire investigation.

c. No single ignition source of the fire was conclusively identified.

DETERMINATION:

The most probable initiator was an electrical arc in the sector between the —Y and +Z spacecraft axes. The exact location best fitting the total available information is near the floor in the lower forward section of the left-hand equipment bay where Environmental Control System (ECS) instrumentation power wiring leads into the area between the Environmental Control Unit (ECU) and the oxygen panel. No evidence was discovered that suggested sabotage.

2. FINDING:

a. The Command Module contained many types and classes of combustible material in areas contiguous to possible ignition sources.

b. The test was conducted with a 16.7 pounds per square inch absolute, 100 percent oxygen atmosphere.

DETERMINATION:

The test conditions were extremely hazardous.

RECOMMENDATION:

The amount and location of combustible materials in the Command Module must be severely restricted and controlled.

3. FINDING:

a. The rapid spread of fire caused an increase in pressure and temperature which resulted in rupture of the Command Module and creation of a toxic atmosphere. Death of the crew was from asphyxia due to inhalation of toxic gases due to fire. A contributory cause of death was thermal burns.

b. Non-uniform distribution of carboxyhemoglobin was found by autopsy.

DETERMINATION:

Autopsy data leads to the medical opinion that unconsciousness occurred rapidly and that death followed soon thereafter.

4. FINDING:

Due to internal pressure, the Command Module inner hatch could not be opened prior to rupture of the Command Module.

DETERMINATION:

The crew was never capable of effecting emergency egress because of the pressurization before rupture and their loss of consciousness soon after rupture.

RECOMMENDATION:

The time required for egress of the crew be reduced and the operations necessary for egress be simplified.

5. FINDING:

Those organizations responsible for the planning, conduct and safety of this test failed to identify it as being hazardous. Contingency preparations to permit escape or rescue of the crew from an internal Command Module fire were not made.

a. No procedures for this type of emergency had been established either for the crew or for the spacecraft pad work team.

b. The emergency equipment located in the White Room and on the spacecraft work levels was not designed for the smoke condition resulting from a fire of this nature.

c. Emergency fire, rescue and medical teams were not in attendance.

d. Both the spacecraft work levels and the umbilical tower access arm contain features such as steps, sliding doors and sharp turns in the egress paths which hinder emergency operations.

DETERMINATION:

Adequate safety precautions were neither established nor observed for this test.

RECOMMENDATIONS:

a. Management continually monitor the safety of all test operations and assure the adequacy of emergency procedures.

b. All emergency equipment (breathing apparatus, protective clothing, deluge systems, access arm, etc.) be reviewed for adequacy.

c. Personnel training and practice for emergency procedures be given on a regular basis and reviewed prior to the conduct of a hazardous operation.

d. Service structures and umbilical towers be modified to facilitate emergency operations.

6. FINDING:

Frequent interruptions and failures had been experienced in the overall communication system during the operations preceding the accident.

DETERMINATION:

The overall communication system was unsatisfactory.

RECOMMENDATIONS:

a. The Ground Communication System be improved to assure reliable communications between all test elements as soon as possible and before the next manned flight.

b. A detailed design review be conducted on the entire spacecraft communication system.

7. FINDING:

a. Revisions to the Operational Checkout Procedure for the test were issued at 5:30 pm EST January 26, 1967 (209 pages) and 10:00 am EST January 27, 1967 (4 pages).

b. Differences existed between the Ground Test Procedures and the In-Flight Check Lists.

DETERMINATION:

Neither the revision nor the differences contributed to the accident. The late issuance of the revision, however, prevented test personnel from becoming adequately familiar with the test procedure prior to its use.

RECOMMENDATIONS:

a. Test Procedures and Pilot's Checklists that represent the actual Command Module configuration be published in final form and reviewed early enough to permit adequate preparation and participation of all test organization.

b. Timely distribution of test procedures and major changes be made a constraint to the beginning of any test.

8. FINDING:

The fire in Command Module 012 was subsequently simulated closely by a test fire in a full-scale mock-up.

DETERMINATION:

Full-scale mock-up fire tests can be used to give a realistic appraisal of fire risks in flight-configured spacecraft.

RECOMMENDATIONS:

Full-scale mock-ups in flight configuration be tested to determine the risk of fire.

9. FINDING:

The Command Module Environmental Control System design provides a pure oxygen atmosphere.

DETERMINATION:

This atmosphere presents severe fire hazards if the amount and location of combustibles in the Command Module are not restricted and controlled.

RECOMMENDATIONS:

a. The fire safety of the reconfigured Command Module be established by full-scale mock-up tests.

b. Studies of the use of a diluent gas be continued with particular reference to assessing the problems of gas detection and control and the risk of additional operations that would be required in the use of a two gas atmosphere.

10. FINDING:

Deficiencies existed in Command Module design, workmanship and quality control, such as:

a. Components of the Environmental Control System installed in Command Module 012 had a history of many removals and of technical difficulties including regulator failures, line failures and Environmental Control Unit failures. The design and installation features of the Environmental Control Unit makes removal or repair difficult.

b. Coolant leakage at solder joints has been a chronic problem.

c. The coolant is both corrosive and combustible.

d. Deficiencies in design, manufacture, installation, rework and quality control existed in the electrical wiring.

e. No vibration test was made of a complete flight-configured spacecraft.

f. Spacecraft design and operating procedures currently require the disconnecting of electrical connections while powered.

g. No design features for fire protection were incorporated.

DETERMINATION:

These deficiencies created an unnecessarily hazardous condition and their continuation would imperil any future Apollo operations.

RECOMMENDATIONS:

a. An in-depth review of all elements, components and assemblies of the Environmental Control System be conducted to assure its functional and structural integrity and to minimize its contribution to fire risk.

b. Present design of soldered joints in plumbing be modified to increase integrity or the joints be replaced with a more structurally reliable configuration.

c. Deleterious effects of coolant leakage and spillage be eliminated.

d. Review of specifications be conducted, 3-dimensional jigs be used in manufacture of wire bundles and rigid inspection at all stages of wiring design, manufacture and installation be enforced.

e. Vibration tests be conducted of a flight-configured spacecraft.

f. The necessity for electrical connections or disconnections with power on within the crew compartment be eliminated.

g. Investigation be made of the most effective means of controlling and extinguishing a spacecraft fire. Auxiliary breathing oxygen and crew protection from smoke and toxic fumes be provided.

11. FINDING:

An examination of operating practices showed the following examples of problem areas:

a. The number of the open items at the time of shipment of the Command Module 012 was not known. There were 113 significant Engineering Orders not accomplished at the time Command Module 012 was delivered to NASA; 623 Engineering Orders were released subsequent to delivery. Of these, 22 were recent releases which were not recorded in configuration records at the time of the accident.

b. Established requirements were not followed with regard to the pre-test constraints list. The list was not completed and signed by designated contractor and NASA personnel prior to the test, even though oral agreement to proceed was reached.

c. Formulation of and changes to pre-launch test requirements for the Apollo spacecraft program were unresponsive to changing conditions.

d. Non-certified equipment items were installed in the Command Module at time of test.

e. Discrepancies existed between NAA and NASA MSC specifications regarding inclusion and positioning of flammable materials.

f. The test specification was released in August 1966 and was not updated to include accumulated changes from release date to date of the test.

DETERMINATION:

Problems of program management and relationships between Centers and with the contractor have led in some cases to insufficient response to changing program requirements.

RECOMMENDATION:

Every effort must be made to insure the maximum clarification and understanding of the responsibilities of all the organizations involved, the objective being a fully coordinated and efficient program.

Of all congressmen, Representative William F. Ryan of New York was perhaps the most angry and the most alarmed at NASA's refusal to release the controversial Phillips Report. In the following statement, released April 26, 1967, Ryan tells why he was so angry, and shows how closely some of the recommendations of the pre-fire Phillips Report match those of the *Report of Apollo 204 Review Board*, presented (after the fire) sixteen months later:

We are confronted with a very grave question which goes to the heart of the democratic process—whether an agency of our government has the unqualified right to withhold from the public and Members of Congress information which is crucial to a Congressional investigation of a vitally important matter.

If federal agencies have this right, then the elected representatives of the people cannot perform their function of making policy and watching over the expenditures of public funds to insure that they are not squandered and that the recipients of public funds fulfill their commitments. Certainly there is no right to conceal information to avoid embarrassment or to cover up inefficiency and negligence. The matters on which I will comment today constitute a crucial case in the long fight for freedom of information.

As you know, the House Science & Astronautics Committee, of which I am a member, has been investigating the circumstances which led to the Apollo fire on January 27, 1967, which claimed the lives of three brave Astronauts.

Apparently because of failures by NASA and its contractor, North American Aviation, their lives were unnecessarily sacrificed.

During the course of the hearings it was revealed that on December 19, 1965, thirteen months before the Apollo fire, General Samuel C. Phillips, Apollo Program Director, sent a covering letter along with a report to North American Aviation, the principal Apollo contractor. It became clear that the Phillips report critically discussed the performance of North American Aviation. It also became clear that the report has a vitally important bearing on the management competence of North American Aviation and the supervisory competence of NASA, both of which are now in question.

Because of the crucial importance of the Phillips report to our investigation, I requested that it be made available in its entirety to the Science & Astronautics Committee and that NASA and North American Aviation be examined concerning its contents. The public, which pays for the second most expensive governmental program, is entitled to know the facts.

In spite of the obvious relevance and importance of the Phillips report, NASA has refused to produce it. It has not refused because the divulgence of its contents would impair national security. It has not refused because it was a classified document. And it has not refused because the Administration claimed "executive privilege" which can only be asserted by the President. In fact, there is no rationale for the suppression of the report. All that NASA would say was that NASA always complied with Congress' "real needs."

I continued to request the report both privately and publically [sic]. Then on Saturday, April 15, 1967, in response to continuing pressure to release the Phillips Report, Mr. Webb sent a letter to the Subcommittee Chairman with an attached memorandum referred to as a summary. A copy of the so-called summary was made available to me at my request. It is no substitute for the full report. Mr. Webb himself describes it as being in essence the same as the testimony before the Senate Committee on Aeronautics and Space Sciences on April 13.

I have now seen a copy of the Phillips report. It is now clear to me why NASA refused to divulge its contents. The reason is simple. It's not that the report would damage the national interest or security. It's not that the space program would be jeopardized. It's simply that the truth concerning NASA's failure to properly supervise Apollo operations and incredible mismanagement on the part of NASA's major Apollo contractor is highly embarrassing to NASA.

In a democracy no agency should be permitted to withhold critical information for its own protection. On the contrary, the public which at a tremendous cost is financing NASA's efforts in space, has a right to know how its money is being spent. The $25 billion for the moon program is nothing compared to the costs that will ensue later as NASA's future plans unfold. These plans are in some ways inconsistent with the recommendations of the scientific community. These plans are in some ways very exciting and remarkable. To be sure, the costs involved are astronomical. Yet the public has not been allowed to review these plans and to approve of future expenditures.

The Phillips Report does not discuss these future plans. But it does give the American people some basis for evaluating the performance of those who will be shaping these plans at vast public expense.

In its effort to hide the facts NASA tried to convince the Congress that, although the Phillips report might have been critical, all the deficiencies mentioned in the report were cleared up long before the Apollo fire. The facts are to the contrary.

On April 5, 1967, the Apollo Review Board made its findings. These findings were made 16 months after the Phillips report was sent to North American Aviation. The similarity between the two sets of findings shows that NASA knew of management's incompetence a full 13 months before the tragic fire. The only reasonable and objective conclusion is that North American Aviation did not clear up the deficiencies pointed out in the Phillips report and that NASA did not exercise proper supervision thereafter.

The covering letter dated December 19, 1965, from General Samuel C. Phillips to Mr. J. L. Atwood, President of North American Aviation, states: "I am definitely not satisfied with the progress and outlook of either program (S–II and CSM) . . . Even with due consideration of hopeful signs, I could not find a substantive basis for confidence in future performance."

According to the Phillips Report, "The review was conducted as a result of the continual failure of NAA to achieve the progress required to support the objective of the Apollo Program."

The following abbreviated items from the Phillips report of December 19, 1965, and their close correlation with many findings of the Apollo Review Board may be of interest:

PHILLIPS REPORT.

"AT THE START OF THE CSM AND S–II PROGRAMS, KEY MILESTONES WERE AGREED UPON, PERFORMANCE REQUIREMENTS ESTABLISHED AND COST PLANS DEVELOPED. THESE WERE ESSENTIALLY COMMITMENTS MADE BY NAA TO NASA. AS THE PROGRAM PROGRESSED NASA HAS BEEN FORCED TO ACCEPT SLIPPAGES IN KEY MILESTONE ACCOMPLISHMENTS, DEGRADATION IN HARDWARE PERFORMANCE, AND INCREASING COSTS."

Apollo Review Board.

". . . during this period (October 7 to December 20, 1966) the Apollo Program Director made a decision to conduct a Recertification Review to be conducted during the month of December 1966. This action was deemed necessary in view of the large number of action items resulting from the initial review, with many remaining open. The selected date of December 21, 1966, for this second review was influenced by a slippage in the launch schedule caused by the delay in completion of the Environmental Control Sub-system . . . to correct a previously identified deficiency . . ."

PHILLIPS REPORT.

"INADEQUATE PROCEDURES AND CONTROLS IN BONDING AND WELDING, AS WELL AS INADEQUATE MASTER TOOLING, HAVE DELAYED FABRICATION. IN ADDITION THERE ARE STILL MAJOR DEVELOPMENT PROBLEMS TO BE RESOLVED. SPS ENGINE LIFE, RCS PERFORMANCE, STRESS CORROSION, AND FAILURE OF OXIDIZER TANKS HAS RESULTED IN DEGRADATION OF THE BLOCK I SPACECRAFT AS WELL AS FORCED POSTPONEMENT OF THE RESOLUTION OF THE BLOCK II SPACECRAFT CONFIGURATION."

Apollo Review Board.

"The purpose of the First Article Configuration Inspection (FACI) is to establish the Configuration Baseline for the spacecraft. It is accomplished by establishing the relationship of the spacecraft as described by released engineering documentation (drawings, specifications) to the spacecraft as manufactured, assembled, and tested. The FACI checkpoint has been implemented for Block II spacecraft only. It was not implemented for S/C 012 . . ."

PHILLIPS REPORT.

"NAA PERFORMANCE ON BOTH PROGRAMS (S–II & CSM) IS CHARACTERIZED BY CONTINUED FAILURE TO MEET COMMITTED SCHEDULE DATES WITH REQUIRED TECHNICAL PERFORMANCE AND WITHIN COSTS. THERE IS NO EVIDENCE OF CURRENT IMPROVEMENT IN NAA'S MANAGEMENT OF THESE PROGRAMS OF THE MAGNITUDE REQUIRED TO GIVE CONFIDENCE THAT NAA PERFORMANCE WILL IMPROVE AT THE RATE REQUIRED TO MEET ESTABLISHED APOLLO PROGRAM OBJECTIVES."

Apollo Review Board.

"At the time of shipment of the spacecraft to KSC, the contractor submitted an incomplete list of open items. A revision of the said list significantly and substantially enlarged the list of open items. The true status of the spacecraft was not identified by the contractor."

PHILLIPS REPORT.

"WITH THE FIRST UNMANNED FLIGHT SPACECRAFT FINALLY DELIVERED TO KSC, THERE ARE STILL SIGNIFICANT PROBLEMS REMAINING FOR BOTH BLOCK I AND BLOCK II CSM'S. TECHNICAL PROBLEMS WITH ELECTRICAL POWER CAPACITY, SERVICE PROPULSION, STRUCTURAL INTEGRITY, WEIGHT GROWTH, ETC., HAVE YET TO BE RESOLVED. TEST STAND ACTIVATION AND UNDERSUPPORT OF GSE STILL RETARD SCHEDULE PROGRESS. DELAYED AND COMPROMISED GROUND AND QUALIFICATION TEST PROGRAMS GIVE US SERIOUS CONCERN THAT FULLY QUALIFIED FLIGHT VEHICLES WILL NOT BE AVAILABLE TO SUPPORT THE LUNAR LANDING PROGRAM."

Apollo Review Board.

"Unsatisfactory Report. Category: Spacecraft/ System: EPS/ U.R. No.: A–054/ Contractor Part Name: Cable Harness Assembly (Crew Compartment)/ Date reported: 10–11–66/ Supplier: NAA/ Mission: Apollo/ Serial No.: 012/ Unsatisfactory Condition: This Unsatisfactory Report documents a recurring problem concerning bent pins in S/C electrical connectors, which if not corrected, could seriously impair the checkout schedules and/or jeopardize subsequent Apollo Missions."

Review of Pre-FRR (Flight Readiness Review) report completed by NAA on January 27, 1967: "During the Combined Systems Test at Downey, several caution and warning light indications could not be verified. Troubleshooting isolated the problem to an open circuit within terminal block assembly No. 1 behind the Main Display Console. An x-ray examination . . . revealed seven pins not properly inserted. The pin insertions in the remaining 31 similar TB assemblies installed in the S/C were examined. This examination revealed nine additional discrepant terminal block assemblies."

PHILLIPS REPORT.

"EFFECTIVE PLANNING AND CONTROL FROM A PROGRAM STANDPOINT DOES NOT EXIST . . . THE PROGRAM MANAGERS DO NOT DEFINE, MONITOR, OR CONTROL THE INTERFACES BETWEEN THE VARIOUS ORGANIZATIONS SUPPORTING THEIR PROGRAM."

Apollo Review Board.

"300 Materials do not meet the (flammability test) criteria established . . . 650 Materials have no status as to acceptability. Due to the type of information . . . used by NAA to compile the material usage list, exact location and amount used is not available in the majority of the cases. Such information is obtainable only by drawing review. This activity is not planned by NAA. In addition, subcontractor compliance has not been either imposed or obtained in all cases. Due to this lack of information, an engineering decision cannot be made on whether a serious problem does or does not exist nor can an assessment be made on the effect on the reliability from a toxicity and flammability standpoint."

PHILLIPS REPORT.

"THE CONDITION OF HARDWARE SHIPPED FROM THE FACTORY, WITH THOUSANDS OF HOURS OF WORK TO COMPLETE, IS UNSATISFACTORY TO NASA. S&ID MUST COMPLETE ALL HARDWARE AT THE FACTORY AND FURTHER IMPLEMENT, WITHOUT DELAY, AN ACCURATE SYSTEM TO CERTIFY CONFIGURATION OF DELIVERED HARDWARE, PROPERLY RELATED TO THE DD 250."

Apollo Review Board.

"Two revisions were made to the original Command Module DD Form 250. The first (original) DD 250 did not reflect the true status of the Command Module in that it did not include all of the actual part shortages nor did it list the equipment removed to facilitate shipment. To correct the status of the Command Module, the second CM DD 250 was written. After shipment, additional discrepancies were discovered in the 'as shipped' hardware configuration status . . . The third CM DD 250 was written to correct the status of the Command Module . . . items requiring Downey action which were not completed at NAA-Downey were transferred to KSC on the DD 250."

PHILLIPS REPORT.

"NAA QUALITY IS NOT UP TO NASA REQUIRED STAND-ARDS. THIS IS EVIDENCED BY THE LARGE NUMBER OF 'CORRECTION' E.O.'S AND MANUFACTURING DISCREPAN-CIES. THIS DEFICIENCY IS FURTHER COMPOUNDED BY THE LARGE NUMBER OF DISCREPANCIES THAT ESCAPE NAA INSPECTORS BUT ARE DETECTED BY NASA INSPEC-TORS. NAA MUST TAKE IMMEDIATE AND EFFECTIVE AC-TION TO IMPROVE THE QUALITY OF WORKMANSHIP AND TO TIGHTEN THEIR OWN INSPECTION. PERFORMANCE GOALS FOR DEMONSTRATING HIGH QUALITY MUST BE ESTABLISHED, AND TREND DATA MUST BE MAINTAINED AND GIVEN SERIOUS ATTENTION BY MANAGEMENT TO CORRECT THIS UNSATISFACTORY CONDITION."

Apollo Review Board.

". . . As a result of review of open work, it was found that a large number of engineering changes (had to be) incorporated into the S/C at KSC. Many of these changes resulted from non-fit or non-function problems . . . The large number of changes made it difficult to establish the vehicle configuration."

PHILLIPS REPORT.

"POOR WORKMANSHIP IS EVIDENCED BY THE CONTINUAL HIGH RATES OF REJECTION AND MRB ACTIONS WHICH RESULT IN REWORK THAT WOULD NOT BE NECESSARY IF THE WORKMANSHIP HAD BEEN GOOD . . . A PRAC-TICAL SYSTEM OF MEASURING WORK ACCOMPLISHED VS. WORK PLANNED MUST BE IMPLEMENTED AND USED TO GAUGE AND TO IMPROVE THE EFFECTIVENESS OF THE LABOR FORCE."

Apollo Review Board. Review of test findings, August 19, 1966.

"Failure of ECS Measurements. The water-glycol pump package pressure measurements was found defective . . . The transducer for water-glycol pump inlet pressure measurements was not replaced and NAA's request for waiver was granted . . . CO_2 Partial Pressure Gage. When power was turned on, the gage went to full scale deflection and triggered the caution and warning system. Additional testing was accomplished prior to shipment and gage operation was determined to be satisfactory although Automatic Checkout Equip-ment readouts did not correspond . . . The master caution and warn-ing light triggered with no visible indication on the individual dis-play when the glycol evaporator steam backpressure was operated. The problem was found to be a switch which was removed and replaced. A retest with the new switch was not performed and was transferred as open work to KSC . . . Use of Velcro and other materials in the CM was not considered desirable and was unsatisfactory for flight. Investigation of the CM crew compartment was performed with identification of undesirable materials listed prior to shipment of the spacecraft."

PHILLIPS REPORT.

"WORK TASK MANAGEMENT—GENERAL ORDERS, TASK AUTHORIZATIONS, PRODUCT PLANS, ETC., ARE BROAD AND ALMOST MEANINGLESS FROM A STANDPOINT OF DEFINING END PRODUCTS. DETAILED DEFINITIONS OF WORK TASKS ARE AVAILABLE AT THE 'DOING LEVEL'; HOWEVER, THESE 'WORK PLANS' ARE NOT REVIEWED, APPROVED, OR CONTROLLED BY THE PROGRAM MANAGERS. THERE IS NO EFFECTIVE REPORTING SYSTEM TO MANAGEMENT THAT EVALUATES PERFORMANCE AGAINST PLANS. PLANS ARE CHANGED TO REFLECT PERFORMANCE. TRENDS AND PERFORMANCE INDICES REPORTING IS ALMOST NONEXISTENT."

Apollo Review Board.

"The purpose of a CDR (Critical Design Review) is to formally review the design of a spacecraft when the design is essentially complete and is intended to precede the release of engineering drawings for manufacture. This review for S/C 012 . . . was accomplished after the S/C had been released for manufacturing."

"Shakedown inspection is . . . to detect and record hardware discrepancies . . . On investigation, it was learned that there were shakedown inspections performed prior to major test and milestones. However, these inspections were performed without definitive inspection criteria."

". . . Inspection procedures just prior to C/M hatch installation were reviewed . . . White Room space and weight loading limitations prevented having an Inspector witness these functions . . ."

"Analysis revealed that constraints lists are signed only by NASA/NAA Operations and Engineering with no NASA or NAA Quality control signature indicating approval of the constraints lists."

"Panel 6 investigated the requirements for retesting of components or subsystems after rework. APOP–T–502, Discrepancy Recording System," covers the retest requirement, but there is no requirement to keep the discrepancy records open until the retest has been verified. The records are closed out with a statement that the retest will be done in a subsequent test. This can then be deleted by on-the-spot deviations in a subsequent test."

"In an attempt to obtain a complete subsystem history from the records, considerable difficulty was experienced. This was due to the fact that the records are not maintained by subsystem."

PHILLIPS REPORT.

"INCENTIVIZATION OF THE S-II PROGRAM SHOULD BE

DELAYED UNTIL NASA IS ASSURED THAT THE S-II PRO-
GRAM IS UNDER CONTROL AND A RESPONSIBLE PRO-
POSAL IS RECEIVED FROM THE CONTRACTOR. DECISION
ON A FOLLOW-ON INCENTIVE CONTRACT FOR THE CSM,
BEYOND THE PRESENT CONTRACT PERIOD, WILL BE
BASED ON CONTRACTOR PERFORMANCE."

Apollo Review Board.

"The overall communication system was unsatisfactory . . . Deficiencies in design, manufacture, installation, rework and quality
control existed in the electrical wiring . . . These deficiencies created
an unnecessarily hazardous condition and their continuation would
imperil any future Apollo operations . . . There were 113 significant
Engineering Orders not accomplished at the time Command Module
012 was delivered to NASA . . . Problems of program management
. . . and with the contractor have led to insufficient response to
changing program requirements."

The danger of an agency arrogating to itself the power to suppress
important facts is clear. It is time for NASA to face Congress and the
public. NASA's refusal to let the public know what failures General
Phillips found and to compare these failures with the continued failures
which led up to the Apollo fire deprives the public and the Congress
of the means to pass judgment upon NASA's operations. NASA should
have made the full report public in the first instance. It can still do so.

In the past NASA has pursued a policy of openness in conducting
the space program. That is consistent with our society and with the
original NASA act which provides that "information obtained or
developed by the Administrator in the performance of his functions
shall be made available for public inspection . . ." and that nothing in
the NASA act "shall authorize the withholding of information by the
Administrator from the duly authorized committees of the Congress."

APPENDIX G

The Apollo 204 Review Board included, in its Appendix D, a summary of other "oxygen fires," including the Brooks Air Force Base fire of January 31, 1967, which killed two airmen. At the time of the Apollo 204 fire, highly placed NASA officials were apparently ignorant of the many similar fires that had occurred in the past. The Board omitted at least one other fire, as the authors point out in Chapter 8.

SUMMARIES OF OTHER OXYGEN FIRES

A review of one unmanned and four manned experiments in which there were fires shows that the exact ignition source in four of the fires was undetermined. They were believed to be electrical in nature. The only fatalities occurred in the two accidents in which there was a flash fire. In all five fires, inadequate safety precautions had been taken to either prevent or extinguish the fire or to protect the occupants.

BROOKS AIR FORCE BASE, SEPTEMBER 9, 1962

A fire occurred in the Space Cabin Simulator at Brooks Air Force Base on September 9, 1962. Test conditions were 5 psia 100 percent oxygen and the test had been in progress fourteen days at the time of the fire. The odor removal system used activated charcoal and the Carbon Dioxide (CO_2) removal system had an aluminum cover and consisted of a 500-pound bed of a mixture of 80-percent calcium hydroxide and 20-percent barium hydroxide. The Environmental Control System circulated cabin air progressively through the hydroxide, the charcoal, through the temperature controller (electric heater and refrigerant evaporator coil), then through an aluminum duct to the circulation fan. From the fan, ducts distributed air over the area behind the electronic test panel (cyclomotor). The air then leaked through openings in the panel back into the cabin. Both occupants wore pressure suits and one was asleep. Immediately upon noticing a glow behind the cyclomotor, one occupant awoke the other, grabbed a CO_2 extinguisher, and fought the fire until he collapsed from smoke inhalation. The awakened occupant immediately opened his face plate with the apparent intention of donning an oxygen mask, but he collapsed from smoke inhalation before he could get a mask or assist in extinguishing the fire. Both occupants were treated for smoke inhalation and neither received burns. There was no flash fire and damage was confined to the end of the chamber in the vicinity of the cyclomotor. Photographs of the aluminum duct immediately downstream of the temperature controller show definite signs of an implosion-explosion in the duct with a three-inch to four-inch diameter hole burned through one duct wall at the center of the imploded area. This was never fully clarified during the investigation and testimony revealed insufficient fuel had been consumed (burned) in the vicinity of the hole to melt the aluminum. Testimony also revealed that a small explosion could have occurred in the duct without being heard by either of the helmeted occupants. The investigating board concluded that the most likely source of ignition was a short or arc in an undetermined electronic component behind the cyclomotor panel.

BROOKS AIR FORCE BASE, JANUARY 31, 1967

A second fire occurred on January 31, 1967, in the same Brooks Air Force Base facility described in the first accident. Test conditions were 7.2 psia 100-percent oxygen. The test was in the first day of a planned 67-day test to study hematology of 16 rabbits. Two men had been in the simulator 12 minutes at the time of the fire, which was fatal to both. Both men suffered second and third degree burns over 90 percent of their bodies. An outside observer witnessed a flash fire which engulfed the chamber. A final report by the investigating board is at present unavailable and details of the facility design, and its differences with the design at the time of the 1962 fire, are therefore also unavailable. However, progress reports of the investigating board have provided the following information. Examination of the blower motor after the fire showed that the impeller was binding against the motor case and application of power to the motor resulted in blowing the fuses. Relationship of the motor malfunction to start of the fire has not yet been determined. The motor was downstream of the CO_2 absorbent bed. A short has been positively identified in an unspecified electrical fixture. The unanimous opinion of the investigating board and its observers-advisors and consultants is that the most probable cause of the fire was the existence of a combustible atmosphere within the chamber. The combustible atmosphere is believed (by the board) to be primarily hydrogen and possibly included hydrocarbons as a result of the animal experiment. Experiments conducted on-site have conclusively shown that the CO_2 absorbent reacted with water and aluminum and generated hydrogen. The ducting and the CO_2 absorber materials are the same as at the time of the 1962 fire; i.e., 80 percent calcium hydroxide and 20 percent barium hydroxide in aluminum ducting. There is evidence of intense heat in the CO_2 absorbent bed and intense exothermic chemical reactions were present in the air conditioning duct. This can be explained by an additional reaction which would have resulted from aluminum and iron oxide being reacted in the presence of a hydrogen-oxygen flame which can cause fusing of metals such as stainless steel, chromium, and other metals. This is known as a "thermite reaction" and the AF Materials Laboratory has determined that it can be initiated at 2352°F, the reactants being stainless steel and oxygen. The reaction is self-sustaining and reaches a temperature of 2550 to 2650°F. The reaction is suppressed in the presence of steam or about 35 percent CO_2. A possible source of the initiating temperature is the burning tape which was around the top of the CO_2 absorber filters. This tape can initiate the oxygen/stainless steel reaction in three seconds in 14.7 psia oxygen, but its burning temperature is as yet unknown in 7 psia oxygen. The CO_2 fire extinguishers were not removed from their holders and examination of the three oxygen regulators show no indication of malfunction. Ignition sources were considered by the investigation board to include an arc from an electrical short, an electrostatic spark, a friction spark, spontaneous oxidation, heated surfaces (particularly those which might have been in the CO_2 absorbent bed), heated surfaces from friction or hot wire, the electrical motor downstream of the CO_2 absorbent bed, clothing which might have ignited on contact with a heated surface or as a result of spontaneous oxidation, or ignition of a sponge, chair cushion, or rabbit fur from either an electrostatic discharge or spontaneous oxidation. A short in a lighting fixture wire was determined to be the most probable source of ignition.

NAVY EXPERIMENTAL DIVING UNIT, FEBRUARY 16, 1965

A fire occurred in the decompression chamber of the Navy's Experimental Diving Unit (EDU) at Washington, D.C. on February 16, 1965. Conditions at the time of the fire were 28-percent oxygen 36-percent nitrogen, and 36-percent helium at a total pressure of 55.6 psia (92 feet depth) or an oxygen partial pressure of 15.6 psia. About eleven minutes after entering the chamber (via a lock) from an adjacent chamber at 126 psia (250-foot depth) one of the divers reported the fire. Two observers at a viewing port observed a fire four inches in diameter and two feet high coming from the CO_2 scrubber immediately prior to a flash fire which engulfed the entire chamber. During the next minute, chamber pressure rose to 130 psia (260-foot depth). Attempts to rescue were unsuccessful and both occupants died. The CO_2 scrubber was portable and was designed for use as an emergency device for submarine atmosphere control and consisted of a tub containing six cylindrical tubes. The center tube contained the fan motor and outer tubes contained four CO_2 absorbent canisters and one filter element. Flow of chamber air through the scrubber was down through the four absorber canisters and up and out through the filter unit. The absorber elements consisted of a cylindrical metal can with metal screens on each end. The metal cylinder and screen materials are unidentified. The absorber chemical was the same as that in use at the time of Brooks' fires; i.e., 80 percent calcium hydroxide and 20-percent barium hydroxide. The "tub" which housed the entire scrubber assembly was made of an unidentified metal. The filter element was made of convoluted paper (probably Kraft) cylinders supported on the inside by a perforated metal (iron) cylinder and at the ends with stamped aluminum covers cemented to cardboard rings which are in turn cemented to the convoluted paper. Each unused unit weighs 2.1 pounds of which paper and cemented end rings comprise 1 pound. Investigation determined that primary use for this filter was in hydraulic systems and in the fuel systems of jet aircraft, and that common practice is to test every single filter element by immersion in an organic liquid and, while submerged, blow air through the filter to see if flaws existed at the seals of the paper. Tests were performed on two unused filter elements identical in design to the accident-involved filter. An acetone extraction on one showed that it probably contained about 0.3 to 0.4 pounds of kerosene-like liquid. This is consistent with the filter specification which lists maximum dry unit weight at 1.8 pounds. This also shows that the dry weight of the paper and end rings is 0.7 pound, arrived at by subtracting total wieght of metal $(2.1-1.0 = 1.1)$ from the 1.8 pounds total dry weight. A second filter was placed in a CO_2 scrubber, without CO_2 absorbent installed and operated for 2 hours. From this test, it was determined that the volatile liquids would be removed from the filter in 5 to 10 hours depending upon temperature and flow rate through the unit. The accident-involved filter was one of two supplied with the scrubber which had 1-1/2 to 2 years of intermittent use and the time logged on each filter is unknown. The used filter not involved in the accident had no "hydrocarbon" odor and an acetone extraction of the paper revealed a weight loss of only 10.2 percent compared to 36 percent loss on an unused filter. Samples from the used filter and an unused filter were subjected to high-frequency discharge (Tesla coil) in a stream of oxygen. The unused filter ignited easily and the flame spread rapidly whereas the used filter required 5 to 7 seconds of continuous discharge, ignited at the edge of the paper, and did not burn readily. From these tests, it was concluded that most or all of the easily ignitable material (hydrocarbon) had been removed from the filter by use prior to the EDU fire and that a rather strong ignition source would have been required to ignite it. A bench test of the scrubber motor after the fire showed that it ran at a reduced speed and rapidly overheated, the condition being caused by faulty operation of the centrifugal throw-out switch which resulted in the motor running on starting windings. The EDU had no provisions for odor removal (such as activated charcoal). The fire caused extensive damage including complete consumption of untreated cotton terry-cloth bath robes and about twelve feet of flexible air conditioning duct made of fabric-covered spiral wire. Untreated cotton mattresses with flame-proof covers were partially consumed. About five feet of the rubber on the unarmored electric cord to the portable scrubber was consumed as was rubber of armor-covered cables directly above the CO_2 scrubber. A simplified calculation by Naval Research Laboratory personnel showed that the pressure rise experienced during the fire would have caused a 761°F temperature rise and that the temperature rise would require the burning of only about 1.1 pounds of cellulosic material, i.e., cotton or perhaps wood-based paper in the filter. The investigation concluded that the most probable cause of the fire was the overheated scrubber motor causing spontaneous ignition of the filter element in a high-oxygen atmosphere. Fire extinguishing equipment consisted of a bucket of sand and a bucket of water, neither of which was used.

NAVY AIR CREW EQUIPMENT LABORATORY, NOVEMBER 17, 1962

A fire occurred in the Navy's Air Crew Equipment Laboratory (ACEL) on November 17, 1962. Test conditions were 100 percent oxygen at 5 psia and the fire occurred on the 17th day of the test. The fire started on the insulation of the ground wire to a light fixture. The ground wire was loose and an arc ignited the insulation. One of the four occupants tried to smother the fire with a towel which also ignited. Further attempts with an asbestos blanket resulted in ignition of the blanket and clothing worn by occupants. Subsequent attempts by all four to extinguish fire on the clothing of others resulted in the ignition of the clothing of all four, generally on the sleeves and pants legs. One occupant's hand caught on fire. All occupants escaped in about 40 seconds after first report of the fire and all were treated for first and second degree burns over 15 to 20 percent of their bodies. Immediately after exit of the occupants the door was closed, the chamber taken to 80,000 feet and purged for 20 minutes with CO_2 to extinguish the fire. There was no flash fire and there were no extinguishers in the chamber.

APOLLO ECS FIRE AT AIRESEARCH TORRANCE FACILITY, APRIL 28, 1966

A fire occurred in an unmanned qualification test of the Apollo Environmental Control System at Torrance, California, on April 28, 1966. Test conditions at, and 23.5 hours prior to the fire, were 100 percent oxygen at 5 psia. Prior to bringing the test up to 5 psia, the test had included 2456 hours at 10·4 millimeters of mercury (Torr). The investigating board concluded that the most probable cause of the fire was failure of a commercial quality strip heater used to add heat to the steam duct. The strip heater used polyvinyl chloride (PVC) insulation and the manufacturer's temperature rating was 167°F continuous, 190°F maximum in air. There was a sharp bend in the heater strip bearing against an ECU power lead splice at the heater strip entry into asbestos tape wrapped over the steam duct in the test set-up. Under high temperature conditions, the heater tape wire was demonstrated to extrude through the PVC insulation and a fire was initiated under simulated test conditions. Three other ignition causes were considered as possibilities. Strip heaters of the same type as above, but covered with aluminum foil, were on the potable water and dew point line sensor. Deterioration of insulation could have caused a short between one of the wires and the aluminum foil. Dew point measurements within the cabin showed that some metal surface temperatures were such that water could have condensed on them causing arcing on open terminal strips, unpotted connectors, or the 400-cycle unit, igniting adjacent materials. One of the ECU high pressure oxygen check valves, which use an elastomeric (DPR) seal, was severely damaged and it was theorized that high pressure "impact" of the 900 psia oxygen could have ignited the EPR. AiResearch ran a series of 3000 psi impact tests without ignition, and although the test results were not absolutely conclusive, it was concluded that this was the least probable of the possible causes presented. Other damage caused by the fire included excessively burned insulation of the test set-up wiring, fusing and burning of ECU wire harness, and burned polyurethane foam insulation on the oxygen and water-glycol lines. The investigating board concluded that, although 16 components had malfunctioned prior to and during the test and 18 had failed due to damage by the fire, the ECS qualification unit was not the direct cause of the fire. Also, test equipment and materials were improper for the environment, there was no fire detection or extinguishing equipment, and there were no emergency procedures. The board also concluded that improvement in the selection of some materials used in the ECS and the Apollo Command Module (C/M) could be made to control fire. Also, the C/M electrical circuits and wiring have potential hazards from arcing or direct short circuits. Also concluded was the fact that AiResearch procedures and documentation were inadequate, that quality control (QC) personnel were provided inadequate direction and that a NASA Test Readiness Review might have precluded the incident. The board recommended that all action necessary be taken to preclude initiation of a fire in the C/M with special emphasis on adequacies of wire bundle derating, circuit breaker/ wire compatibility, and elimination of all possible nonmetallic materials in contact with wire bundles. The board also recommended the imposition of nonmetallic materials specification requirements on all contractors and other suppliers of flight equipment, and to strengthen the materials selection and application program.

APOLLO ECS EXPLOSION AT AIRESEARCH, APRIL 13, 1965

An explosion occurred in an unmanned qualification test of the Apollo ECS at AiResearch on April 13, 1965. The explosion occurred after 127 hours of a planned 141-hour test. Conditions were corrosive contaminants, oxygen, and humidity (CCOH) per qualification test procedure SS-1224-R, paragraph 6.8. Failure reports were prepared for four components; a sensor (P/N 820110-1), a fan (P/N 826310-2-1), a valve (P/N 850028-1-1), and an absolute pressure transducer (P/N 837044-1-1). The explosion was determined to be the result of polyurethane foam swelling underneath a water tank causing a suspended electrical immersion heater to touch the bottom of the tank. Sufficient localized heat was generated to ignite the oxygen-saturated foam. Electrical connections did not indicate evidence of shorting and it was noted that all units were operable after the test was aborted. Corrective action included use of Teflon sheets in place of polyurethane foam and neoprene to isolate the units electrically, connection of the unit mounting frame and tank to a common ground, potting of heater leads, installation of a commercial submersion heater in the water tank by welding a boss.

APOLLO ECS EXPLOSION AT AIRESEARCH, JULY 1, 1964

An explosion occurred in unmanned qualification test in the explosion proof chamber at AiResearch on or about July 1, 1964. The test had been in progress 30 minutes and test conditions were in accordance with explosion proof test SS-1218-R, paragraph 6.9.2. A cabin air temperature sensor, P/N 820100-1, was damaged to the extent that the glass bead around the thermistor was bubbled and pitted from the heat. Conclusion as to the cause of the explosion was that the insulation around the heater coil broke down from heat inside the explosion chamber while the explosion proof test was in progress. Corrective action was to retest the sensor for temperature versus resistance per SS-1113-R, revision 1. paragraph 4.2. The sensor was retested, witnessed by NAA and Air Force QC, and released for future testing on July 1, 1964

APPENDIX H

The use of 100 percent oxygen as a space-cabin environment was plainly based on engineering considerations. Human safety was secondary. This simple truth is nowhere more evident than in the following three tables included in NASA publication SP–118, "Space-Cabin Atmospheres, Part IV—Engineering Tradeoffs of One- Versus Two-Gas Systems." This publication, prepared considerably earlier, was not released until after the Apollo 204 fire.

TABLE 34.—*Physiological Factors*

Factor [a]	Mixed 7-psia 1. 3.5-psia O$_2$ / 3.5-psia N$_2$	Mixed 7-psia 2. 3.5-psia O$_2$ / 3.5-psia He	Mixed 5-psia 3. 3.5-psia O$_2$ / 1.5-psia N$_2$	Mixed 5-psia 4. 3.5-psia O$_2$ / 1.5-psia He	Single 5-psia 5. 5-psia O$_2$	Selection order [b]
1. Aural atelectasis (Part I) (fig. 2)	No problem	No problem	No problem	No problem	Does occur in laboratory	(1 2 3 4) 5
2. Pulmonary atelectasis (Part I) (fig. 2)	No problem	No problem	No problem	No problem	Does occur in laboratory	(1 2 3 4) 5
3. Vital capacity reduction (Part I) (fig. 2)	No problem	No problem	No problem	No problem	Has occurred in laboratory; ? significance	(1 2 3 4) 5
4. Hemolytic anemia (Part I)	No problem	No problem	No problem	No problem	Has occurred in laboratory; ? significance	(1 2 3 4) 5
5. Urinary abnormalities (Parts I and III)						
6. Radiation sensitivity (Parts I and III)	No change	No change	No change	No change	No change at this pressure	(1 2 3 4 5)
7. Voice pitch change (Part III)	Insignificant	Minimal	Insignificant	Minimal	Insignificant	1 (3 5) (4 2)
8. Decompression time prior to symptoms of hypoxia (table 6)	Longest available	Intermediate	Next to shortest	Shortest available	Intermediate	1 (5 2) 3 4
9. Alteration of trace contaminant effects (Part II)	None expected	None expected	None expected	None expected	Has occurred in laboratory	1 3 2 4 5
10. Abdominal gaseous distress	Least, same as 2	Least, same as 1	Most, same as 4 and 5	Most, same as 3 and 4	Most, same as 3 and 4	(1 2) (3 4 5)
11. Decompression sickness:						
(a) Bends (Part III)	Rare but most susceptible	Same as 1	Very rare intermediate susceptibility	Same as 3	Probably will not occur when fully denitrogenated	5 (4 3) (1 2)
(b) Neurocirculatory collapse (Part III)	Extremely rare; most susceptible	Extremely rare; Intermediate susceptibility	Very extremely rare	Insignificantly low possibility	Probably will not occur when fully denitrogenated	5 4 3 2 1
(c) Ebullism survival time (Part III)	Least time	Intermediate time	Intermediate time	More time	Most time	5 4 (2 3) 1
12. Explosive decompression (Part III)	Extremely rare; most susceptible	Extremely rare; low susceptibility	Extremely rare; Intermediate susceptibility	Extremely rare; lowest susceptibility	Extremely rare; Intermediate susceptibility	4 2 (3 5) 1
13. Blast overpressure (Parts II and III)	Intermediate lung damage; Worst gas emboli	More favorable than 1	More lung damage; less dangerous emboli than 1	More lung damage; less dangerous emboli than 2	Same lung damage; less dangerous emboli than 3	(2 4) 5 3 1
14. Flash blindness from meteoroid penetration. (Part II)	Least dangerous	Same as 1	Intermediate	Intermediate	Most dangerous	(1 2) (3 4) 5
15. Possible metabolic side effects (Part III)	Least	Slightly more than 4	Slightly greater than 1	Slightly less than 2	Most likely	1 3 4 2 5
16. Tolerance of high air temperature (table 3)	Least	Most	Slightly more than 1	Next to 2	Same as 3	2 4 (3 5) 1
17. Changes in bacterial flora of skin and mouth	Least	Same as 1	Much less expected than in 5	Much less expected than in 5	Does occur in laboratory	(1 2) (3 4) 5

[a] Parts I, II, and III refer to SP–47, SP–48, and SP–117 which are parts of the Space-Cabin Atmospheres series and are listed as references 90, 91, and 92 in this report. Tables and figures cited are in this report.

[b] Mixtures are presented in descending order of desirability; those within parentheses are equally desirable.

TABLE 35.—Fire and Blast Hazards

Factor [a]	Mixed 7-psia		Mixed 5-psia		Single 5-psia	Selection order [b]
	1. 3.5-psia O_2 3.5-psia N_2	2. 3.5-psia O_2 3.5-psia He	3. 3.5-psia O_2 1.5-psia N_2	4. 3.5-psia O_2 1.5-psia He	5. 5-psia O_2	
1. Burning rate of fabrics and plastics (Part II) and (ref. 40)	Slowest rate	Greater than 1 but hardest to ignite by contact with hot solid	Slightly greater rate than 2	Greater than 3 but harder to ignite by contact with hot solid	Fastest burning rate	(2 1) (4 3) 5
2. Flame temperature of burning hydrocarbon vapor (Part II)	Lowest	Probably same as 1	Slightly higher than 1	Probably same as 3	Highest	(2 1) (4 3) 5
3. Decompression time to extinguish flame (Part II) (table 6)	Longest	Intermediate	Next to shortest	Shortest	Intermediate	4 3 (2 5) 1
4. Selectivity of cabin materials (Part III)	Least restrictive	Same as 1	Intermediate	Same as 3	Most restrictive	(2 1) (4 3) 5
5. Flash oxidation from meteorite penetration (Part II) (See no. 14 of table 34)	Least dangerous	Slightly more dangerous than 1	Slightly more dangerous than 1	Slightly more dangerous than 3	Most dangerous	1 2 3 4 5
6. Reduction of fire hazard by zero-gravity (Part II)	Slightly more reduced than 3	Probably most reduced; most diffusible inertant at flame front.	Slightly less than 4	Slightly less than 2	Markedly reduced but least susceptible to zero-gravity effects	2 4 1 3 5
7. Toxicity of oxidation products of atmosphere (Part II)	Most toxic; oxides of nitrogen	Least toxic	Slightly less than 4	Least toxic	Same as 4	(2 4 5) (3 1)
8. See no. 13 of table 34						
9. Overall fire hazard (Part II)	Least severe	Same as 1	Intermediate	Intermediate	Most severe	(1 2) (3 4) 5

[a] Parts I, II, and III refer to SP–47, SP–48, and SP–117 which are parts of the Space-Cabin Atmospheres series and are listed as references 90, 91, and 92. Tables and figures cited are in this report.

[b] Mixtures are presented in descending order of desirability; those within parentheses are equally desirable.

TABLE 36.—*Engineering Factors for 30-Day, 2-Man Orbiting Mission*

Factor [a]	Mixed 7-psia		Mixed 5-psia		Single 5-psia	Selection order [b]
	1. 3.5-psia O$_2$ 3.5-psia N$_2$	2. 3.5-psia O$_2$ 3.5-psia He	3. 3.5-psia O$_2$ 1.5-psia N$_2$	4. 3.5-psia O$_2$ 1.5-psia He	5. 5-psia O$_2$	
1. Gas storage:						
Overall tankage weight penalty (figs. 34 to 43 and table 31).	Less than 2	Greatest	More than 5	Less than 1	Least	5 3 4 1 2
Weight of diluent gas used (table 31)	Most	Slightly more than 4	Slightly less than 1	Least used	None	5 4 2 3 1
Total gas storage weight. (table 31)	Most	Intermediate	Intermediate	Least	Slightly more than 4	4 5 (2 3) 1
2. Fan power weight (table 23):						
Atmosphere control (tables 27 to 30)	Most	Slightly more than 4	Intermediate	Least	Intermediate	4 2 (3 5) 1
Ventilation and heat transfer (tables 24 to 26, 30).	Most (same as 3 and 5)	Least	Most (same as 1 and 5)	More than 2	Most (same as 1 and 3)	2 3 (5 4 1)
3. Controls, weight and complication.	More complicated than 5	Same as 1	Same as 1	Same as 1	Least weight and complication	5 (1 2 3 4)
4. Total ECS weight penalty (tables 31, 32, 33).	Most	Intermediate	Intermediate	Least	Intermediate	4 5 (2 3) 1
5. Development time and cost	Intermediate	High	Intermediate	Slightly more than 2 (if small diluent tankage)	Least	5 (1 3) (2 4)
6. Reliability of hardware	Less than 5	Less than 1	Same as 1	Less than 3	Most	5 (1 3) (2 4)
7. Compatibility with current reentry modules.	Least	Same as 1	Intermediate	Intermediate	Most	5 (3 4) (1 2)
8. Sensitivity to extension of active missions to 90 days.	Little	Some increase in storage efficiency less than 4	Little	Value does gain slightly because of increased storage efficiency	Little	4 2 (1 3 5)
9. Sensitivity to standby operations.	Gaseous storage insensitive, cryogenic is same as 3 and 5	Sensitive due to greater heat sink of cryogenic helium; gaseous may leak at high pressure	Same as 1	Slightly greater than 2 due to greater heat leak; gaseous may leak at high pressure	Same as 1	(1 3 5) 2 4

[a] Tables and figures cited are in this report.

[b] Mixtures are presented in descending order of desirability; those within parentheses are equally desirable.

Senator Walter F. Mondale of Minnesota appended "Additional Views" to the *Report of the Senate Committee on Aeronautical and Space Sciences on the Apollo 204 Accident.* His views were both more critical and more pessimistic than any of his colleagues on the Committee, who felt that while NASA had erred, the space agency had succeeded in correcting its wrongs and could be relied upon to function effectively and alertly in the future.

ADDITIONAL VIEWS OF MR. MONDALE
(On Apollo 204 Accident, Report of the Committee on Aeronautical and Space Sciences, United States Senate.)

I am in general agreement with the committee report as it now stands. However, one issue which arose during the committee's investigation into the Apollo 204 tragedy—the so-called Phillips report—requires further elaboration and emphasis.

The committee report rightly admonishes the National Aeronautics and Space Administration and its Administrator, the Honorable James E. Webb, for failing to appraise the committee of the serious contractor deficiencies which prompted the Phillips report at the time these problems were being investigated.

The Phillips report represented the most far-reaching and fundamental official criticism ever made of a major NASA program. The biggest and most ambitious NASA program of all—man's flight to the moon—was in deep and perilous trouble, and Congress was unaware of that fact.

Thus NASA's failure to inform the Congress of this grave situation was an unquestionably serious dereliction. But that this failure should be followed and compounded by deliberate efforts to mislead committee members and evade legitimate congressional inquiries during an investigation of this Nation's worst space tragedy, raises basic issues regarding the role of the committee vis-a-vis NASA and the ability of the committee and Congress to fulfill their responsibilities to the Nation. Specifically, the Phillips report incident raises the question of whether the committee and the Congress are to be limited to only that information which NASA sees fit to provide or whether the Congress will be supplied with complete and candid information regarding basic problems and difficulties being experienced in various NASA programs.

NASA has an unfortunate habit of swamping Congress with engineering details and starving it for policy and management information.

And it is in this second area—policy and management—not the first, where the responsibility of Congress lies.

Obviously, it is neither necessary nor desirable that the committee be inundated with every detail of NASA's relations with its contractors. But the Congress should be able to count on frank answers to pertinent, responsible, and legitimate inquiries.

Nonetheless, in response to such questions about the Phillips report, both NASA officials and representatives of the NASA contractor attempted to mislead the committee and evaded giving frank answers. When I first asked about the Phillips report on February 27, 1967, NASA officials responded with puzzlement and such statements as: "I know of no unusual General Phillips report." "I don't know of a specific report such as that." And "I cannot identify the (report) Senator Mondale was talking about." Representatives of the NASA contractor, North American Aviation, responded in a similar vein in testimony before the House Subcommittee on NASA Oversight on April 11. When asked about the Phillips report, NAA President Atwood replied:

> The Phillips report to whom? I have heard it mentioned, but General Phillips has not given us a copy of any report.

A month later, on May 4, the same North American officials were talking knowledgeably before the Senate committee about the review and report of the "General Phillips task force." Mr. Atwood described the review as "a very comprehensive and very complete * * * review and performance assessment," and said that he personally "put a tremendous amount of emphasis on it" and that NAA formed an action group consisting of "top corporate executives" to carry out the recommendations.

Similarly, the same NASA officials who knew of "no unusual General Phillips report" in February were calling it "a high-level review" and "an extraordinary effort" in testimony before the Senate committee on May 9.

These eventual admissions of the importance of the Phillips report did not come until after the existence of the document was an established fact. Unfortunately—and despite repeated requests to NASA—the Phillips report was first made available to the committee and Congress through sources other than official NASA channels, and throughout the hearings Congress was dependent upon an unofficial surreptitious source for the most significant single document involved in the Apollo 204 investigation.

Even when the facts of the Phillips review became known, NASA and NAA officials attempted to mislead members of the committee by engaging in a "semantic waltz" as to whether there was in fact a "report" or merely some informal "notes" made by the general and his associates. (The Phillips report is entitled "NASA Review Team Report" and is called a report not less than 10 times in the text.)

NASA's performance—the evasiveness, the lack of candor, the patronizing attitude exhibited toward Congress, the refusal to respond fully and forthrightly to legitimate congressional inquiries, and the solicitous concern for corporate sensitivities at a time of national tragedy—can only produce a loss of congressional and public confidence in NASA programs. And neither NASA nor the Nation can afford such a loss.

The very least this situation warrants is a thorough review and reassessment by NASA of its policies and practices regarding congressional inquiries and its responsibilities to keep the appropriate committees of Congress fully appraised of all basic aspects—good and bad—of NASA programs.

Unfortunately, there has been no indication to my knowledge that NASA intends to review or change the policies and practices brought to light by the Phillips report incident. Instead, there have been indications from the highest level of NASA management that such policies and practices will continue.

WALTER F. MONDALE.

Source Notes

CHAPTER 1

Page   QUOTES AND SOURCES

3   Just after dawn . . .   Sunrise occurred at 7:13
                                         a.m. on January 27, 1967.
                                         Gordon Harris, NASA chief
                                         of public affairs at Cape
                                         Kennedy.

3   "no earlier than February   NASA Release No. 67–9;
         21"   Jan. 23, 1967.

4   "routine"   *Time*, Feb. 3, 1967, p. 13;
                                         Today, "Florida's Space
                                         Age Newspaper," Brevard
                                         County, Fla., Jan. 27, 1968.

4   "standard procedure . . .   "Status Report on A/S 204
         several times before."   Accident," Cape Kennedy,
                                         Fla., Jan. 27, 1967, Maj.
                                         General Samuel C. Phillips,
                                         Apollo Program Director,
                                         Washington, D.C., presid-
                                         ing.

4   "bland mission"   Dr. Joseph F. Shea, Apollo
                                         Spacecraft Program Man-
                                         ager, Manned Spacecraft
                                         Center, transcript of Apollo
                                         News Media Symposium
                                         (Dec. 15–16, 1966, at
                                         Houston), p. 32.

4   The astronauts . . . making   Report of the Apollo 204
         the rounds at the Cape   Review Board (abbrevi-
                                         ated hereafter "RARB),
                                         Appx. D. p. D-11-6.

         within 10 to 12 feet   RARB, Appx. B, p. B-43.

8	"a popular new astronaut"	*American Space Exploration*, The First Decade, by William Roy Shelton, Little, Brown, 1967, p. 307.
8 *ftnt.*	"I don't bear any scars . . ."	*Men of Space*, Vol. 7, by Shirley Thomas, Chilton, 1965, p. 105.
8-9	"the largest and most complex," etc.	Hearings before the House Subcommittee on NASA Oversight (Apr. 10, 1967), Vol. I, p. 7.
9	"combination of building pyramids," etc.	Senate Hearings, NASA Appropriations (H.R. 124-74) 90th Congress, First Session, Fiscal Year 1968, p. 24. Dr. George E. Mueller paraphrase of Robert Hotz of *Aviation Week*.
9	"facetious" exchange about "causing," etc.	RARB, Appx. B, p. B-170.
9	"sent most of our guys down"	RARB, Appx. B, p. B-63.
9	whereabouts of reporters	*Editor and Publisher*, Feb. 4, 1967, p. 9.
10	public enthusiasm . . . on the rise again	A Public Opinion Survey, "Attitude Towards the Government Space and Moon Program," conducted for Thiokol Chemical Corporation, Sept., 1967, by Trendex, Inc.
10	"emergency egress" drill	RARB, Sum. Vol., p. 4-3.
11	objectives of plugs-out test	RARB, Sum. Vol., p. 4-3.
11	"worked around"	RARB, Appx. D, p. D-13-7.
11	believed to have come from Grissom	RARB, Sum. Vol., p. 5-8.
13	believed to be from Chaffee	RARB, Sum. Vol., p. 5-8.
13	loss of consciousness . . . 15 to 30 seconds "after first suit failed"	RARB, Sum. Vol., p. 5-9.

14	twenty-seven pad crewmen . . . overnight	NASA releases from JFK Space Center: AS 204 Release No. 2 and AS 204 Release No. 3, Jan. 27, 1967.
14	Donald K. Slayton . . . recalled, etc.	RARB, Appx. B, p. B-162.
14	"The Pad Leader . . ."	RARB, Sum. Vol., p. 4-8.
14	"in the interests of . . . after the accident"	RARB, Sum. Vol., p. 4-8.
15	standard NASA procedure	NASA "Management Instruction" Apr. 14, 1966, reproduced in RARB, Sum. Vol., pp. 1-3 to 1-4.
15	"never know . . . or pinpoint"	Dr. Robert C. Seamans, testimony in Hearing before the Senate Committee on Aeronautical and Space Sciences (Feb. 7, 1967), Part 1, pp. 26, 53.
16	"We know . . . astronaut"	A/S 204 Release No. 6, Jan. 28, 1967, JFK Space Center.
16	"every step . . . safety"	Hearing before Senate Committee on Aeronautical and Space Sciences (Feb. 7, 1967) Part 1, p. 40.

CHAPTER 2

19 chapter head	Grissom quote	Quoted in *Time*, Feb. 3, 1967, p. 13.
19	"inexcusable casualness . . ."	Dr. Ralph E. Lapp, personal communication.
19	"change the atmosphere . . ."	Quoted in *U.S. News & World Report*, Feb. 13, 1967, p. 31.
20	"standard procedure"	Maj. Gen. Samuel C. Phillips, Apollo Program Director, "Status Report on A/S 204 Accident," Cape Kennedy, Fla., Jan. 27, 1967.

20	"a new unified hatch . . . under testing"	Personal communication, Mark Bloom, N.Y. *Daily News.*
20	at least a minute	RARB, Appx. D, p. D-13-4.
21	TV camera . . . absent	RARB, Appx. D, pp. 1-16 and 13-7.
22	TV image . . . poor at best	RARB, Appx. B, p. B-157.
22	emergency exit drill had been added . . . at the request of astronauts	RARB, Sum. Vol., p. 4-3.
22	simulated trial of . . . ELS had to be canceled	RARB, Appx. D, p. 7-49.
23	support crew . . . fully installed	RARB, Appx. B, p. B-77 and Appx. D, p. D-12-25.
24	fifty-six were significant . . .	RARB, Appx. D, p. 1-19.
25	Grissom quote: "they can't even . . ."	Richard Lewis in *New York Post*, Feb. 3, 1967.
25	microphone . . . could not be turned off	RARB, Sum. Vol., pp. 4-3–4-4.
25	"minor" problem	Seamans to Webb memo of Feb. 3, 1967, included in RARB, Sum. Vol., p. 3-48. See Appendix A.
25	random switching of channels	RARB, Appx. B, pp. B-69-72.
25	"Astronaut communications all screwed up"	RARB, Appx. B, p. B-149.
25	"The overall communications problem . . ."	RARB, Appx. B, p. B-142.
26	"shortly before the accident . . . interfering with our conversation"	RARB, Appx. B, p. B-167.
26	"Up to this time . . . opportunity to improve communications between the spacecraft and ground crew"	RARB, Sum. Vol., p. 3-48; see Appendix A.
26	"worked around"	RARB, Appx. D, p. D-13-7.

26	"We . . . agreed to pick up the count"	RARB, Appx. B, p. B-161.
26-7	"'funny' . . . peculiar and unwelcome odor . . . buttermilk	RARB, Appx. B, pp. B-148 and B-175.
27	Two or three . . . "purges" of pure oxygen without cause of sour "buttermilk" odor . . . found	RARB, Appx. B, pp. B-52, B-77, B-175.
27	"significant"	RARB, Sum. Vol., p. 4-5.
27	"No Unexplained . . . Permitted"	*Gemini Midprogram Conference* (Feb. 23-25, 1966), p. 143.
28	"No failure"	*Ibid.*, p. 98.
28	"Mission success and Crew Safety"	*Ibid.*, p. 90.
29	"people working . . . flight safety implications of the program"	*Ibid.*, p. 9.
29	frantic men . . . one fire extinguisher . . . (level A-8)	RARB, Sum. Vol., p. 4-5.
29	This extinguisher . . . 30-day period . . . CO_2 extinguishers . . . operable 10-35 seconds	RARB, Appx. D, p. D-13-7.
31	Of the 80 masks . . . dense smoke that prevailed	RARB, Appx. D, pp. D-13-7, 8.
31	Donald Babbitt testimony	RARB, Appx. B, p. B-52.
31	L. D. Reece testimony	RARB, Appx. B, p. B-79.
31	When the Pan American firemen . . . finally arrived . . . airpacks . . . left behind.	RARB, Appx. D, p. D-12-28.
32	"we immediately . . . I almost ran over Mr. . . ."	RARB, Appx. B, p. B-73.
32	Some fully expected . . . "it would be 500° on the ground"	*Today*, "Florida's Space Age Newspaper," Brevard County, Fla., Jan. 27, 1968, quoting James E. Cramer, emergency elevator operator at time of fire.

32	. . . as long as they remained inside.	RARB, Appx. B, pp. B-163–B-164.
32	"space suits would protect them . . ."	RARB, Appx. B, p. B-154.
32	"blow the hatch"	*Ibid.*
32	they saw head and arm movements	RARB, Appx. B, p. B-153, p. B-167, etc.
33	Donald K. Slayton testimony	RARB, Appx. B, p. B-161.
33	During the frenzy . . . locked out of White Room	RARB, Appx. B, p. B-56.
33	"in a tool box with 34 other items"	RARB, Appx. B, p. B-63; p. B-79. *Today,* "Florida's Space Age Newspaper," Brevard County, Fla., Jan. 27, 1968, p. 2A.
33	At 6:30:21 p.m. some change . . . returned to normal	RARB, Sum. Vol., p. 4-4.
35	They were still alive and breathing "soot within nose, oral cavity, trachea and bronchi"	See Appendix C.
35	By about 6:36 p.m. . . . open the hatches . . . no attempt at removal or resuscitation	RARB, Sum. Vol., p. 4-6.
35	"Continue Mission"	RARB, Appx. D, p. D-20-15.
35	"as soon as conditions permitted"	AS 204 Release No. 3, NASA, JFK Space Center, released 10:50 p.m., Jan. 27, 1967.
35	They . . . arrived fourteen to eighteen minutes after fire was discovered	RARB, Appx. D, p. 11-3 states "approximately 6:45 p.m." Testimony by Dr. Berry before Senate set limits at 14 to 18 minutes.
35	Two NASA physicians . . . after being alerted by . . . Donald Slayton	RARB, Appx. B, p. B-161.

36	"After a quick evaluation . . . crew had not survived the heat, smoke, and thermal burns"	RARB, Sum. Vol., p. 4-8.
36	Slayton testimony	RARB, Appx. B, pp. B-161 and B-162.
37	The hatches . . . "off at 6:36 p.m.," or about five minutes after the fire was detected	RARB, Appx. D, p. D-12-29.
37	L. D. Reece . . . what the cabin contained	RARB, Appx. B, p. B-79.
37	One of the support crew . . . uncharred leg	RARB, Appx. B, p. B-178.
37	"cause of death . . . burns"	See Appendix C.
37	agency's "preliminary" . . . pronouncement	See Appendix A.
37-8	Dr. Berry's testimony	Senate Committee on Aeronautical and Space Sciences, Feb. 27, 1967, Part 2, p. 65.
38	Senator Clinton Anderson remark	Senate Committee on Aeronautical and Space Sciences, Feb. 27, 1967, Part 2, p. 66.
38	". . . 20,000 separate failures . . ." more than 100 important design changes in spacecraft	*Aviation Week*, Dec. 26, 1966, p. 18.
39	Shea remark	"Apollo News Media Symposium," Manned Spacecraft Center, Houston, Texas (Dec. 15–16, 1966), p. 8.
39	220 failures in Environmental Control System . . .	*Ibid.*, p. 15.
39	In December . . . still undergoing "a rebuild and retest cycle."	*Ibid.*, p. 35.

39	Loose wires . . . careless workmen	*Mercury Project Summary* (May 15–16, 1963), published by NASA October, 1963, pp. 248-249.
39	"Early in the Mercury program . . . free-floating debris . . ."	*Ibid.*, p. 248.
39	even the oxygen and water supplies contaminated	*Ibid.*, p. 249.
39-40	Webb, cited by *Fortune*	*Fortune*, August, 1967, p. 87.
40	Williams left NASA	William Hines in the *Nation*, April 24, 1967.
40	When Walter Schirra's Gemini 6 . . . saving the rocket . . . himself and . . . Stafford	*Today*, "Florida's Space Age Newspaper", Jan. 27, 1968.
40	According to Mark Bloom . . . major disaster	Personal communication.
40	"hung a lemon on it"	1968 NASA Authorization Hearings before the House Subcommittee on Manned Space Flight (March 14, 1967), Part 2, p. 44.

CHAPTER 3

41	"springboard to the Moon"	Robert Hotz editorial in *Aviation Week & Space Technology*, June 20, 1966, p. 21.
41	operated by Trans World Airlines . . .	*Forbes*, July 1, 1968, p. 96.
41	"monument to man's questing spirit"	Robert Hotz editorial in *Aviation Week & Space Technology*, June 20, 1966, p. 21.
41	tourist buses . . . right on schedule	*Editor and Publisher*, February 4, 1968, p. 10.
42	majority of the press . . . was some distance removed	*Ibid.*, p. 9.

42	experience . . . taught . . . interest could not be kept at fever-pitch forever	A Public Opinion Survey, "Attitude Towards the Government Space and Moon Program," conducted for Thiokol Chemical Corporation, September 1967, by Trendex, Inc.
43	"suit-donning and doffing . . . helmets and gloves?"	Apollo News Media Symposium at Manned Spacecraft Center, Houston, Texas (December 15–16, 1966), p. 385 of transcript.
43	Shea space jingle	*Ibid.*, p. 1 of transcript.
43	"It's almost a bland mission . . ."	*Ibid.*, p. 32 of transcript.
43	Jack King . . . news bulletins	*Editor & Publisher*, Feb. 4, 1967, p. 9.
44-5	Quotation from John Lear	*Saturday Review*, March 4, 1967, p. 51.
45	At approximately 7:00 p.m. . . . fire on the launch pad	*Editor and Publisher*, Feb. 4, 1967.
45	Finally, at about 8:32 . . . NASA all three . . . had been killed	*Ibid.*, p. 10.
45	The official NASA justification . . . inform next of kin	A/S 204 Release No. 1, JFK Space Center, Fla., Jan. 27, 1967.
46	This release was then re-typed . . . the word "a" was dropped	AS 204 Release No. 1, JFK Space Center, Fla., Jan. 27, 1967.
46	"unauthorized"	Personal communication, NASA Headquarters, Jan. 1967.
47	Subsequent releases . . . "flash" fire	A/S 204, Release No. 2, JFK Space Center, Fla., Jan. 27, 1967, etc.
47	He [Jack King] instructed to "save his eyewitness reports"	*Editor and Publisher*, Feb. 4, 1967, p. 9.
47	The General . . . "internal" power	"Status Report on A/S 204 Accident," Cape Kennedy, Fla., Jan. 27, 1967, p. 5.

47	The same error . . . by Paul Haney	"Statement of Apollo 1 Crew Death," Jan. 27, 1967, 11:05 p.m. at Manned Spacecraft Center, Houston, Tex., Tape 1, p. 4.
47	Attempts . . . drew "no comment."	John Noble Wilford, *The New York Times*; personal communication.
48	NASA countered . . . George Alexander . . . "still recognizable" flight plan book	*Editor and Publisher*, Feb. 4, 1967, p. 10.
48	Over a month after the accident, John Lear . . . spoke of "three charred skeletons"	*Saturday Review*, March 4, 1967, p. 53.
48	Almost three months after, ABC Science editor . . . mentioned astronauts . . . "instantly cremated."	ABC's "Issues and Answers," April 16, 1967.
50	UPI . . . personal memories of the dead astronauts	*Editor and Publisher*, Feb. 4, 1967, p. 10.
50	John Lear quotation	*Saturday Review*, March 4, 1967, p. 52.
51	John Noble Wilford . . . story reported anguished cries . . .	*The New York Times*, Jan. 31, 1967.
51	NASA was forced to correct . . . before he [White] was overcome	See Appendix A.
51	In Houston . . . Haney . . . "saturates all the insulation . . ."	"Statement of Apollo 1 Crew Death," January 27, 1967 11:05 p.m. at Manned Spacecraft Center, Houston, Tape 2, p. 3.
52	"No, the spacecraft . . . not pressurized . . ."	*Ibid.*, Tape 2, p. 4.
52	When Major General Phillips . . . questioned . . . "To the best of my knowledge there was not."	"Status Report on A/S 204 Accident," Cape Kennedy, Fla., Jan. 27, 1967, p. 4.

52	"You might recall . . . the only thing . . . I can recall."	"Statement of Apollo 1 Crew Death," Jan. 27, 1967, 11:05 p.m., at Manned Spacecraft Center, Houston, Tex., Tape 2, p. 3.
53	"Let's knock it off! . . . maudlin, saccharine concern"	*Technology Week*, Feb. 6, 1967, p. 50.
54	"Astronauts Public Affairs Activities"	Apollo News Media Conference, Dec. 15–16, 1966, Houston, Texas, follows page 377 of transcript.
55	Joseph Shea . . . "control release of all information . . . amplification of inconsequentials . . . what they might not resonate on"	RARB, Appx. A, p. A-20.
55	"very gratuitous and generous build-up"	Hearings before the House Subcommittee on NASA Oversight (May 10, 1967) Vol. 1, p. 558.
55	"It tolls . . . from euphoria to exaggerated detail . . ."	*Ibid.* (April 10, 1967), Vol. 1, p. 7.
56	Skardon quote	*Columbia Journalism Review*, Winter 1967/1968, pp. 34-35.
56	F. J. Hendel quotations	*Journal of Spacecraft and Rockets*, Vol. 1, No. 4, July-August, 1967, p. 353 and p. 361.
57	"largest and most complex . . ."	Hearings before the House Subcommittee on NASA Oversight (April 10, 1967) Vol. 1, p. 7.

CHAPTER 4

58	"with the launching of small, unmanned . . . satellites as part of International Geophysical Year . . ."	Quoted by Wernher von Braun in *Astronautics & Aeronautics*, Oct. 1967, p. 45.

| 58-9 | "the startling impact . . . of Sputnik 1 . . ." | Nicholas E. Golovin, *Astronautics & Aeronautics*, Oct. 1967, pp. 50–51. |

| 59 | "overnight . . . Even the moral fiber of our people came under scathing examination" | Wernher von Braun, quoted in *Fortune*, October 1967, p. 166. |

| 59 | "Russians captured all the German scientists at Peenemunde" | Dwight D. Eisenhower, quoted in *Fortune*, October, 1967, p. 166. |

| 59 | "most significant booty" | *Fortune*, October, 1967, p. 166. |

| 59 | The big lift . . . 341 box cars of V–2's equipment and records | *Rockets, Missiles, and Men in Space*, by Willy Ley, Viking Press, 1967, p. 223; *History of Rocketry & Space Travel*, by Wernher von Braun and Frederick I. Ordway III, Thomas Y. Crowell, 1966, p. 118. |

| 61 | Project Orbiter . . . during the summer of 1956 | *Rockets, Missiles and Men in Space*, op. cit., p. 306. |

| 62 | Russians delivered an official report . . . four months before Sputnik 1 . . . even announced frequency on which it was to transmit | *Rockets, Missiles and Men in Space*, op. cit., p. 384. *History of Rocketry & Space Travel*, op. cit., p. 180. |

| 63 | Air Force Committee on Space Technology . . . "Sputnik . . . created a national emergency." | *USAF Scientific Advisory Board, 1944–1964*, Washington 1967, p. 8. |

| 63 | American Rocket Society, with the Rocket and Satellite Panel of the National Academy of Sciences . . . felt a manned Moon landing could be accomplished by 1968. | Senate Special Committee on Space and Astronautics, *No. 1* Washington, 1958, pp. 17–19. |

64   "outer space . . . only for peaceful purposes"   Dwight D. Eisenhower, quoted in *The Genesis of the National Aeronautics and Space Act of 1958*, by E. Allison Griffith, Wash., 1962.

64-5   Four factors cited . . . as underlying America's Space program . . .   President's Scientific Advisory Committee, *Introduction to Outer Space*, March, 1958.

65   Dr. Van Allen . . . advised that an annual budget of $500 million . . .   Eugene M. Emme, *Historical Perspectives on Apollo*, AIAA paper No. 67-389, delivered at AIAA Annual Meeting, Anaheim, Calif., October 23-27, 1967.

66   [NASA's] goal to "demonstrate, soon and safely, man's capacity for space flight."   *Ibid.*

67   "The alumni of NACA . . . dominating influence . . ."   *Fortune*, August, 1967, p. 84.

67   Headed by H. Guyford Stever manned lunar landing "within the next 10 years"   NACA Special Committee on Space Technology, Working Group on Vehicular Program "Interim Report: National Integrated Missile and Space Development Program," April 1, 1958, p. 9.

67   "There is a possibility (of) a manned lunar landing (by) July, 1966."   NACA Special Committee on Space Technology, Working Group on Vehicular Program, *A National Integrated Missile and Space Vehicle Development Program*, July 18, 1958, p. 7.

68   Saturn cluster-engine . . . "quickest and surest way to . . . million-pound class."   Senate Staff Report on *Manned Space Flight*, Sept., 1959, p. 165.

68   "in accord with . . . outer   Eugene M. Emme, *op. cit.*
               space"

69   The United States chose to   *History of Rocket & Space*
               wait (for) a compact   *Travel,* by Wernher von
               nuclear warhead . . . the   Braun and Frederick I.
               Atomic Energy Commis-   Ordway, III, Thomas Y.
               sion could deliver "by 1965   Crowell, 1966, pp. 129, 132.
               at the latest" . . . relatively
               small launch vehicles . . .

69-70   "The Soviets were far   *History of Rocketry &*
               behind the U.S. in nuclear   *Space Travel, op. cit.,* p. 14.
               technology . . . space
               exploration"

CHAPTER 5

74   "If man orbits earth this   John F. Kennedy, quoted
               year his name will be Ivan"   by Eugene M. Emme, *op.
                                                  cit.*

74   "We are in a strategic space   John F. Kennedy in *Mis-*
               race . . . we must be first"   *siles and Rockets,* October
                                                  10, 1960.

74   "All these things and more   John F. Kennedy in *Mis-*
               we should accomplish as   *siles and Rockets,* October
               swiftly as possible"   10, 1960.

74   "This is the new age of ex-   John F. Kennedy, quoted
               ploration; space is our great   by Eugene M. Emme, *op.
               new frontier"   cit.*

74-5   no missile gap in 1960   Ralph   E.   Lapp,   *The
                                                  Weapons Culture,* W. W.
                                                  Norton & Co., New York,
                                                  1968, pp. 38–41.

75   Eisenhower quote   Remark attributed to Presi-
                                                  dent Eisenhower, *Fortune,*
                                                  August, 1967, p. 84.

75   "the cost of a manned   Eugene M. Emme, *op. cit.*
               lunar landing would range
               from $20 to $40 billion"

76   "organization and manage-   "Wiesner report," prepared
               ment deficiencies"   by President Kennedy's
                                                  nine-man Ad Hoc Com-
                                                  mittee on Space, released
                                                  Jan. 12, 1961.

76	"executive and other . . . levels . . ."	*Ibid.*
76	"virtually challenged . . ."	Eugene M. Emme, *op. cit.*
76	"marginal . . . not endorse . . . possible failures"	"Wiesner report," *op. cit.*
76	"seemed satisfied . . . less than competent"	Eugene M. Emme, *op. cit.*
76	"We should stop advertising Mercury . . ."	"Wiesner report," *op. cit.*
78	"recommend . . . national interest"	Eugene M. Emme, *op. cit.*
78-9	"renewed emphasis on manned space flight . . . bolstered"	"Man's Role in the National Space Program," submitted by Space Science Board of National Academy of Sciences to President Kennedy on March 31, 1961.
80	Webb indicated . . . "to proceed faster . . . the atomic bomb"	"Discussion of Soviet 'Man-in-Space Shot'," House Committee on Science and Astronautics (April 13, 1961), pp. 1–5, 31.
80-1	Seamans . . . replied "This is really a very major undertaking . . ."	1962 NASA Authorization hearings, before the House Committee on Science and Astronautics (Part 1), pp. 374–8.
82	The President . . . responded by saying . . . "Nothing is more important"	Emme, *op. cit.*
84	He [Kennedy] reportedly did not even brief NASA officials . . .	*The Rise and Fall of the Space Age*, by Edwin Diamond, Doubleday, 1964, p. 12.
84	EOR . . . particularly favored by Wiesner	*Ibid.*, p. 44.
85	promised to cut "from six to fifteen months" from . . . EOR . . .	*Ibid.*, p. 43.

86	Webb quote	*Space: The New Frontier,* NASA, U.S. Government Printing Office, 1967, 0-223-626, p. 2.
86	George M. Low quote	Speech to NASA-Industry Conference, Washington, D.C., Feb. 11, 1963, NASA SP-29, p. 33.
87	Kistiakowsky's "Hogwash"	*Science U.S.A.,* by William Gilman, Viking, 1965, p. 81.
89	Seamans' quote	*Aviation Week and Space Technology,* Jan. 20, 1964, p. 27.
89	"unexpected technical troubles"	*Ibid.*
89	Webb quotes: "if the space agency misses . . ." "inaccurate"	*Ibid.,* p. 29.
89	"[D. Brainerd Holmes] resigned to take a $90,000 job . . . at Raytheon"	*Fortune,* August, 1967, p. 87.
91	"U.S. space medicine program . . . weakest link . . . Mr. McNamara's biggest blunders"	Robert Hotz editorial in *Aviation Week,* Oct. 19, 1964, p. 21.
93	"On Gemini 10 . . . they had to open their face plates to take eyedrops."	*Rockets, Missiles, and Men in Space,* Willy Ley, Viking, 1968, p. 398.
94	"overconfidence and complacency"	Report on the Apollo 204 Accident by the Senate Committee on Aeronautical and Space Sciences (Jan. 30, 1968), p. 10.
95	Dr. Seamans . . . read into Apollo fire hearings . . . . . . Apollo program is predicated on a success schedule . . .	Apollo Accident, Hearings before the Senate Committee on Aeronautical and Space Sciences (Feb. 7, 1967) Part 1, p. 53.
95	Russians said "haste" and "flaws"	*Trud,* quoted in *The New York Times,* Jan. 30, 1967.

CHAPTER 6

98	letter transmitting "herewith"	Letter dated April 5, 1967, reproduced as opening page of RARB, Sum. Vol., signed by all Review Board members except George T. Malley, Legal Counsel.
99	"whitewash"	William J. Coughlin, *Technology Week*, April 17, 1967.
99	"harsh, scathing report"	*Ibid.*
99	Senator Smith quote	Hearings before the Senate Committee on Aeronautical and Space Sciences (April 11, 1967), Part 3, p. 195.
99	Representative Hechler quote	Hearings before the House Subcommittee on NASA Oversight (April 10, 1967), Vol. 1, p. 25.
99-100	Representative Rumsfeld quote	*Ibid.*, pp. 11–12.
100	Representative Wydler quotes	*Ibid.*, pp. 22–23.
100	Webb quote: "to search for error in the most complex research and development program ever undertaken"	*Ibid.*, p. 7.
100	Dr. Seamans quote	Hearings before the Senate Committee on Aeronautical and Space Sciences (Feb. 7, 1967), Part 1, p. 51.
101	Webb quote on Board's independence being a "technical question"	Hearings before the House Subcommittee on NASA Oversight (April 10, 1967), Vol. 1, p. 24.
102	Webb quote: "Whatever our faults, we are today an able-bodied team"	Hearings before the House Subcommittee on NASA Oversight (April 10, 1967), Vol. 1, p. 7.

103	"blue-ribbon Board"	*Murder on Pad 34*, by Eric Berghaust, G. P. Putnam's Sons, 1968.
104	Webb on Dr. Thompson	Hearings before the House Subcommittee on NASA Oversight (April 10, 1967), Vol. 1, p. 7.
104	Representative Downing on Dr. Thompson	*Ibid.*, pp. 17–18.
105	Dr. Seamans on Colonel Strang	*Ibid.*, p. 19.
108	Dr. Seamans on Dr. Long	*Ibid.*, p. 25.
108	Dr. Seamans on George Jeffs	*Ibid.*, p. 23.
109	Jeffs's testimony	Hearings before the House Subcommittee on NASA Oversight (April 11, 1967), Vol. 1, p. 207.
109	Dr. Thompson on Jeffs	RARB, Appendix A, p. A-68.
116	Baron testimony	Hearings before the House Subcommittee on NASA Oversight (April 21, 1967), Vol. 1, pp. 483–499.
116	Hechler remarks	*Ibid.*, p. 493.
116	Mervin Holmburg . . . called before the Subcommittee hearing	Hearings before the House Subcommittee on NASA Oversight (April 21, 1967), Vol. 1, p. 499.
117	Propst testimony to Review Board	RARB, Appx. B, p. B-154.
117	Propst remarks to reporter	*Today*, "Florida's Space Age Newspaper," Jan. 27, 1968.
118	Review Board records . . . not . . . confidential, [but] will be treated as "Confidential"	RARB, Sum. Vol., p. 3-14.
118-19	A typical "complete transcript"	RARB, Appx. A, p. A-27.

119	Senator Young–Colonel Borman exchange	Hearings before the Senate Committee on Aeronautical and Space Sciences (April 11, 1967), Part 3, p. 231.
120	Colonel Borman quote	*Ibid.*, p. 242.
120	Colonel Borman quote	*Ibid.*, p. 243.
120	Dr. Thompson quote	*Ibid.*, p. 235.
120-21	Webb quote	*Ibid.*, Part 2, p. 109.
121	Review Board statement	RARB, Sum. Vol., p. 5-12.
122	Representative Bell–Webb exchange	Hearings before the Subcommittee on NASA Oversight (April 10, 1967), Vol. 1, p. 25.

CHAPTER 7

124	Apollo and Titanic parallels clear to some NASA spokesmen	*Fortune*, August 1967, p. 192.
124	"nonhazardous"	Col. Frank Borman, on ABC-TV *Issues and Answers*, April 16, 1967.
126	1,412 potential combustibles	*Status of Actions Taken on Recommendations of the Apollo 204 Review Board*, House Subcommittee on NASA Oversight—Serial L —forwarded to George P. Miller, Chairman, Committee on Science and Astronautics, January 27, 1968.
126-27	"No point of culpability was found"	Rep. Olin E. Teague (D. Texas), Chairman, House Subcommittee on NASA Oversight, NBC-TV *Today Show*, April 21, 1967.
127	faulty, even "poor"	William J. Coughlin, *Technology Week*, p. 50, April 17, 1967.
128	Senator Anderson–Dr. Thompson exchange	Hearings before the Senate Committee on Aeronautical and Space Sciences, April 11, 1967, Part 2, p. 220.

128-29	Dr. Emanuel M. Roth quote	A.I.A.A. paper No. 67-855 delivered at Anaheim, Calif., October 1967, p. 1.
130	"one in a million"	William J. Coughlin, in *Technology Week*, p. 50, February 6, 1967.
130	Senator Mondale quote	Hearings before Senate Committee on Aeronautical Sciences, April 11, 1967, Part 2, p. 125.
133	Dr. Charles A. Berry quote	Hearings before the Senate Committee on Aeronautical. and Space Sciences (Feb. 7, 1967), Part 1, p. 16.
133	North's collapse was due to leaky lines	*Ibid.*, p. 17.
134	Quote from editors of *Fortune* magazine	*The Space Industry: America's Newest Giant*, by the Editors of *Fortune*, Prentice-Hall, Inc. 1962, p. 161.
135-36	Dr. Berry testimony	Hearings before the Senate Committee on Aeronautical and Space Sciences (Feb. 7, 1967), Part 1, p. 15–22.
136	Doctors . . . found a host of medical complications with pure oxygen.	Letter to the Editor, *Aviation Week*, February 27, 1967, p. 98.
137	Members of the scientific community grew more and more uneasy . . . the argument *against* pure oxygen, and *for* a mixed-gas as atmosphere grew more audible and noticeably more heated.	*Aviation Week*, letter to Editor, Feb. 27, 1967, p. 98.
138	Dr. Berry testimony	Hearings before the Senate Committee on Aeronautical and Space Sciences (Feb. 7, 1967), p. 19.
140	Dr. Berry testimony	*Ibid.*, p. 20.

141 *ftnt.*	Republic Aviation test	NASA TN D-2506 (January 1965), pp. 118, 121, 122.
142	Dr. Roth quote	NASA SP-48 (1964), p. 107.
142	Dr. Lawrence E. Lamb quote	*Aviation Week*, Nov. 23, 1964, p. 54.
144	Dr. Berry quote	NASA SP-121 (*Gemini Midprogram Conference*, Feb. 23-25, 1966), p. 235.
144	Dr. Roth quote	A.I.A.A. paper No. 67-855, delivered at Anaheim, Calif., October, 1967.
146	Col. Borman testimony	Hearings before the Senate Committee on Aeronautical and Space Sciences, April 11, 1967, Part 3, p. 198.
146-47	Senator Anderson quote	*Ibid.*, p. 221
147	Senator Smith– Col. Borman exchange	*Ibid.*, p. 198.
147	Senator Curtis– Col. Borman exchange	*Ibid.*, p. 207.
147	Senator Percy– Col. Borman exchange	*Ibid.*, p. 217.
148	Dr. Mueller– Senator Dodd exchange	*Ibid.*, Feb. 27, 1967, Part 2, p. 114.
148	Webb quote	Hearings before Senate Subcommittee on Appropriations, July 26, 1967, p. 25.
149	Dr. John McCarthy– Representative Karth exchange	Hearings before House Subcommittee on NASA Oversight, April 11, 1967, p. 165.

CHAPTER 8

| 151-52 | Technical description of Navy Air Crew Equipment Laboratory fire, Nov. 17, 1962. | NASA SP-48, p. 100. |

152-53	Detailed 45-page report published by NASA in January, 1965.	NASA TN D—2506.
153-54	"Fumes . . . alerted the cabin crew . . . instead of focusing attention on the hazards of fire, the accident gave a false sense of security."	NASA SP-48 [date of fire not given]
154	Soviet designer	*Fortune*, October, 1967, p. 168.
155	Representative Olin Teague quote	Remarks on ABC's "Issues and Answers," April 16, 1967.
155	Dr. Berry quote introducing Dr. Roth reports to Senate	Hearings of Senate Committee on Aeronautical and Space Sciences, Feb. 7, 1967, Part 1, p. 13.
156-60	Dr. Roth quotes	All quotes by Dr. Roth from his "Space-Cabin Atmospheres Part 2—Fire and Blast Hazards."
161	Dr. Mueller quotes	Authorization hearings before House Subcommittee on Manned Flight, March 14, 1967, part 2, p. 66.
161	Frank J. Hendel paper	*Spacecraft and Rockets*, July-August 1964, pp. 360–362.
168	Dr. Wallace O. Fenn quotes	*Inert Gases*, pp. 104–6, reprinted from Publication 1485B, *Physiology in The Space Environment*, Vol. II: Respiration; National Academy of Sciences—National Research Council.
168 *ftnt.* **	diluents under consideration	*Science News*, Oct. 5, 1965, p. 343.
169	Accordingly, the Academy . . . "post-Apollo flights."	Personal communication.

CHAPTER 9

175-76	According to NASA, hazards associated with fire in flight are far less than on the ground . . . because of three factors . . . the cabin . . . replenished with fresh, clean oxygen supply	Hearings before Senate Committee on Aeronautical and Space Sciences, Feb. 7, 1967, Part 1, p. 40; p. 43. Also April 11, 1967, Part 3, p. 198; p. 202.
180	NASA compared the relative testing and check-out periods of Mercury . . . Gemini . . . and Apollo systems on the ground . . .	Hearings before Senate Committee on Aeronautical and Space Sciences, Feb. 7, 1967, Part 1, p. 36.
181	"Apollo . . . plagued by troubles . . . 20,000 changes . . ."	*Ibid.*, pp. 54–55.
181-82	Exchange among Dr. Mueller, Dr. Berry, Senator Holland, staff counsel James J. Gehrig, and Senator Cannon	*Ibid.*, Part 2, pp. 84–85.
183	Roth quotes	NASA SP-48, pp. 82–83.
183	Roth quote	*Ibid.*, p. 108.
185	The 400°F. cut-off point was selected . . . there would be no fire of catastrophic proportion.	Hearings before the House Subcommittee on Manned Flight Committee on Science and Astronautics, March 14, 1967, Part 2, p. 8 . . . also Senate Committee on Aeronautical and Space Sciences, Feb. 27, 1967, Part 2, p. 107.
186-87	[Senate's] final Apollo 204 Report	*Apollo 204 Accident*, Report of the Committee on Aeronautical and Space Sciences, United States Senate, with Additional Views 90th Congress, 2nd Session, Report No. 956, Jan. 30, 1968—ordered to be printed, p. 6.

187	Webb quote, "we have incorporated many changes . . ."	Hearings before the Senate Committee on Aeronautical and Space Sciences on "NASA's Proposed Operating Plan for fiscal year 1968 (Nov. 8, 1967), p. 14.
187-88	"no changes in the existing spacecraft environmental control system" (which supplies pure oxygen in flight)	NASA News Release 68-47, March 13, 1968.
190-91	Dr. Chryssanthos Chryssanthou research on bends	Authors' interview, also *Aerospace Medicine*, August, 1964.
193	Roth quote	NASA SP-117, p. 116.

CHAPTER 10

196	. . . NASA claimed "secret" and "private" information	John Noble Wilford, *The New York Times*, August 14, 1968.
197	Visit of two congressmen to Cape Kennedy and then to Brooks	RARB, Appx. A, p. A-33.
197	Chairman L. Mendel Rivers . . . described in *Science*	*Science*, March 15, 1968, pp. 1217–19.
198	The CIA wanted it [MOL] . . .	*Aviation Week & Space Technology*, Sept. 20, 1965, pp. 26–27.
	so did the Air Force	*Ibid.*
199-200	Pentagon strategists planned on frequent trips of thirty-day duration . . . using procedures developed during the Gemini program . . . "itself and the rest of the world" "it is technically feasible and nationally necessary"	Robert Hotz in *Aviation Week*, editorial, Sept. 6, 1965.
202	USIA's mission . . . to make [MOL] . . . look as "peaceful as possible"	*Report to the Congress from the President of the United States, U.S. Aeronautics and Space Activities, 1967*, p. 116.

202	Description of AAP's mission	*Ibid.*, p. 14.
202	Wydler quote: "same program doing essentially the same things"	"Authorizing Appropriations to NASA," *Congressional Record*, Vol. 113, No. 103, June 28, 1967.
203	Ryan quote: "parallel program objectives"	Representative William F. Ryan of New York in a "Dear Colleague" letter of March 20, 1968.
203	Lapp remarks	transcript of radio interview with Representative Ryan, March 25, 1968.
203-4	"the actual experiments . . . selected jointly by NASA and DOD . . . all original seven NASA astronauts were military trained personnel"; quotations from Humphrey and Paul.	*The National Space Program — Its Values and Benefits*, prepared by staff of House Subcommittee on NASA Oversight, Feb. 1967, pp. 20–22.
204	Mueller testimony	NASA Authorization for Fiscal Year 1968, Hearings before the Senate Committee on Aeronautical and Space Sciences (April 19, 1967), Part 1, p. 143.
204	In return, Air Force MOL [would] test a NASA experiment	*Ibid.*
206-7	Richard D. Lyons quote	*The New York Times*, Oct. 21, 1968.
207	"NASA assists the military . . . the military . . . supports NASA's requirements"	1968 NASA Authorization Hearings before the House Committee on Science and Astronautics (March, April, 1967), Part 4, p. 199.
207	"DOD . . . taken into account in the formulation of practically all of NASA's research and technology . . ."	*Ibid.*, p. 198.

207	Webb quote	NASA Authorization for Fiscal Year 1968, Hearings before the Senate Committee on Aeronautical and Space Sciences (April 18, 1967), Part 1, p. 51.
207-8	NASA proudly boast(s) of (hours testing for USAF)	1968 NASA Authorization Hearings before the House Committee on Science and Astronautics (March-April, 1967), p. 199.
208	"In summary . . . 75 percent of NASA's Space Vehicle Division effort . . . is of direct benefit to DOD . . . and the specific military requirements"	1968 NASA Authorization (Part 4) Hearings before House Committee on Science and Astronautics (March-April, 1967), p. 199.
208	"growing role of the civilian space agency in the Vietnam War . . . that NASA's office of Advanced Research and Technology is spending between $4 and $5 million a year directing the efforts of 100 scientists and engineers to tasks vital to the Vietnam War"	Thomas O'Toole in *The Washington Post*, December 4, 1967.
209	NASA could loft a synchronous satellite over the Vietnamese jungles—a satellite equipped with a huge mirror [that would illuminate the night landscape]	*The National Space Program, op. cit.*, p. 20.
210	NASA's wind tunnels and tracking stations "are operated for the Department of Defense" . . . without reimbursement to NASA	1968 NASA Authorization (Part 4) Hearings before House Committee on Science and Astronautics (March-April, 1967), p. 840.

210   DOD would "support and eventually operate the NASA tracking facilities on Grand Bahama Island"   *Report to the Congress from the President of the United States, U.S. Aeronautical and Space Activities, 1967,* p. 43.

210   Nimbus B carried a "piggyback" DOD payload . . . "as part of an inter-agency program . . ."   NASA Release No. 68-64, May 10, 1968.

211   Statement by House Subcommittee on NASA Oversight   *The National Space Program — Its Value and Benefits,* staff study for the House Subcommittee on NASA Oversight, 1967, p. 19.

212   Representative Wydler quote   1968 NASA Authorization (Part 4) Hearings before House Committee on Science and Astronautics (March-April, 1967), p. 302.

213   General Schriever quote   *Space: Its Impact on Man and Society,* ed. Lillian Levy, W. W. Norton, 1965, p. 67.

216 *ftnt.* **   AEC budget   *Science News,* Vol. 93 (Feb. 10, 1968), p. 133.

217   Webb, Senator Anderson exchange   *Aviation Week & Space Technology,* Nov. 27, 1967, p. 15.

218   Webb's remarks on retirement of Admiral W. F. Boone from NASA   NASA Release No. 67-314, December 29, 1967.

218   "big decisions . . ."   NASA's Proposed Operation Plan for Fiscal Year 1968, p. 33; NASA Authorization for Fiscal Year 1968, before the Senate Committee on Aeronautical and Space Sciences, (April 18, 1968), p. 54; etc.

219	John Noble Wilford quote	*The New York Times,* April 16, 1968.
219-21	General Schriever quotes	*Space: Its Impact on Man and Society,* ed. Lillian Levy, W. W. Norton, 1965, p. 68, p. 63.
223	Secretary of Defense McNamara and FOBS	Transcript of "News Conference of Secretary of Defense, Robert S. McNamara at Pentagon, Friday, Nov. 3, 1967."
224	Lapp quote	*Science News,* Aug. 24, 1968, p. 181.
226	Quote of NBC official	Author interview.
227	PSAC statement	*The Space Program in the Post Apollo Period,* a Report of the President's Science Advisory Committee prepared by the Joint Space Panels, The White House, Feb. 1967, p. 11.

CHAPTER 11

231	President Johnson quote	Remarks at NASA's Michoud Assembly Facility, near New Orleans, La., March 2, 1968.
233	President Johnson quote	*Forbes,* July 1, 1968, p. 58.
233-34	General Schriever quotes	*Aerospace Technology,* March 11, 1968, p. 16.
234	John P. Rogan quote	*Forbes,* July 1, 1968, p. 55.
234	Martin Goland quote	*Space: Its Impact on Man and Society,* Ed. Lillian Levy, W. W. Norton, 1965, p. 47.
236-37	A whole generation of scientist-astronauts . . . were considering resignations . . .	*The New York Times,* Feb. 11, 1968. *Aviation Week,* Sept. 2, 1968, p. 15.
237-38	Karl G. Harr statement	*Technology Week,* Jan. 16, 1967.

241	California aerospace employment statistics	"The Impact of the Cold War on California and Utah," by Dr. James L. Clayton, in the *Pacific Historical Review*, pp. 449–473.
242	Dupré and Gustafson observation	Quoted in *Space: Its Impact on Man and Society*, in essay by Joseph A. Beirne "Labor in the Age of Space"; ed. Lillian Levy, W. W. Norton, 1965, p. 23.
243	One anonymous spokesman . . . complained that North American Aviation . . . "gave us a black eye"	*Forbes*, July 1, 1968, p. 67.
244	Mueller quote; further questioning elicited similar dissembling from NASA	See Appendix I.
	John Leland Atwood— Representative Ryan exchange	Hearings before the House Subcommittee on NASA Oversight (April 11, 1967), Vol. 1, p. 265.
244	James Webb refused (to release Phillips report) giving as [reasons] . . .	*Ibid.*
	Webb quote	Hearings before the Senate Committee on Aeronautical and Space Sciences (Feb. 27, 1968), Part 2, p. 128.
245-46	Representative Roudebush, John L. Atwood exchange	Hearings before the House Subcommittee on NASA Oversight (April 11, 1967), Vol. 1, p. 161.
246	Martin Goland quote	Essay, "The Aerospace Industry," in *Space: Its Impact on Man and Society*, ed. Lillian Levy, W. W. Norton, 1965, p. 40.
247	Rocketdyne . . . the Nova vehicle	*The Space Industry: America's Newest Giant*, by the Editors of *Fortune*, Prentice-Hall, 1962, p. 108.

247   NASA chose to chastise   *Fortune*, August, 1967, p.
       North American by assign-   192.
       ing Boeing . . .

248   John Moore quote   *Forbes*, July 1, 1968, p. 67.

248   Willard F. Rockwell quote   *Ibid.*

249   "bicycles, toys, etc."   *The Wall Street Journal*,
                                    Nov. 6, 1968, p. 1.

251   SST seismic waves   *Science News*, Nov. 23,
                                    1968, p. 521.

251   Pentagon interest in SST as *American Engineer*, April,
       troop transport   1968, p. 33.

CHAPTER 12

255   Webb quote, "It's not   Hearings   before   Senate
       possible . . ."   Committee on Aeronautical
                                    and Space Sciences (Jan.
                                    25, 1967), p. 16.

256   Webb quote "'for whom   Hearings   before   House
       the Apollo bell tolls'"   Subcommittee   on   NASA
                                    Oversight (April 10, 1967),
                                    Vol. 1, p. 7.

256   Colonel Borman began an   Hearings   before   Senate
       impromptu elaboration . . . Committee on Aeronautical
       Dr. Thompson said . . .   and Space Sciences (April
                                    11, 1967), Part 3, p. 185.

256-57 James Webb asked con-   *Ibid.*, (Feb. 17, 1967), Part
       gressional indulgence say- 2, p. 115.
       ing ". . . sure we are ac-
       curate."

257   Chairman Olin Teague told   Hearings   before   House
       Berry . . . Dr. Berry . . . Subcommittee   on   NASA
       testified . . . to the negative Oversight (April 12, 1967),
                                    p. 310.

257   "It would be an insult to   *Aviation Week*, Feb. 20,
       NASA."   1967, p. 15.

258   "possible whitewash . . ."   Hearings   before   House
       "nothing behind scenes"   Committee on Science and
                                    Astronautics   (Feb.   28,
                                    1967), Part 1, p. 33.

258	Senator John Stennis . . . special effort to express . . . gratitude . . . [to Mr. Webb]	Hearings before Senate Committee on Aeronautical and Space Sciences (April 18, 1967), p. 31.
259	"confidential Committee print" . . . circulated for months	Printed on title page of "Apollo Accident — Draft Report of the Committee on Aeronautical and Space Sciences, United States Senate, which is dated September, 1967.
259	According to William Hines	*Washington Star*, Feb. 2, 1968.
260	Congressman Ryan . . . Senate Report . . . "whitewash."	*Ibid.*
260	Hines . . . "nearly a whitewash"	*Ibid.*
261	A member of the Boeing team . . . "It is a good immediate goal . . ."	A. H. Phillips in *Apollo Pace and Progress*, Staff Study for House Subcommittee on NASA Oversight, Serial F (March 10, 1967), Appendix B, p. 101.
261	Boeing's Douglas Serrill ". . . politically or publicly acceptable"	*Ibid.*, p. 102.
262	Senator Allen J. Ellender . . . Webb replied in the affirmative	Hearings before the Senate Subcommittee of the Committee on Appropriations (July 26, 1967) on H.R. 12474 for Fiscal Year 1968, p. 35.
262	Senator Ellender observed . . . Webb could only reply . . . Ellender said ". . . without the space program"	*Ibid.*, p. 35.
262	Webb . . . "best for the United States . . ."	*Ibid.*, p. 37.
262-63	Exchange involving James Webb, Senators Ellender and Holland on cutting certain NASA programs	*Ibid.*, p. 77.

263	Pressing his point, Webb informed . . . "They have beat us on every single major thing . . ."	*Ibid.*, p. 81.
	Senator Holland . . . "I am surprised . . . rather than evade our questions."	*Ibid.*
264	"Rose by any other name"	*Aerospace Technology*, January 1, 1968.
265	"Dear Mr. Fulton" letter	House Report (No. 1181) Authorizing Appropriations to National Aeronautics and Space Administration (March 19, 1968), p. 178.
267	a poll of leading businessmen	"A Survey of Views of Leading Industrial Executives on the National Space Program," House Committee on Science and Astronautics Serial P, April 24, 1968.
268	James Wilson . . . most frequently [asked] "how will this affect . . . the schedule and the budget"	*Apollo Pace and Progress*, Staff Study for House Subcommittee on NASA Oversight, Serial F, (March 10, 1967).
268	General Phillips . . . "cut to the bare bones" . . .	*Ibid.*, p. 873.
268	would not be "prudent"	*Ibid.*, p. 847.
267-68	Quotation from Elmer P. Wohl	*Ordnance*, July-August, 1968, pp. 65–67.

CHAPTER 13

270	Webb quote	*The New York Times*, Sept. 16, 1968.
272	Wilford quote	*Ibid.*, Dec. 8, 1968.
272	Quote from *Time*	*Time*, Nov. 22, 1968.
272	Reputed Lovell quotes, "sickens me," "just plain silly"	*The New York Times*, Nov. 21, 1968.

272	Lovell quote, "one of the deepest follies . . ."	*U.S. News & World Report*, Feb. 13, 1967.
272	Lovell quote, "On a scientific basis . . ."	*Time*, Dec. 6, 1968.
273	Quote from *The Economist*	*The Economist*, Nov. 23, 1968
273	Lapp quote	*The New Republic*, Dec. 14, 1968.
273 *ftnt.*	"simulated rescue . . . around the moon."	*The New York Times*, Oct. 13, 1968.
274	Mueller quote	*Ibid.*, Nov. 21, 1968.
276	"Russians might launch . . . October 15 or 16"	*Ibid.*, Oct. 9, 1968.
276	Sedov quotes	*Ibid.*, Oct. 15, 1968.
278	space officials were describing . . .	*Christian Science Monitor*, Nov. 5, 1968.
278	One rumor . . . December 2nd.	*The New York Times*, Nov. 19, 1968.
278 *ftnt.*	Krivsky quotes	*Ibid.*, Nov. 3, 1968.
279	"soon," . . . one, two, or three cosmonauts	*Ibid.*, Nov. 30, 1968.
279	quote from *Tass*	*Ibid.*, Nov. 24, 1968.
279	quote from *Izvestia*	*Ibid.*, Nov. 26, 1968.
279	UPI report from Moscow	*Ibid.*, Nov. 27, 1968.
279	quote from *Tass*	*Ibid.*, Nov. 30, 1968.
280	Russia finally concede	*Ibid.*, Dec. 18, 1968.
281	Phillips and North American quotes	*Ibid.*, Nov. 10, 1967.
282	"not considered serious"	*Ibid.*
283	by changing the flight plan	*Science News*, Feb. 3, 1968.
283	"there have been many other difficulties"	*Ibid.*, Nov. 2, 1968.
283	substitute aluminum replacements	*Aviation Week & Space Technology*, Jan. 15, 1968, p. 29.
284	"headache producing"	*Science News*, Nov. 2, 1968.

284	Wilford quote	*The New York Times*, Jan. 22, 1968.
284 *ftnt.*	McDivitt quote	*Ibid.*
285	Quote from *The New York Times*	*Ibid.*, April 6, 1968.
285	Mueller quotes	*Ibid.*, April 5, 1968.
285	"greater risks . . ."	*Time*, Nov. 22, 1968.
287	"to reduce . . . their helmets"	*The New York Times*, Oct. 11, 1968.
287	650 pounds	*Ibid.*
288	Phillips quote	*Ibid.*, Oct. 23, 1968.
288	A more dispassionate view	*Science News*, Nov. 2, 1968.
289	"someone on the launching tower"	*The New York Times*, Oct. 12, 1968.
289	power failure . . .	*Ibid.*
289-90	On the second day of the mission . . . "out there."	*Ibid.*, Oct. 13, 1968.
290	Late into the third day . . . minimum of power.	*Ibid.*, Oct. 24, 1968.
290	During the fifth day . . . accounted for.	*Ibid.*, Oct. 16, 1968.
290	A week into the mission . . .	*Ibid.*, Oct. 19, 1968.
290-91	On the eighth day . . . were lost.	*Ibid.*, Oct. 20 and Oct. 23, 1968.
291	Another significant problem . . .	*Science News*, Nov. 2, 1968.
291-92	According to UPI . . .	*The New York Times*, Dec. 12, 1968.
292	"minor glitch"	*Newsweek*, Dec. 30, 1968.
292	no duplicate . . . parts	*The New York Times*, Dec. 26, 1968.
293	Phillips quotes	*Time*, Dec. 6, 1968.
293 *ftnt.*	The Soviet Soyuz 3 . . .	*Ibid.*, Nov. 25, 1968.
293-94	Petrov quote	*The New York Times*, Dec. 24, 1968.

294	"far less spectacular"	*Science News*, Jan. 4, 1969.
294 *ftnt.*	Kraft quote	*The New York Times*, Dec. 22, 1968.
296 *ftnt.*	Mueller quote	Hearings before the House Subcommittee on Manned Flight of the Committee on Science and Astronautics, March 14, 1967, p. 45.
297	firm denial by Gen. Phillips	*Time*, Jan. 3, 1969.
297	Grumman official quote	*Science News*, Dec. 7, 1968.
298-99	Mitchell quote	*Aerospace Technology*, June 17, 1968.
301	*New York Post* editorial	*New York Post*, Dec. 23, 1968.
302	"several thousand" . . . calls of protest	*New York Post*, Dec. 23, 1968.
303 *ftnt.*	lucrative spin-off . . . for astronauts	*Aviation Week & Space Technology*, Nov. 25, 1968.
304-5	ten Russian cosmonauts ". . . noble goal"	*Time*, Jan. 10, 1969.
305	One congressman . . . Congressional Medal of Honor	*The New York Times*, Dec. 29, 1968.
306	Quote from National Academy of Sciences report	*The New Republic*, Jan. 11, 1969.
306-7	Quote from National Academy of Sciences report	*The New York Times*, Aug. 15, 1968.
307	Borman quote	Transcript of news conference at the State Dept. Auditorium, Wash., D.C., Jan. 9, 1969.
307 *ftnt.*	Anders quote	*Time*, Dec. 6, 1968.
308	Lyons quote	*The New York Times*, Oct. 20, 1968.
309	"some sort of disorientation"	*The New York Times*, July 29, 1968.
309	Disorientation . . . retarded.	*Science News*, July 27, 1968.
309	Adey quote	*Ibid.*

310	Sulzberger quote	*The New York Times*, Dec. 29, 1968.
310	NASA officials . . . *military* experiments	*Aviation Week & Space Technology*, Dec. 23, 1968, p. 17.
310	Paine quote	*The New York Times*, Dec. 28, 1968.
310-11	Anderson quotes	UPI dispatch, carried in *Hartford Times*, Jan. 12, 1969.
311	Commoner quote	*The New York Times*, Dec. 28, 1968.
311	Mead quote	*Ibid.*
311-12	*New York Times* editorial	*Ibid.*, Dec. 30, 1968.
312	Bryant quote	*New York Post*, Jan. 8, 1969.
312	As billions . . . 0.2 per cent of NASA's budget	*Science News*, June 1, 1968.
314	Hornig quote	*Ibid.*, Sept. 28, 1968.
314	Shannon and Abelson quotes	*The New York Times*, Dec. 28, 1968.
315	Karth quote	*Space Digest*, April, 1968, p. 124.
315	DuBridge quote	*The New York Times*, Dec. 17, 1968.

INDEX

Abelson, Philip, 314
Adams, Michael J., 309
Adey, W. Ross, 309
Advanced Research Projects Agency (ARPA), 63, 66, 67
Aerospace industry, public relations and the, 229–254
Aerospace Medical Association, 147 fn.
Aerospace Technology, 53, 55, 264, 273 fn.
Agriculture, Department of, 214 fn.
A.I.A.A., *see* American Institute of Aeronautics and Astronautics
Air Force Committee on Space Technology, 63
Air Force Satellite Test Center (California), 198 fn.
Air Force School of Aerospace Medicine, 131, 136
Aircraft industry, development of, 230
Airesearch Corporation, 166–167
Alden, John D., 250
Aldrin, E. E., Jr., 93, 270, 298
Alexander, George, 9, 48
Alexander the Great, 230, 231, 254
Allnutt, Robert F., 265
Altitude tests, 21, 23, 24, 52, 57
American Association for the Advancement of Science, 75, 311
American Aviation, 209 fn.
American Broadcasting Corporation, 257
American Engineer, 250
American Institute of Aeronautics and Astronautics, 53, 56
American Rocket Society, 63
Ames Research Center, 209 fn.
Anders, William A., 230, 274, 285, 288, 291, 294, 300, 303, 304, 305, 307 fn.
Anderson, Clinton P., 38, 89, 98, 114, 120, 128, 147, 217, 243, 262, 266, 310–311
"Anomalies," 27, 28, 288–291
Anoxia, 21
Apollo 4, 281–282, 293

Apollo 5, 112, 282–284, 294
Apollo 6, 284–286, 292
Apollo 7, 7, 17, 43, 113, 191 fn., 192, 227–228, 270–271, 276, 286–291, 293, 307, 308, 315
Apollo 8, 271–274, 278, 279, 280, 281, 283, 285, 286, 288, 289, 291–294, 300–307, 311
Apollo 9, 273, 283, 294–296
Apollo 10, 293, 296–298
Apollo 11, 286, 297–299
Apollo 12, 286, 300
Apollo 012, 3, 4 fn., 10, 25, 57
Apollo 201, 281
Apollo 202, 281
Apollo 203, 281
Apollo 204, 4–18
Review Board, 15, 17, 22, 27, 33, 37, 48, 50, 51, 55, 57, 97, 98–122, 127, 128, 130, 147, 150, 158, 166, 167, 175, 176, 178, 179, 181, 182, 183, 186, 197, 243, 244–245, 256, 258. *See also* Report of Apollo 204 Review Board
Apollo Applications Program (AAP), 202, 204, 310
Apollo Lunar Surface Experiments Package (ALSEP), 299
"Apollo News Media Conference," 43, 54
Apollo Project, 68 fn., 73, 78, 86–89, 95, 100, 128
Armstrong, Neil, 92, 284, 298
Army Ballistic Missile Agency (ABMA), 70
Army Ordnance Missile Command (AOMC), 67, 68 fn.
Associated Press, 45, 190, 297
Astronauts, original seven, 6 fn.
Atomic Energy Commission, 69, 214 fn., 217, 262
budget, 216 fn., 228
Atwood, John Leland, 113, 244–246
Aviation Week, 38, 48, 55, 62, 88, 91, 143, 200, 208, 241, 265